ILLUSTRATED ADVANCED BIOLOGY

Genetics & Evolution

Also in this series:

Mammals: Structure & Function 0 7195 7551 6

Artwork credits

The following are sources from which artwork or data have been adapted and redrawn: **Figure 3.22 (p.30)** data adapted from I. Knight (1984) *The Height and Weight of Adults in Great Britain*, Table 4.1 (male data) page 25, with permission from the Office for National Statistics, ©Crown copyright 1998; **Figure 3.28 (p.33)** adapted from P.M. Shepherd (1958) *Natural Selection and Heredity*, Figure 6 page 90, Hutchinson, London; **Figure 3.30 (p.34)** data adapted from Mark Ferguson and Ted Joanen (1982) *Nature* **296**(April), page 29; **Figure 4.14 (p.45)** adapted from E.J Wood, C.A. Smith and W.R. Pickering (1997) *Life Chemistry and Molecular Biology*, Figure 6.9 page 176, by permission of Portland Press Ltd, London; **Figure 5.6 (p.51)** adapted from E.J. Wood, C.A. Smith and W.R. Pickering (1997) *Life Chemistry and Molecular Biology*, page 173, by permission of Portland Press Ltd, London; **Figure 6.27 (p.74)** adapted from R.J. Berry (1977) *The New Naturalist Inheritance and Natural History*, Figure 40 page 133, by permission of the author and HarperCollins Publishers Ltd, London; **Figure 6.31 (p.76)** adapted from Ray North (1996) *Ants*, page 58, by permission of Whittet Books Ltd, Suffolk; **Figure 6.33 (p.78)** adapted from C.J. Clegg with D.G. Mackean (1994) *Advanced Biology: Principles and Applications*, Figures 30.26 & 30.28 pages 669 & 671, John Murray, London; **Figure 6.38 (p.81)** adapted from C.J. Clegg with D.G. Mackean (1994) *Advanced Biology: Principles and Applications*, Figure 30.22 page 674, John Murray, London; **Figure 6.43 (p.82)** adapted from R. Lewin (1989) *Human Evolution An Illustrated Introduction*, page 67, by permission of Blackwell Science Ltd, Oxford; **Figure 6.44 (p.83)** adapted with permission from Pete Wheeler (1988) *New Scientist* 12 May, pages 62–65; **Figure 6.48 (p.85)** adapted from R. Lewin (1989) *Human Evolution An Illustrated Introduction*, page 100, by permission of Blackwell Science Ltd, Oxford; **Figure 6.50 (p.86)** adapted from R. Lewin (1989) *Human Evolution An Illustrated Introduction*, page 103, by permission of Blackwell Science Ltd, Oxford; **Figure 6.51 (p.86)** adapted from R. Lewin (1989) *Human Evolution An Illustrated Introduction*, page 112, by permission of Blackwell Science Ltd, Oxford; **Figure 6.52 (p.87)** adapted from S. Tomkins (1984) *The Origin of Mankind*, Figure 8.2 page 62, by permission of Cambridge University Press, Cambridge; **Figure 6.53 (p.87)** adapted from S. Tomkins (1984) *The Origin of Mankind*, Figure 10.6 page 90, by permission of Cambridge University Press, Cambridge.

Photo credits

Thanks are due to the following copyright holders for permission to reproduce photographs: **Cover** Dr Kari Lounatmaa/Science Photo Library; **p.1** *top* ©L. Lee Rue/Frank Lane Picture Agency, *middle* ©R.P. Lawrence/Frank Lane Picture Agency, *bottom* Dr C.J. Clegg; **p.3** *both* Dr C.J. Clegg; **p.9** *left* ©Kevin Schafer/NHPA, *right* ©Lynn Stone/BBC Natural History Unit; **p.11** *top* Chris Bjornberg/Science Photo Library, *bottom left & right* Dr C.J. Clegg; **p.16** Nigel Cattlin/Holt Studios International; **p.18** ©Jane Gifford/NHPA; **p.19** Willem Harinck/Holt Studios International; **p.21** ©Biophoto Associates; **p.23** ©Biophoto Associates; **p.25** *top* Adam Hart-Davis/Science Photo Library, *bottom left & right* Dr C.A. Sewry, Neuromuscular Unit, Imperial College School of Medicine, Hammersmith Hospital; **p.26** Prof. P. Motta/Dept of Anatomy/University "La Sapienza", Rome/Science Photo Library; **p.29** ©Andrew Henley/Biofotos; **p.34** ©David Hosking/Frank Lane Picture Agency; **p.35** *top left & middle* Nigel Cattlin/Holt Studios International, *top right* ©John B. Free/BBC Natural History Unit, *bottom* ©Stephen Dalton/NHPA; **p.36** Professor A. Gray; **p.37** *all* Dr C.J. Clegg; **p.39** Eric Grave/Science Photo Library; **p.40** *top* ©Biophoto Associates, *bottom* Dr Kari Lounatmaa/Science Photo Library; **p.41** Biozentrum, University of Basel/Science Photo Library; **p.42** The Randall Institute, Kings College London; **p.51** Julia Kamlish/Science Photo Library; **p.52** Dr Jeremy Burgess/Science Photo Library; **p.53** Associated Press/John Hopkins University; **p.58** *top* CC Studio/Science Photo Library, *bottom left* ©Murdo MacLeod, *bottom right* Professor J.M.W. Slack, University of Bath; **p.59** *left* ©Morley Read/BBC Natural History Unit, *right* Dr C.J. Clegg; **p.60** *top* Ken Lucas/Plant Earth Pictures, *middle* Sinclair Stammers/Science Photo Library, *bottom* Rover Group/BMIHT/Beaulieu; **p.64** *top right* ©Henry Ausloos/NHPA, *top middle* ©Andy Rouse/NHPA, *top left* ©Gerard Lacz/NHPA, *bottom left* ©A.P. Barnes/NHPA, *bottom middle* ©Gerard Lacz/NHPA, *bottom right* ©B. & C. Alexander/NHPA; **p.65** Dr C.J. Clegg; **p.67** *all* Dr C.J. Clegg; **p.72** Dr C.J. Clegg; **p.73** *left* Gene Cox, *right* INS News Agency Ltd; **p.76** *left* ©David Hosking/Frank Lane Picture Agency, *right* ©Stephen Dalton/NHPA; **p.82** John Reader/Science Photo Library; **p.83** ©Peter Blackwell/BBC Natural History Unit; **p.85** ©National Museums of Kenya; **p.87** Sheridan Photo Library/Ancient Art and Architecture Collection.

First published in 1999
by John Murray (Publishers) Ltd
50 Albemarle Street
London W1X 4BD

Illustrations by Ethan Danielson, Philip Ford, Wearset and Tony Randell
Layouts by Eric Drewery
Cover design by John Townson/Creation

Typeset in 10/12pt Galliard by Wearset, Boldon, Tyne and Wear
Printed and bound in Great Britain by the Alden Group, Oxford

A catalogue entry for this title is available from the British Library

ISBN 0 7195 7552 4

Front cover: The organism that may cause pneumonia in humans (and mice), *Streptococcus pneumoniae*, exists in two forms – one with a capsule (left), and the other without a capsule (right). This bacterium was first used many years ago in laboratory experiments that led eventually to the discovery that DNA controls and directs all aspects of cell activity, and is also the hereditary material.

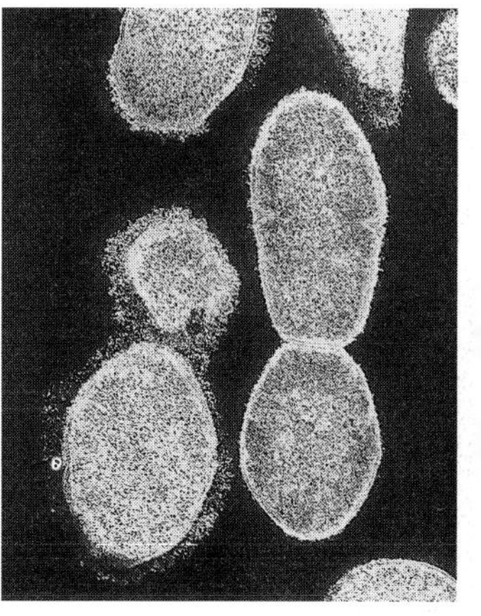

Contents

Abbreviations used in text

ATP	adenosine 5'-triphosphate
CF	cystic fibrosis
df	degree of freedom
DNA	deoxyribonucleic acid
mRNA	messenger ribonucleic acid
mtDNA	mitochondrial deoxyribonucleic acid
my	million years
mya	million years ago
PHB	polyhydrobutyrate
PKU	phenylketonuria
rDNA	ribosomal deoxyribonucleic acid
RNA	ribonucleic acid
R-plasmid	resistance plasmid
SEM	scanning electron microscope
TDF	testis determining factor
TEM	transmission electron microscope
tRNA	transfer ribonucleic acid
TSD	temperature sex determination
ya	years ago

Preface

The mechanism of inheritance has been a challenge ever since humans wondered why 'like begets like' in the living world. Modern genetics has grown from the pioneering experiments of Gregor Mendel, to be at the heart of the discipline we call cell biology. Now, genetics is of great economic and medical importance through its applications in the technology of genetic engineering. The manipulation of genes is virtually a daily news item, raising social and ethical issues that have to be understood and addressed.

However, modern genetics has also made sense of the mechanisms of organic evolution by natural selection. This theory was proposed by Charles Darwin at a time when evolution was a revolutionary idea that profoundly challenged science and society. Today, we accept evolution as an organising principle of modern biology.

In this book the ideas of genetics and evolution are outlined in a pictorial format. Our current understanding of inheritance is developed from its early beginnings. Then, the biochemistry of the gene is shown to underpin the processes of genetic engineering. Next, the fact of evolution is introduced, and mechanisms examined. Evidence for natural selection in speciation is presented. Finally, current ideas concerning human evolution are reviewed.

All these facets are covered using drawings, genetic diagrams, flow-diagrams, graphs and notes, accompanied by photomicrographs, electronmicrographs and photographs. The treatment is ideal for students at AS and A level, and for GNVQ courses, in Biology, Environmental Studies, Social and Human Biology, and all related disciplines, as well as being of general interest.

Taking your studies further

- You can read more about the background to these topics, and learn about how they have been investigated in the laboratory and in nature from:
  CJ Clegg with DG Mackean (1994) *Advanced Biology Principles & Applications*, John Murray, London.
- Related laboratory practicals, projects and investigations, and details of other resources for learning are available in:
  CJ Clegg with DG Mackean, PH Openshaw and RC Reynolds (1996) *Advanced Biology Study Guide*, John Murray, London.
- Keeping up to date with developments is possible with the help of articles in:
  New Scientist, a weekly review of science and technology, including the occasional series 'Inside Science';
  Biological Sciences Review, a relatively new journal, designed and written for A level biology students;
  Scientific American, a review journal of science, sometimes with articles applicable to this level.

Acknowledgements

To the very many known and unknown scientists, naturalists, teachers, illustrators and writers who have influenced my own understanding I gladly acknowledge my debt. Where copyright material has been used it is acknowledged on page ii.

If the intellectual property of anyone has inadvertently been used without prior agreement, then I ask that John Murray (Publishers) Ltd, of 50 Albemarle Street, London, W1X 4BD are contacted so that correction can be made.

I have sought guidance on specific issues from Professor Neil Jones of University College of Wales, Aberystwyth, and Professor Steve Jones of University College London, and I am most grateful for their observations. I am especially grateful to colleagues whose views have helped and guided my work and not least to Don Mackean for many incisive comments. Any remaining errors are my sole responsibility.

At John Murray the skill and patience of Julie Jones, Helen Townson and Katie Mackenzie Stuart have brought together text, photomicrographs and drawings exactly as I wished, and I am most grateful to them.

CJ Clegg
January 1999

The first geneticists

The practical skills of animal and plant breeding made possible the first great revolution in human history, the **Neolithic revolution**. It started after the last Ice Age, about 10 000 years ago. Groups of *Homo sapiens* stopped their nomadic existence and became farmers in settled communities. At this stage the human population started to grow.

We may remember these ancestors by the great sites they constructed, for example, Stonehenge, without the use of the wheel or metal tools. However, their greatest achievement was the breeding of domesticated animals and the cultivation of many plant crops, all from the 'wild' stock around. This technology, now called **'artificial selection'**, was developed without knowledge of heredity (the transmission of characteristics or traits from one generation to another). Many of the plant and animal species of modern farming were first produced at this time. How was this achieved?

Table 1.1 What domestication of wild animals involved.

- The **identification** of a population of a 'species' as a useful source of hides, meat, etc., and learning how to tell these animals apart from related species. Herd animals (e.g. sheep and cattle) are naturally sociable, and lend themselves to this
- The selective killing (**culling**) of the ***least*** suitable members of this herd in order to meet immediate needs for food and materials for living
- Encouraging **breeding** among the docile, well-endowed members of the herd, and providing protection against predators
- **Selecting** from the progeny individuals with the most useful features, and making them the future breeding stock
- **Maintenance** of the breeding stock during unfavourable seasons
- Ultimately, the **establishment of a domesticated herd**, dependent on the herdspeople rather than living wild, leading to the possibility of trading individuals of a breeding stock with neighbouring herdspeople's stocks

Figure 1.1 The history of modern humans on the 24-hour clock.

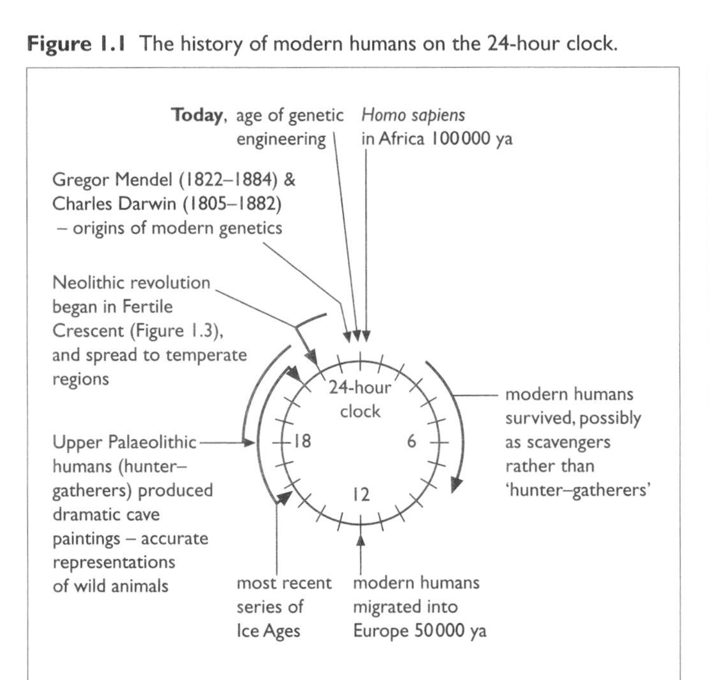

Figure 1.2 From 'wild' to domesticated species.

Wild sheep or mouflon (*Ovis musimon*) occur today on Sardinia and Corsica

Soay sheep of the Outer Hebrides suggest to us what the earliest domesticated sheep looked like

Modern selective breeding has produced a shorter animal with a woolly fleece in place of coarse hair, and with muscle of higher fat content. Many breeds have lost their horns

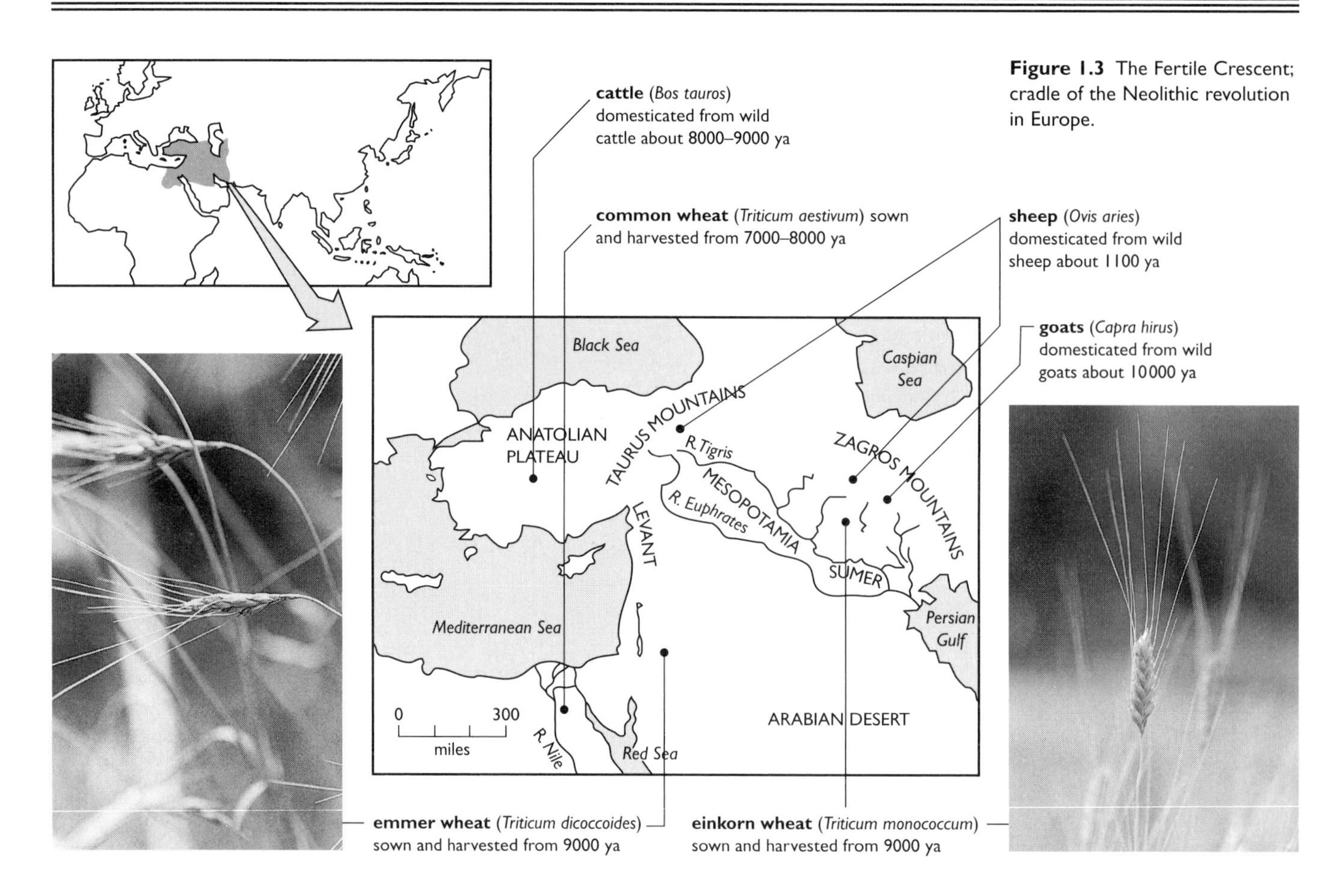

Figure 1.3 The Fertile Crescent; cradle of the Neolithic revolution in Europe.

The evidence for Neolithic agriculture comes from the finds made at archaeological 'digs' at ancient settlement sites, and includes:

- wheat and barley fruits as grains carbonised by fire action, and clay impressions of cereal flowers;
- remains of stored fruits and seeds of cereal plants, of beans, peas and lentils, and of oil-producing plants like olives, sesame, castor oil, rape and flax;
- parts of skeletons and individual bones of dogs (the first animals domesticated), and then of sheep, goats, pigs and cattle that were managed in herds;
- the high proportion (for example 60%) of bones of young animals present (when wild animals were killed by hunter–gatherers, the proportion of young animals in a 'kill' was 25%, at most);
- the subsequent accurate dating of artefacts like these, made by radiometric dating using natural radioactive isotopes.

Since the Neolithic revolution selective breeding of fruits, vegetables, flowers and livestock has continued more or less throughout human history. As a result, new organisms have been added to the list of previously wild species now cultivated, and many new varieties of cultivated organisms have been developed.

In more recent times, investigation of the **mechanisms of inheritance** became possible, once sex cell formation and fertilisation (and pollination) were understood. Partly because these investigations involved the inheritance of many characteristics of the parents by the progeny, the results were often confusing. As a result, an idea known as **'blending inheritance'** was widely accepted. This was the situation when Gregor Mendel began his studies.

Parent 1 }
Parent 2 } — both parents contribute equally to offspring ——→ offspring an **average** of the characteristics of the parents

- The outcome of blending inheritance (if it occurs) is that each successive generation will show *less* variation than the parents, with the trend towards **increasing uniformity**.
- Blending inheritance would **not** provide a basis for natural selection (page 67).

Figure 1.4 The idea of 'blending inheritance'.

Gregor Mendel was born in a small village in Moravia in 1822, the son of a peasant farmer. Mendel had a happy early life, but as he grew older he and his family had to battle against a shortage of money to pay for his education. This struggle affected Gregor's health. At the age of 21 he was offered a place in the monastery at Bruno (now in the Czech Republic) and he accepted, 'feeling compelled to enter a station of life which would free him from the bitter struggle for existence'. In fact the monastery was a centre of research in natural sciences and agriculture, as well as in theology, the arts and music. Mendel was well placed and was successful there. Ultimately he became Abbot, but at a politically turbulent time for his church. His happiest contribution to local society was as a school teacher, but he never succeeded in qualifying as such. His greatest contribution to learning was to discover many of the **underlying principles of heredity** by a painstaking series of experiments using garden pea plants, organised on a large scale. He was a pioneer at applying statistical methods to biological research. At the time, the nucleus of a cell was recognised, but chromosomes and genes were not known. The significance of his work was not appreciated in his lifetime, and Mendel, although now recognised as one of the great figures in modern science, died in relative obscurity. In all his disappointments he was always philosophical. He was heard to say 'Mein Zeit wird schon kommen' ('My time will soon come'). He died in 1884, and his work was rediscovered in 1900. You can read more about this fascinating person in: V Orel (1996) *Gregor Mendel; the First Geneticist*, Oxford University Press, Oxford.

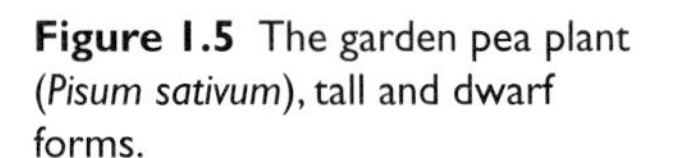

Figure 1.5 The garden pea plant (*Pisum sativum*), tall and dwarf forms.

Mendel was successful because:

- his experiments were carefully planned;
- large samples were used and this minimised chance effects;
- he carefully recorded the numbers of plants of each type formed as this became known (often the following season);
- he expressed his results as ratios;
- his choice of the garden pea meant he worked with an organism with contrasting characteristics that were easily recognised;
- each of these characteristics was controlled by a single factor (gene*), (rather than by many genes, as most characteristics of humans are);
- when he worked on the inheritance of two pairs of contrasting characteristics they were ones controlled by factors (genes) on separate chromosomes*;
- in interpreting his results, Mendel made use of the mathematics he had learnt.

*Genes and chromosomes were not known then.

1 What 'chance effects' might influence the outcome of breeding experiments like these?

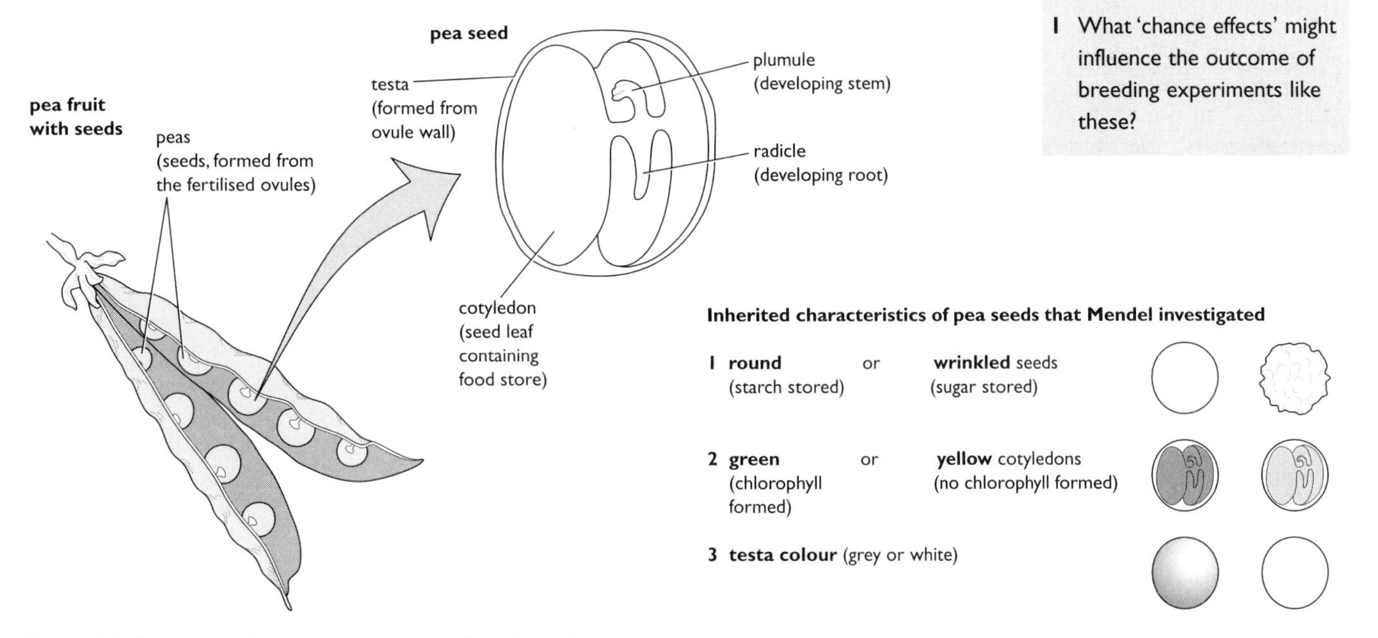

Figure 1.6 Features of the garden pea seed that Mendel studied.

2 Mendelian genetics

What happens to the alternative forms of a characteristic when they are combined together to form a hybrid?

No one had the answer at the time Mendel started his experiments. He investigated this issue exhaustively, using the contrasting characteristics of the garden pea (and later other species of plant, too). Mendel's experimental technique involved:

- **checking that the parent plants 'bred true'**, for example, seeds producing tall plants were from plant stocks that had all been tall for two or more previous generations, and seeds producing dwarf plants were from two or more generations of dwarf plants;
- **crossing plants that are naturally self-pollinating**, that is, the garden pea plant (*Pisum sativum*), which is self-pollinating (pollen from the stamens reaches the stigma of the same flower, germinates successfully there, and fertilisation follows, before pollen from another flower is brought to the stigma). To carry out a breeding experiment between pea plants with contrasting characteristics, very young flowers had to be opened, the immature stamens removed before they shed pollen, and mature pollen introduced from a plant showing the contrasting characteristic. Finally the entry of 'stray' pollen had to be prevented whilst the stigma remained receptive (Figure 2.1);
- **reciprocal crosses**, that is, pollen from tall plants was dusted on to the stigmas of dwarf plants and pollen from dwarf plants was dusted on to the stigmas of tall plants.

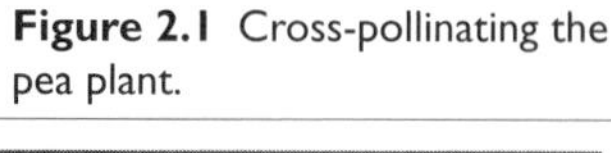

Figure 2.1 Cross-pollinating the pea plant.

Flowers of the pea family have five petals: a rear **standard**, two lateral **wings**, and two **keels** arranged like a boat, surrounding the male (stamens) and female (stigma, style and ovary) parts of the flower.

Insects, such as bees, part the keels on landing, expose the stamens and stigma, and may pollinate the flower

Note: the garden pea plant is naturally self-pollinated

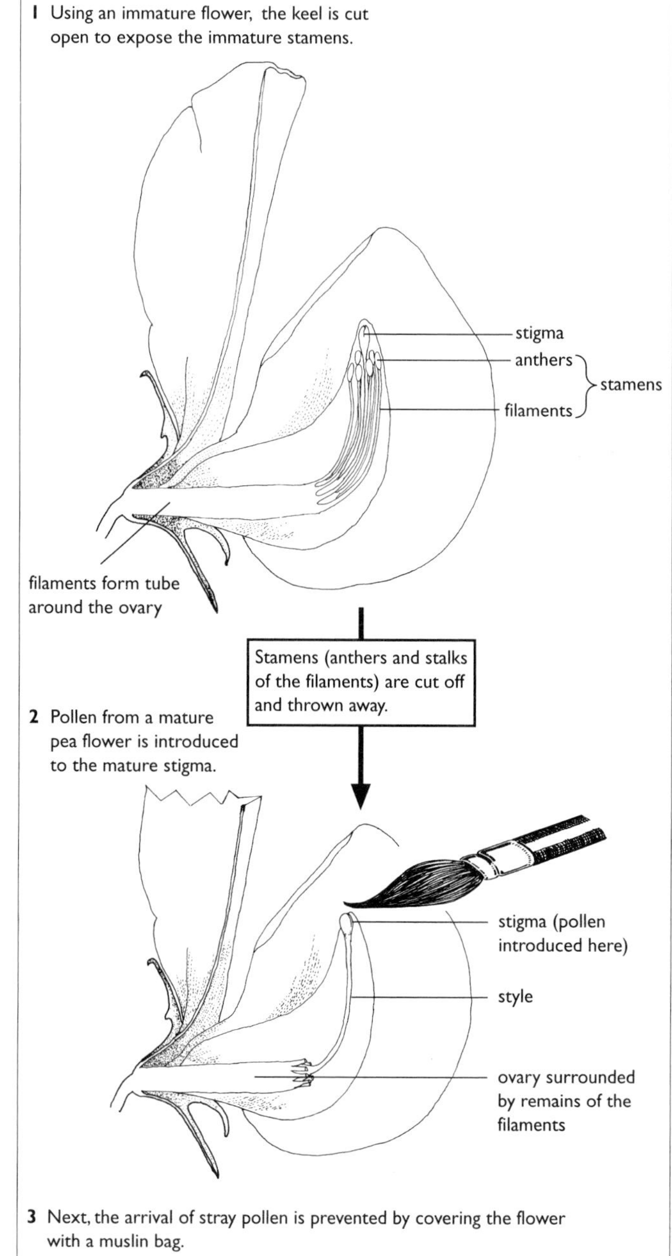

The monohybrid cross

In the monohybrid crosses, Mendel restricted observations to what happened when he crossed pure breeding plants that differed in just ***one*** characteristic. For example, Mendel crossed tall pea plants and dwarf pea plants and then followed the inheritance of height in the subsequent generations of pea plants, produced by self-pollination (Figures 2.2 and 2.3).

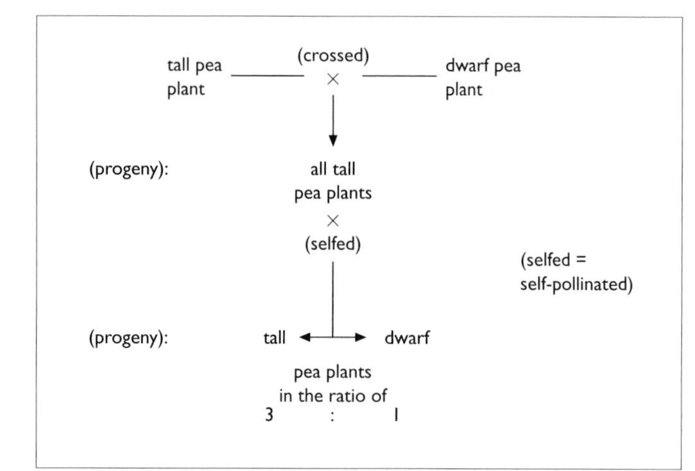

Figure 2.2 Monohybrid cross in summary.

1 What is the term we now use for 'breeding true'?

2 What do we mean by 'pollination' and 'fertilisation'?

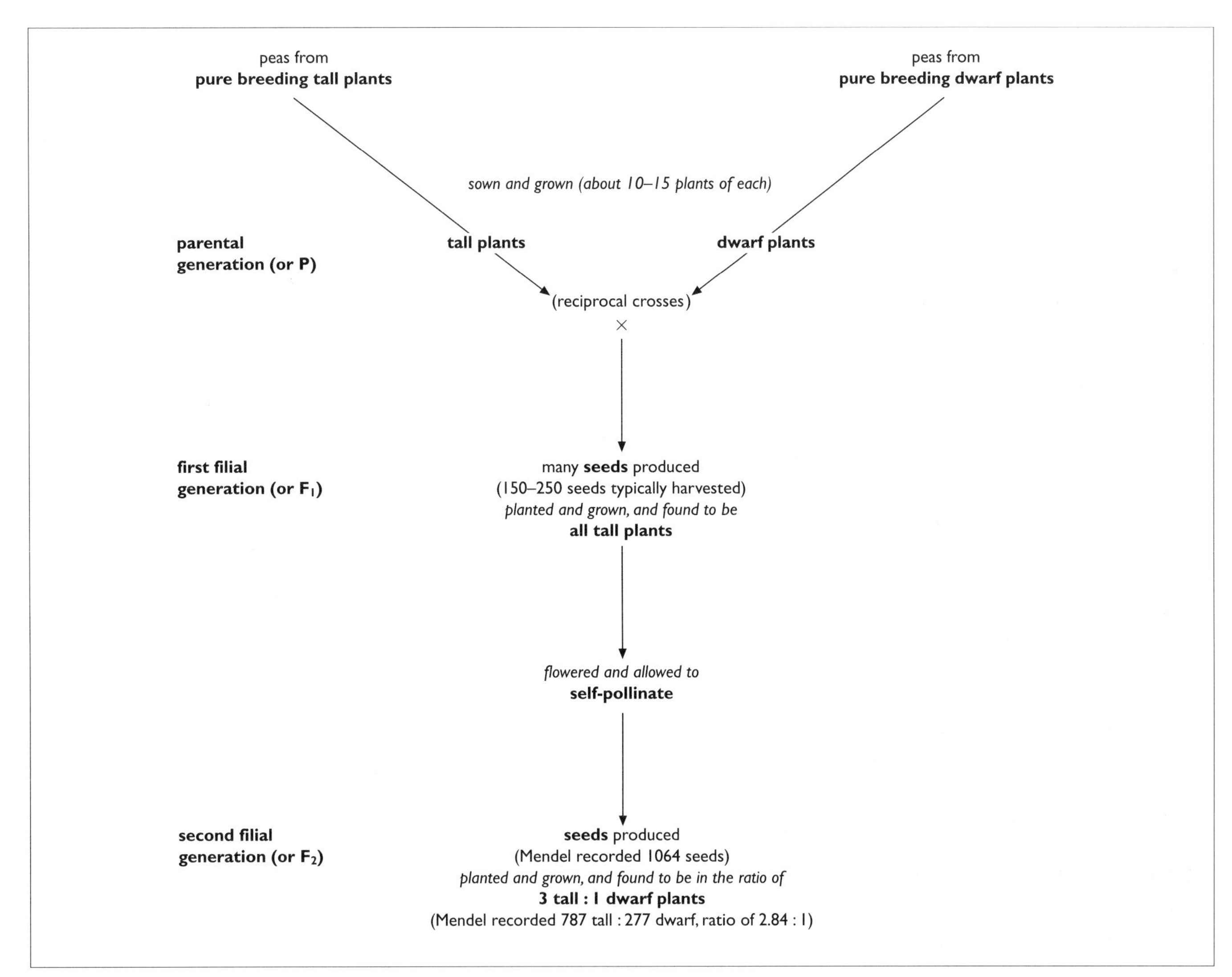

Figure 2.3 The steps to Mendel's monohybrid cross.

Mendel's interpretation

Because the 'dwarf' characteristic had apparently 'disappeared' in the F_1 generation and reappeared in the F_2 generation, there must be a 'factor' controlling 'dwarfness' that remained intact from one generation to another. However, this factor did not express itself in the presence of a similar factor for 'tallness'. Logically there must be two independent factors for height, one from one parent and the other factor from the other parent, in the cells of an organism. A sex cell (**gamete**) must contain only one of these factors.

Mendel saw that a 3:1 ratio could be the product of randomly combining two pairs of unlike factors (**A** and **a**).

$$(A + a)(A + a) = 1AA + 2Aa + 1aa$$ (the **binomial expression**)

This can also be shown using a grid, now known as a Punnett square, after the mathematician who first used it (Figure 2.4).

Figure 2.4 The binomial expression by Punnett square.

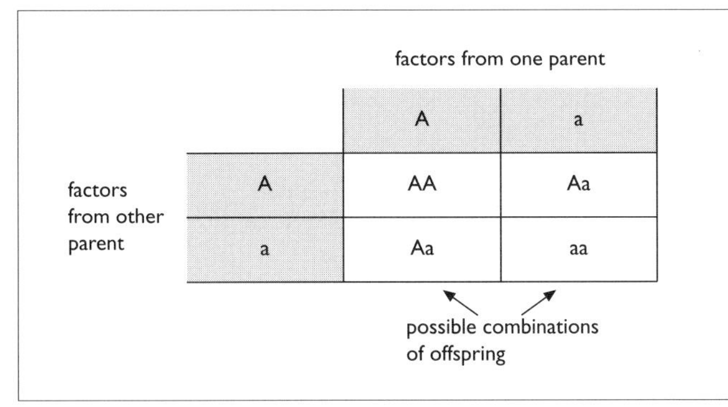

Table 2.1 Mendel's conclusions from the monohybrid cross.

- Within an organism there are breeding 'factors' controlling characteristics such as 'tall' and 'dwarf'
- There are two factors in each cell
- One factor comes from each parent
- The factors separate in reproduction, and either can enter an offspring
- The factor for tall is an alternative form of the factor for dwarf
- The factor for tall is dominant over the factor for dwarf

Interpreting Mendel today

Within the nucleus are chromosomes, which contain DNA (page 40). In non-dividing cells the chromosomes are dispersed as chromatin, but at times of cell division the nucleus divides first, and at this stage, chromosomes are visible. In the time of Mendel the structure and roles of the nucleus were a closed book. We now recognise the nucleus to have a double function; it controls the activity of the cell, and is also the location of the hereditary material.

The **'chromosome theory'** is our way of interpreting Mendel's work today.

- Mendel's 'factors' are **genes** found on chromosomes in the nucleus of every cell.
- Normally, there are at least two forms of a gene and they are called **alleles**. Allele is an abbreviation of allelomorph, meaning 'alternative form'.
- In the garden pea the allele for 'tallness' is **dominant** over the allele for 'dwarfness', which is **recessive**.
- A 'pure breeding' tall plant is **homozygous** for the tall allele, that is, it has two alleles for tallness. A pure breeding dwarf plant is homozygous for the dwarf allele.
- The F_1 progeny in Mendel's monohybrid cross was **heterozygous** tall, with one allele for tallness and one allele for dwarfness.
- In the heterozygous individual the recessive allele is not **expressed**.
- The terms 'homozygous' and 'heterozygous' refer to the genetic constitution or **genotype** of the individual.
- The actual appearance of the organism, that is, whether it is tall or dwarf, is its **phenotype**. This term is important because adverse environmental conditions may cause a tall organism to be stunted in growth, for example.

3 Normally the number of chromosomes per nucleus is unchanged, except when gametes (sex cells) are formed, when the number is halved. By what process is the chromosome number halved, and what is the importance of this reduction?

Figure 2.5 Diagram showing the behaviour of alleles in Mendel's monohybrid cross.

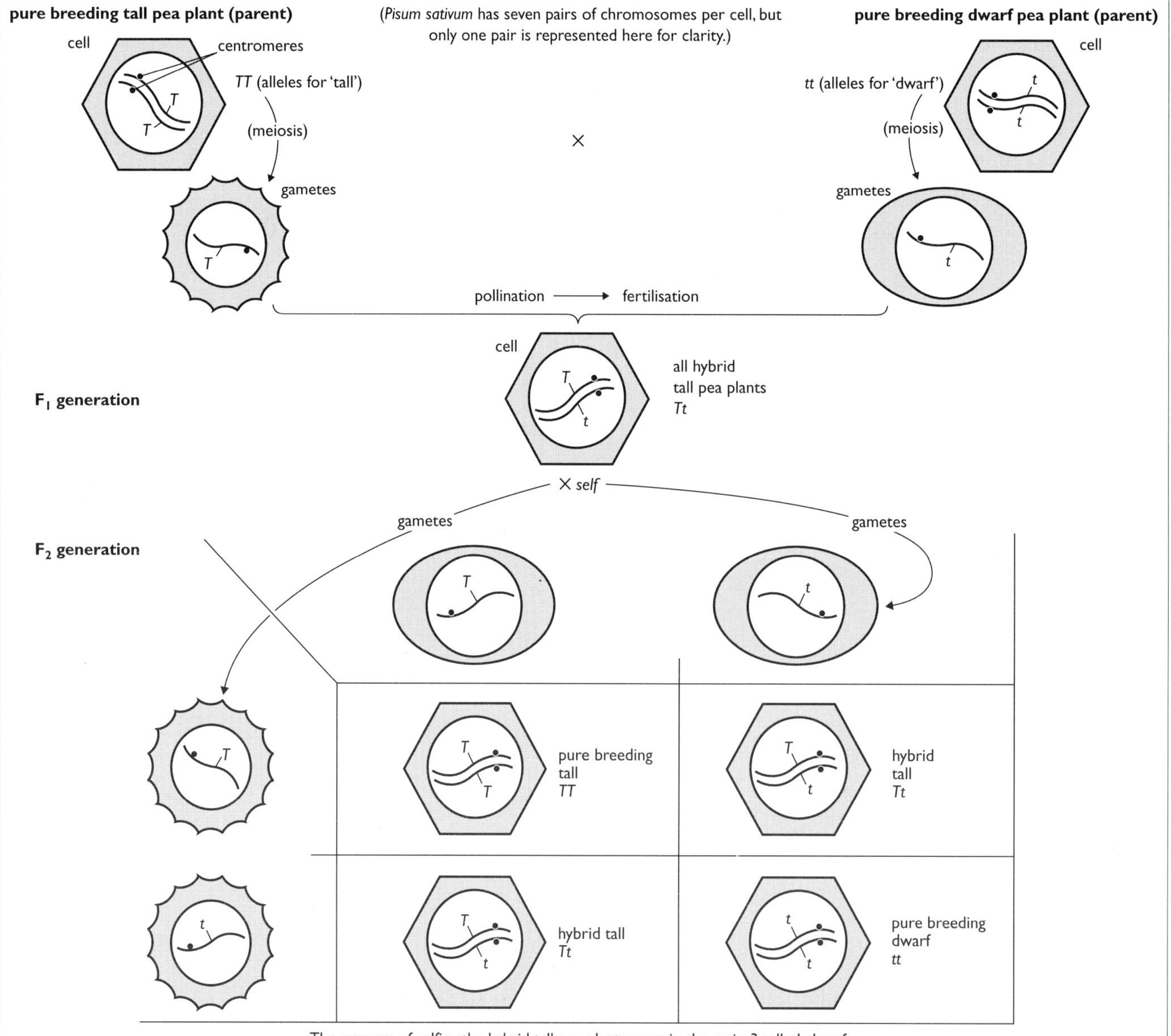

The progeny of selfing the hybrid tall pea plants were in the ratio 3 tall : 1 dwarf.

Mendel never stated his discoveries as **'Laws'** as we do today, but it might have helped others to understand his work had he done so. For example, he might have said 'Each characteristic of an organism is determined by a pair of factors of which only one can be present in each gamete'.

Today we talk of Mendel's 'First Law' as the **Law of Segregation: The characteristics of an organism are controlled by pairs of alleles, which separate in equal numbers into different gametes as a result of meiosis** (page 20).

Figure 2.6 Genetic diagram showing the behaviour of alleles in Mendel's monohybrid cross.

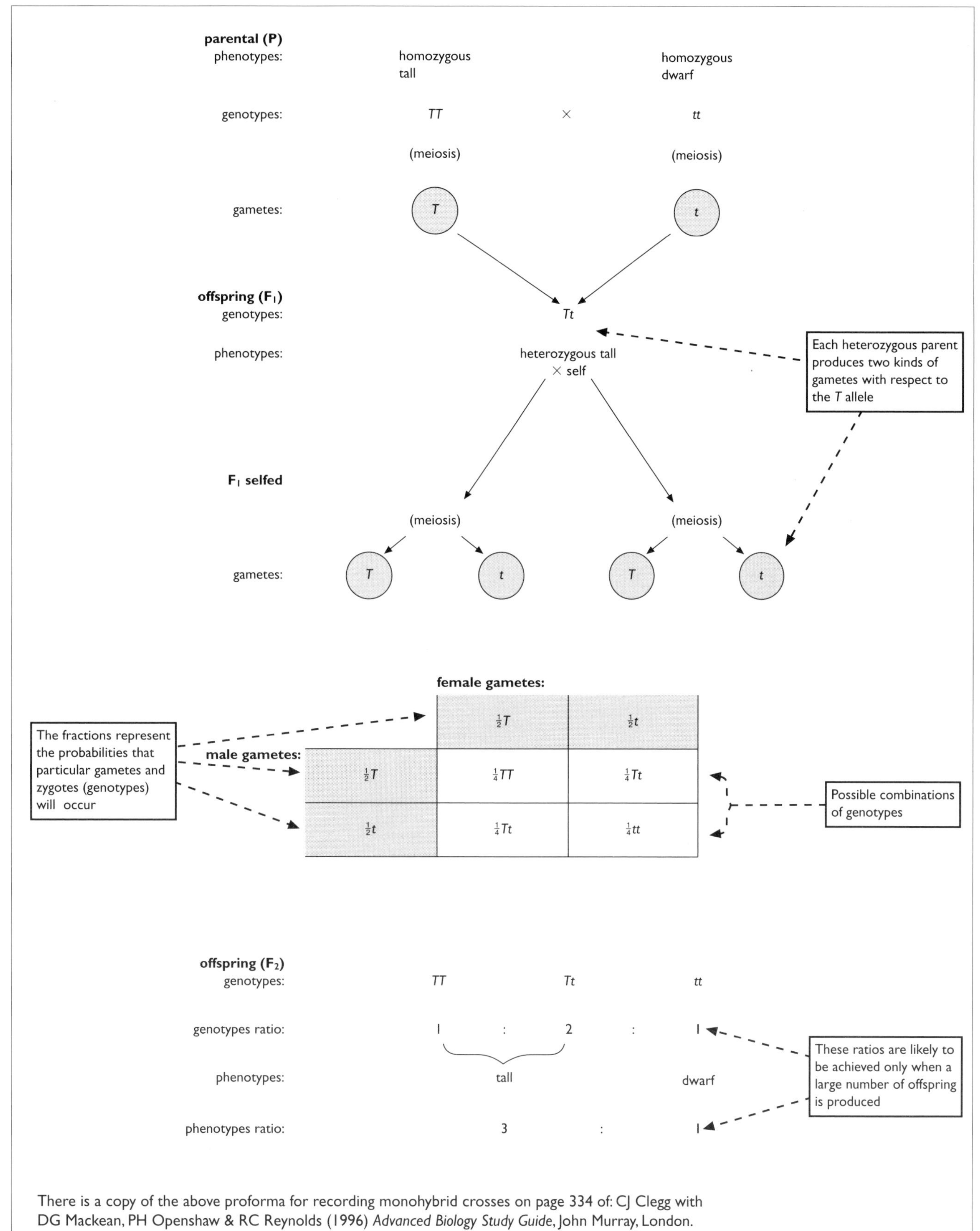

There is a copy of the above proforma for recording monohybrid crosses on page 334 of: CJ Clegg with DG Mackean, PH Openshaw & RC Reynolds (1996) *Advanced Biology Study Guide*, John Murray, London.

Telling 'tall' pea plants apart: Mendel's test cross

Mendel had discovered that tall pea plants of genotypes '*TT*' and '*Tt*' looked alike (but remember, his name for genes was 'factors'). You could tell plants like these apart only by the progeny they produced. He crossed tall plants with the homozygous recessive plants (*tt*), and predicted, correctly, that the cross with **heterozygous** tall (*Tt*) would yield 50% tall and 50% dwarf plants. Of course, sufficient numbers of plants had to be used to obtain this distinctive ratio. This type of cross has become known as a **test cross**.

Figure 2.7 Mendel's test cross in summary.

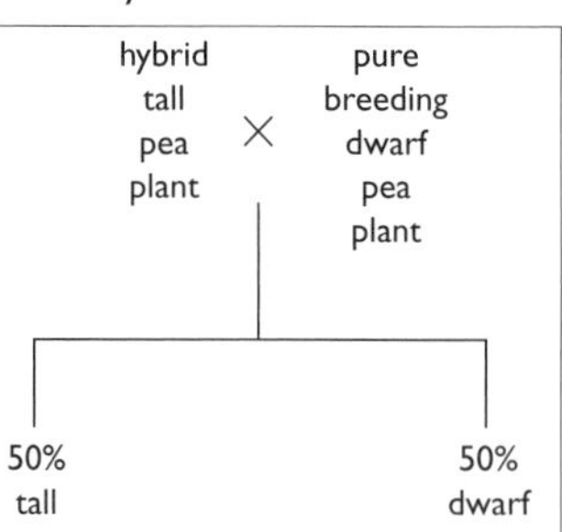

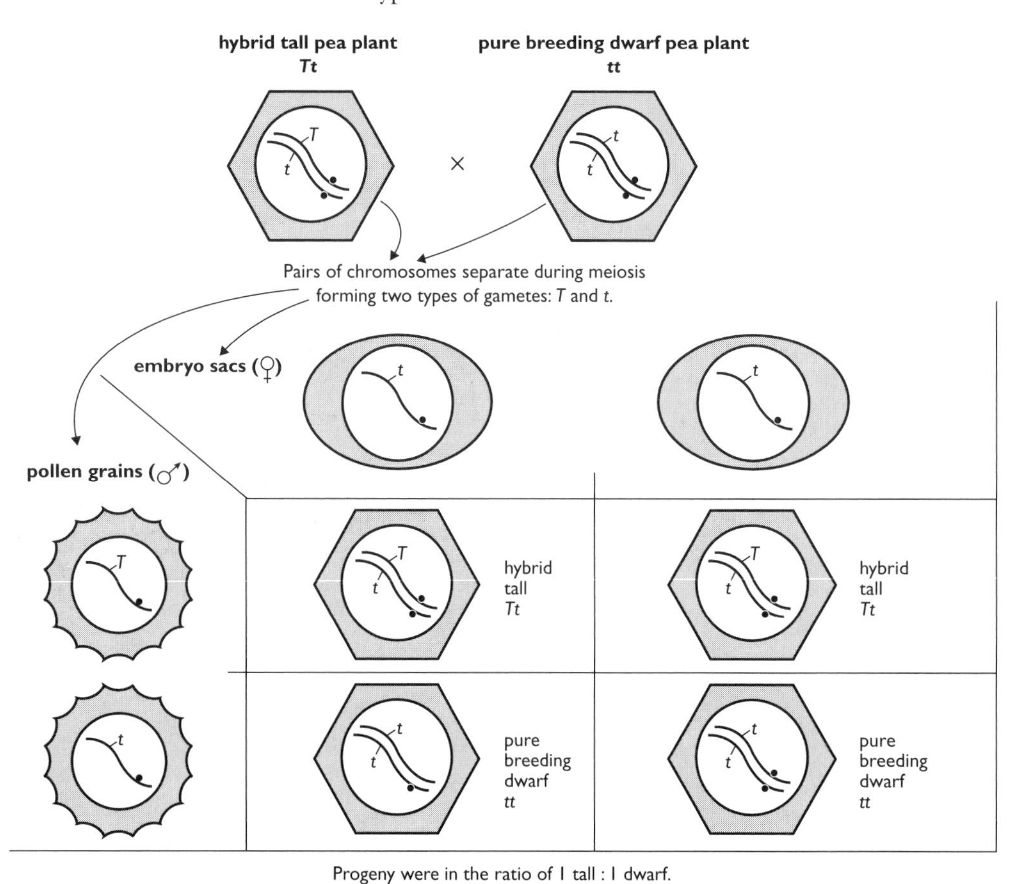

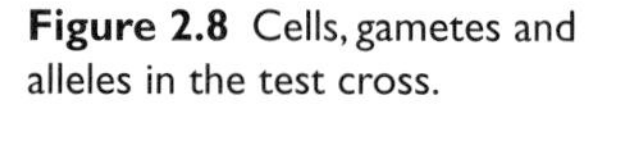

Figure 2.8 Cells, gametes and alleles in the test cross.

parental

phenotypes: tall × dwarf

genotypes: *Tt* × *tt*

(meiosis) (meiosis)

gametes: (*T*) (*t*) (*t*) (*t*)

	$\frac{1}{2}t$	$\frac{1}{2}t$
$\frac{1}{2}T$	$\frac{1}{4}Tt$	$\frac{1}{4}Tt$
$\frac{1}{2}t$	$\frac{1}{4}tt$	$\frac{1}{4}tt$

offspring

genotypes:	*Tt*		*tt*
genotypes ratio:	1	:	1
phenotypes:	tall		dwarf
phenotypes ratio:	50%	:	50%

Figure 2.9 Genetic diagram of Mendel's test cross.

4 What percentage of the progeny are 'tall' when **homozygous** tall peas are crossed with homozygous dwarf pea plants?

Monohybrid inheritance in animals

Leopards and panthers

Leopards and panthers are good examples of 'big cat' mammals. Typically, they prey on medium to large-sized herbivorous mammals, often hauling their catch into trees for safety, prior to feeding. Leopards and panthers used to be widely distributed in tropical and sub-tropical rain forests throughout Africa and over vast areas of Asia. Today, over much of their range they have been exterminated by humans, commonly by habitat destruction.

The leopard and panther were traditionally thought of as separate but closely related species, but we now know that the differences are due to one pair of alleles. The panther is a black variety of the leopard, just as the dwarf garden pea is related to the tall pea! This genetic connection was discovered by breeding in captivity.

Figure 2.10 The leopard and the panther (*Panthera pardus*).

Figure 2.11 Mendelian inheritance of coat colour/pattern in *Panthera pardus*.

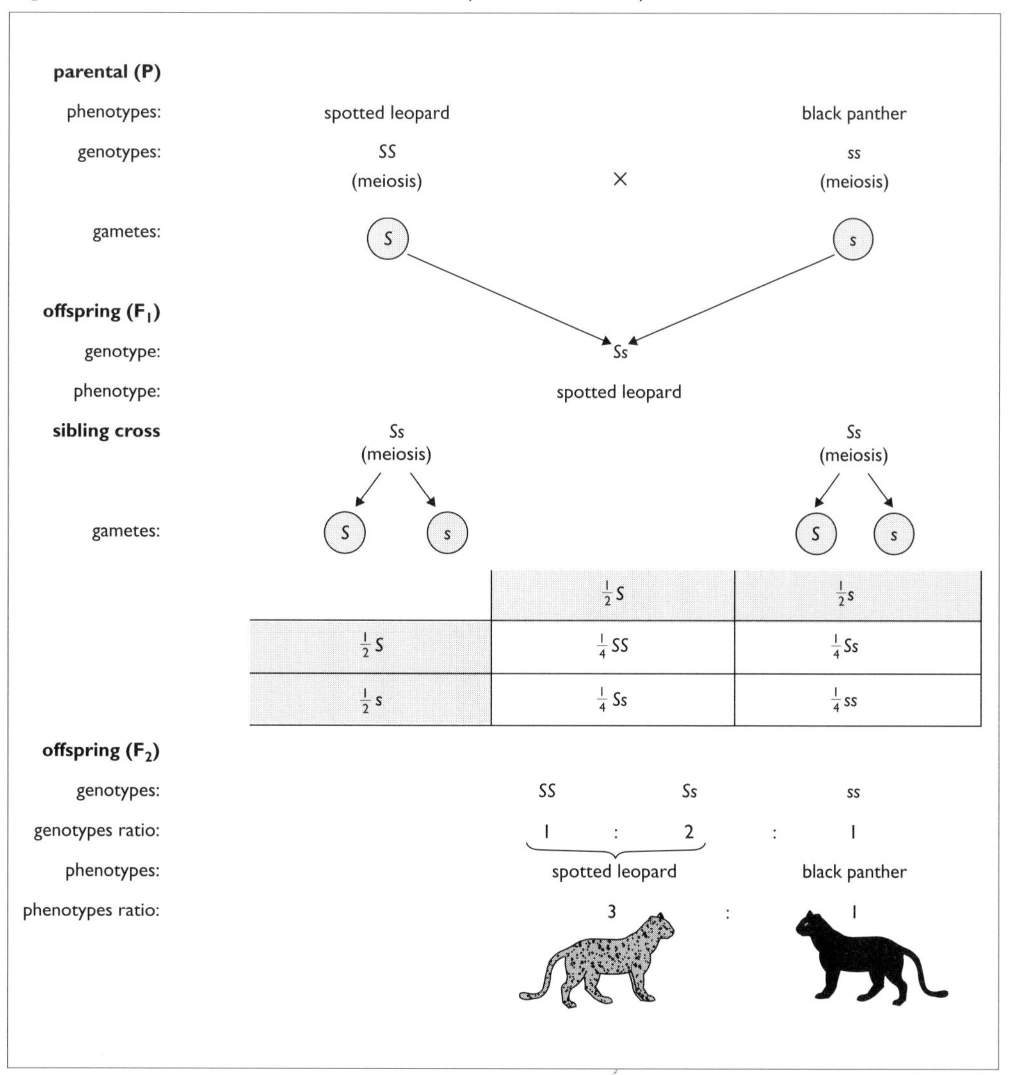

Humans

Studying inheritance in humans by carrying out Mendelian crosses (with experimentally selected parents, sibling crosses and the production of large numbers of progeny) is out of the question. Instead, we may investigate the pattern of inheritance of a particular characteristic by researching a **family pedigree**, where appropriate records of the ancestors exist.

A human pedigree chart uses a set of rules, outlined in Figure 2.12. Using pedigree charts we may identify different patterns of inheritance.

> **5 a)** Who are the female grandchildren of Richard and Judith?
> **b)** Who are Alan's
> i) grandparents
> ii) uncles?
> **c)** How many people in this pedigree chart have parents unknown to us?
> **d)** Name two offspring who are cousins.

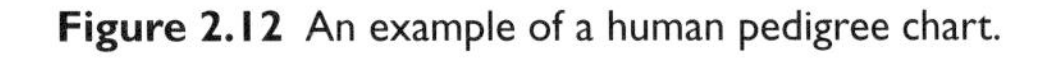

Figure 2.12 An example of a human pedigree chart.

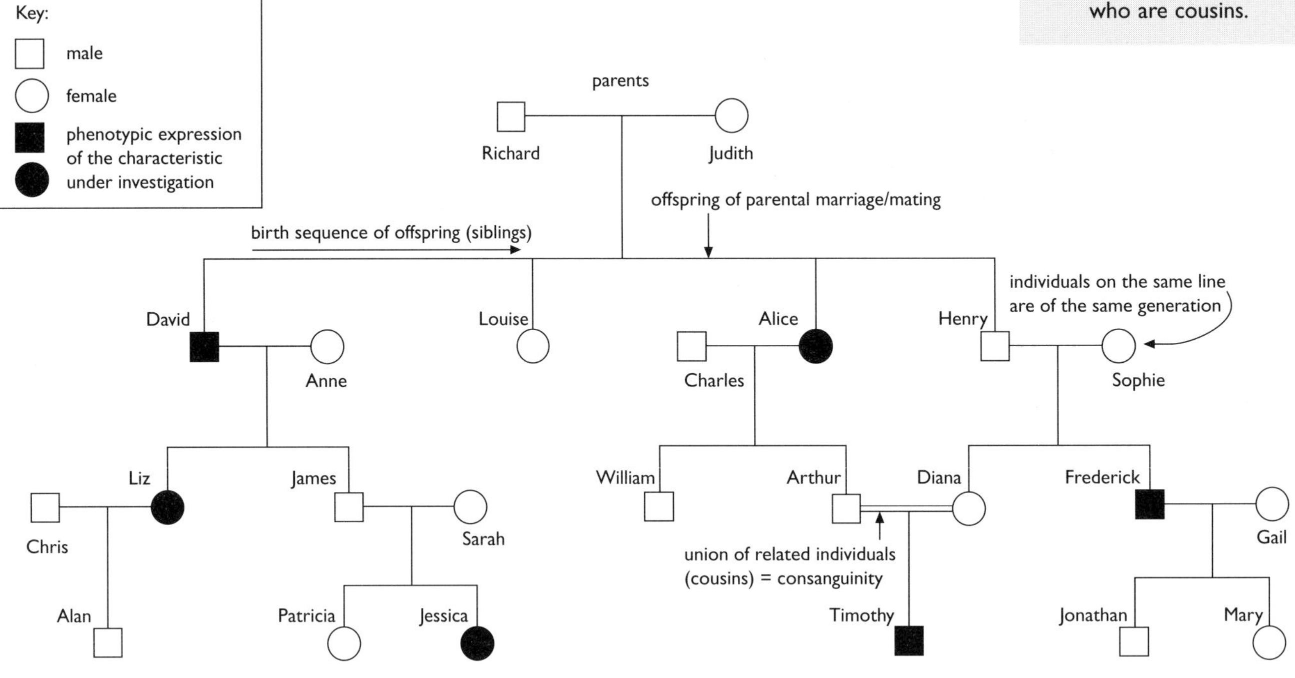

Albinism is a rare inherited condition of humans (and other mammals) in which the individual has a block in the biochemical pathway by which the pigment melanin is formed. Albinos have white hair, very light coloured skin and pink eyes. Albinism shows a pattern of **recessive monohybrid inheritance** in humans; that is to say, in a pedigree chart of a family with albino members, albinism occurs infrequently, often 'skipping' one or more generations altogether.

Figure 2.13 Pedigree chart of a family with albino members.

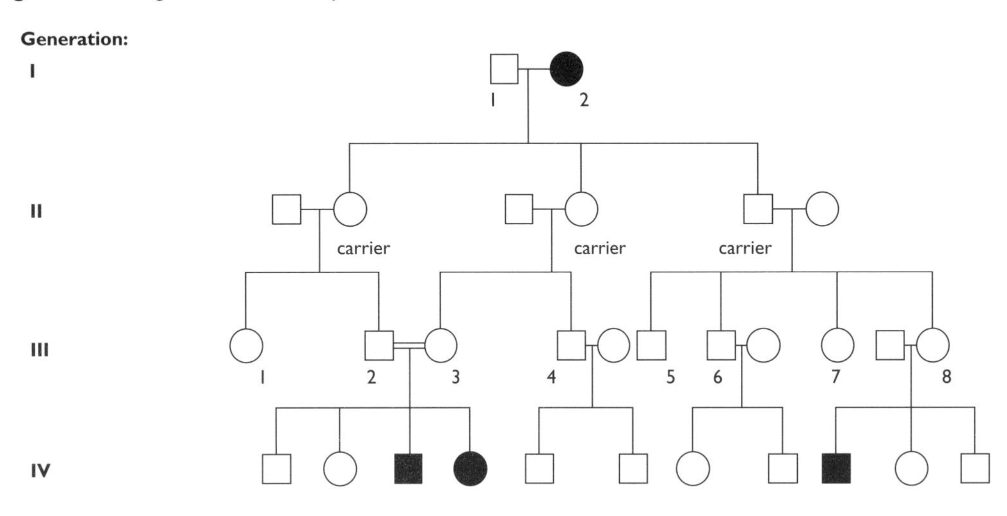

- In **generation I:** individual 1 may be *PP* (homozygous normal pigmentation) or *Pp* (heterozygous normal pigmentation); individual 2 must be *pp* in order to show albinism.
- In **generation II:** all offspring must be carriers *Pp* (heterozygous normal).
- In **generation III:** no individual is albino, but offspring 2, 3 and 8 are carriers (therefore albino offspring) and so is the partner to 8.
- In **generation IV:** three of the 11 offspring are albino (a high incidence), arising because of the cousin marriage (2 and 3) and the unusual chance of 8's partner also being a carrier.

Brachydactyly is a rare condition of humans in which the fingers are very short. Brachydactyly is due to a mutation (page 36) in the gene for finger length. Unusually, the mutant allele is dominant, so brachydactyly shows a pattern of **dominant monohybrid inheritance** among members of a family in which it occurs. A dominant characteristic tends to occur in members of every generation.

Figure 2.14 Brachydactyly. X-ray of bones of hand of normal length (left) and drawing of brachydactylous hand (right).

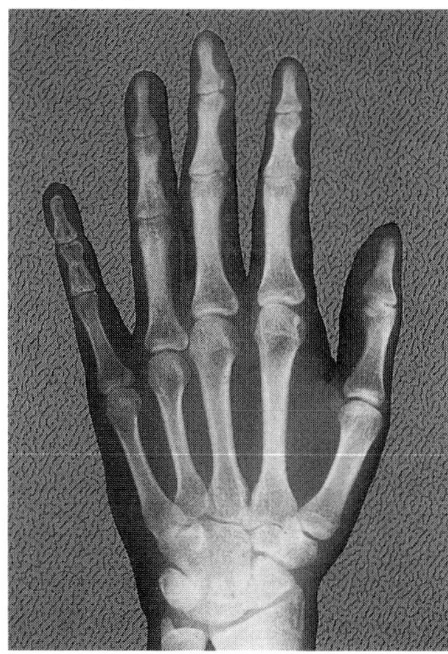

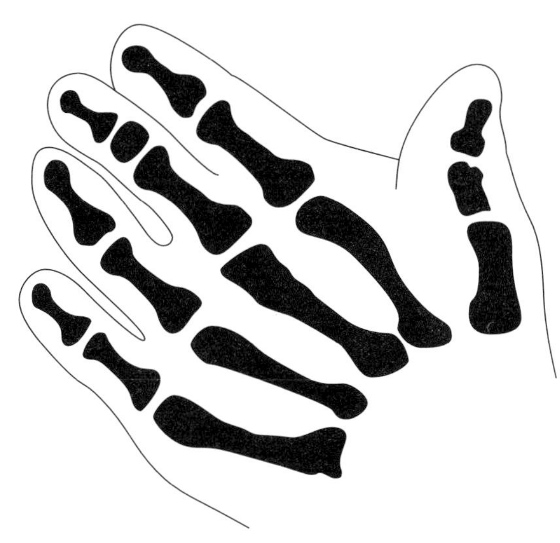

6 If a homozygous normal hand parent (*nn*) were crossed with a heterozygous brachydactylous parent (*Nn*) what is the probability of an offspring with brachydactylous hands? Show your working using a genetic diagram.

Figure 2.15 Pedigree chart of a family with brachydactylous genes.

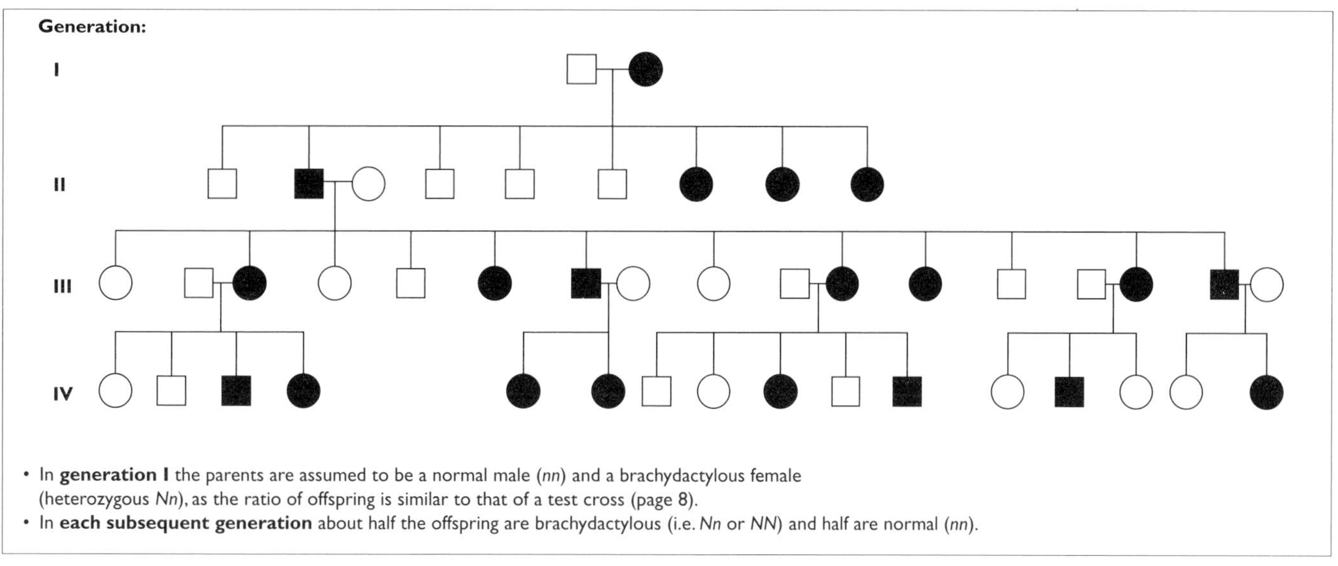

- In **generation I** the parents are assumed to be a normal male (*nn*) and a brachydactylous female (heterozygous *Nn*), as the ratio of offspring is similar to that of a test cross (page 8).
- In **each subsequent generation** about half the offspring are brachydactylous (i.e. *Nn* or *NN*) and half are normal (*nn*).

Figure 2.16 Human characteristics that are not examples of monohybrid inheritance.

The genetics of eye colour is almost certainly a polygenic trait (page 30). Look carefully at the eyes of blue-eyed people. In some it is possible to see tiny patches of green or brown pigmentation. Such people, when they become parents, quite commonly have brown-eyed children. Mendel's First Law cannot be applied to human eye colour until we know how many controlling genes are involved.

Eye colour

Many (but not all) people can roll their tongues. Even members of identical twin pairs may differ in this. If genetically controlled, this facility is likely to be polygenic. However, cultural and social differences, including breast feeding as a baby, are more likely to be involved.

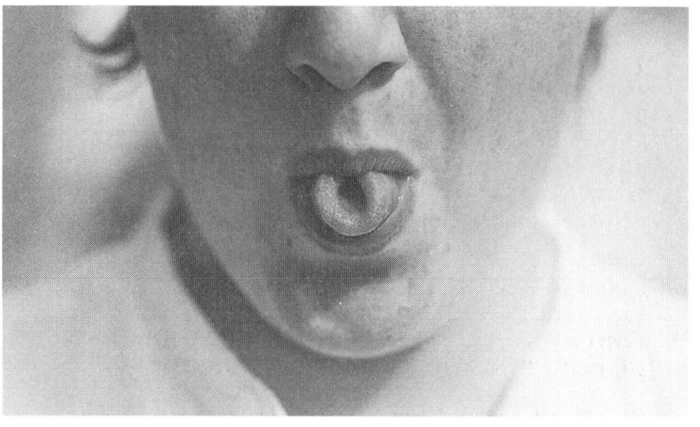

'Tongue rolling'

The dihybrid cross

Mendel also investigated the simultaneous inheritance of two pairs of contrasting characters, using the garden pea plant. This he referred to as a **dihydrid cross**. We can illustrate this series of experiments by reference to the one with pea plants grown from seeds that were round with yellow cotyledons, crossed with plants grown from seeds that were wrinkled with green cotyledons. Mendel confirmed the results by carrying out experiments with peas showing other pairs of contrasting characteristics (and also with other experimental plants). He published his results through his local natural history/agricultural research society, and by regular correspondence with important scientists of the time. We cannot be confident that anyone apart from Mendel saw the significance of his discoveries in his lifetime, however.

Figure 2.17 Mendel's dihybrid cross.

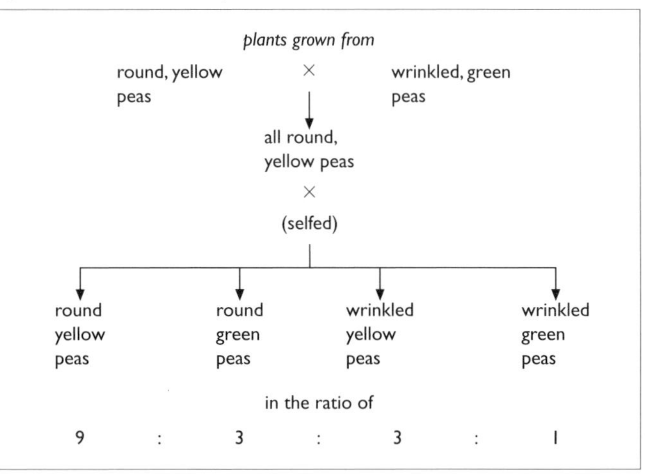

Figure 2.18 The steps to Mendel's dihybrid cross.

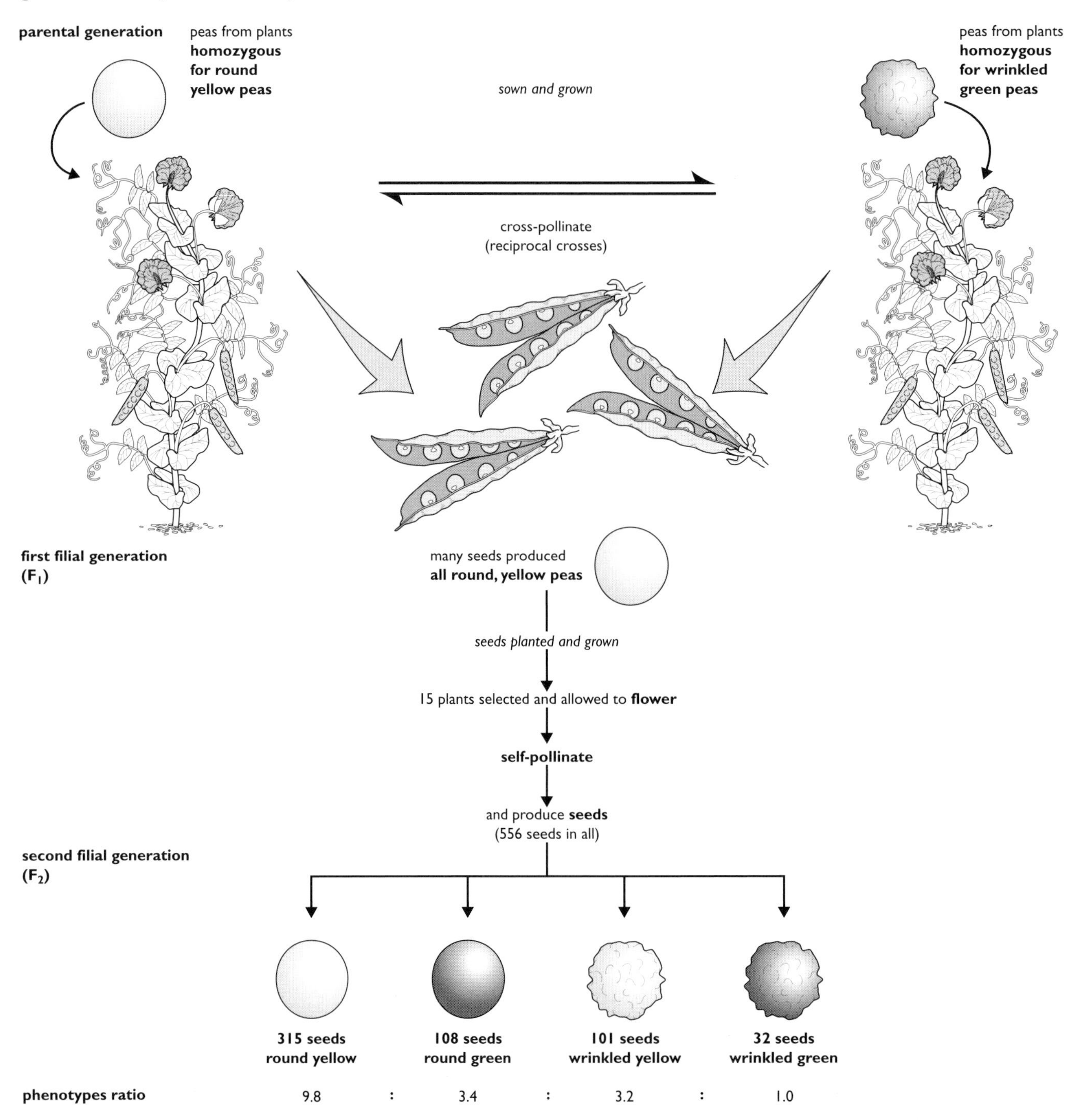

Figure 2.19 Genetic diagram showing the behaviour of alleles in Mendel's dihybrid cross.

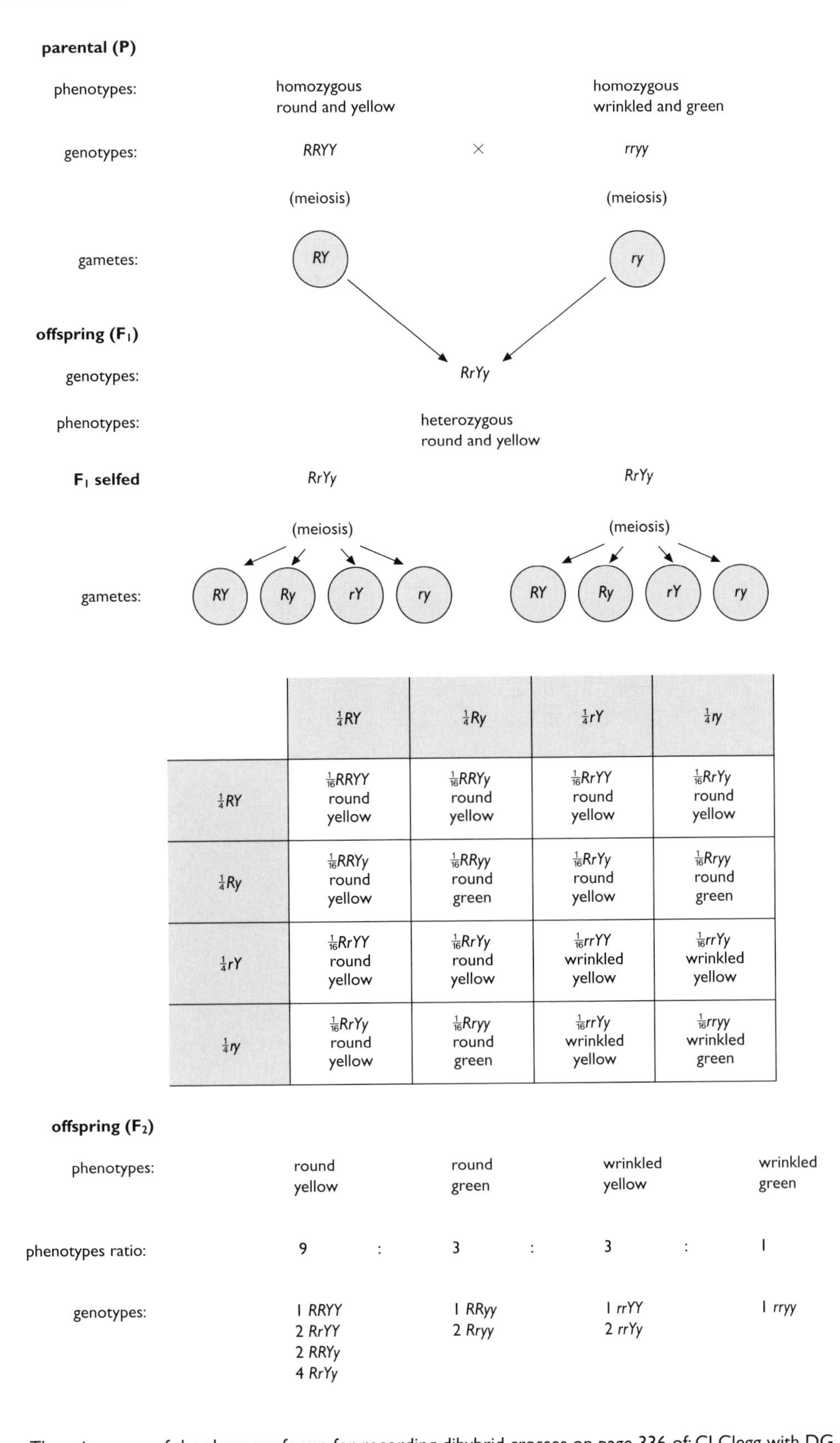

	$\frac{1}{4}$*RY*	$\frac{1}{4}$*Ry*	$\frac{1}{4}$*rY*	$\frac{1}{4}$*ry*
$\frac{1}{4}$*RY*	$\frac{1}{16}$*RRYY* round yellow	$\frac{1}{16}$*RRYy* round yellow	$\frac{1}{16}$*RrYY* round yellow	$\frac{1}{16}$*RrYy* round yellow
$\frac{1}{4}$*Ry*	$\frac{1}{16}$*RRYy* round yellow	$\frac{1}{16}$*RRyy* round green	$\frac{1}{16}$*RrYy* round yellow	$\frac{1}{16}$*Rryy* round green
$\frac{1}{4}$*rY*	$\frac{1}{16}$*RrYY* round yellow	$\frac{1}{16}$*RrYy* round yellow	$\frac{1}{16}$*rrYY* wrinkled yellow	$\frac{1}{16}$*rrYy* wrinkled yellow
$\frac{1}{4}$*ry*	$\frac{1}{16}$*RrYy* round yellow	$\frac{1}{16}$*Rryy* round green	$\frac{1}{16}$*rrYy* wrinkled yellow	$\frac{1}{16}$*rryy* wrinkled green

There is a copy of the above proforma for recording dihybrid crosses on page 336 of: CJ Clegg with DG Mackean, PH Openshaw & RC Reynolds (1996) *Advanced Biology Study Guide*, John Murray, London.

Mendel did not express the outcome of the dihybrid cross as a succinct **'Second Law'**. However, today we call Mendel's 'Second Law' the

Law of Independent Assortment: Two or more pairs of alleles segregate independently of each other as a result of meiosis, provided the genes concerned are not linked by being on the same chromosome.

7 What is significant about the likely positions of the genes for round/wrinkled and for yellow/green cotyledons within the nucleus that we can appreciate, which was unknown to Mendel?

The dihybrid cross and the chromosome theory

Again we can interpret the dihybrid cross in terms of the **chromosome theory** (page 6).

> **8** What are the roles of the centromere in the process of meiosis?

Figure 2.20 Chromosome theory and the dihybrid cross.

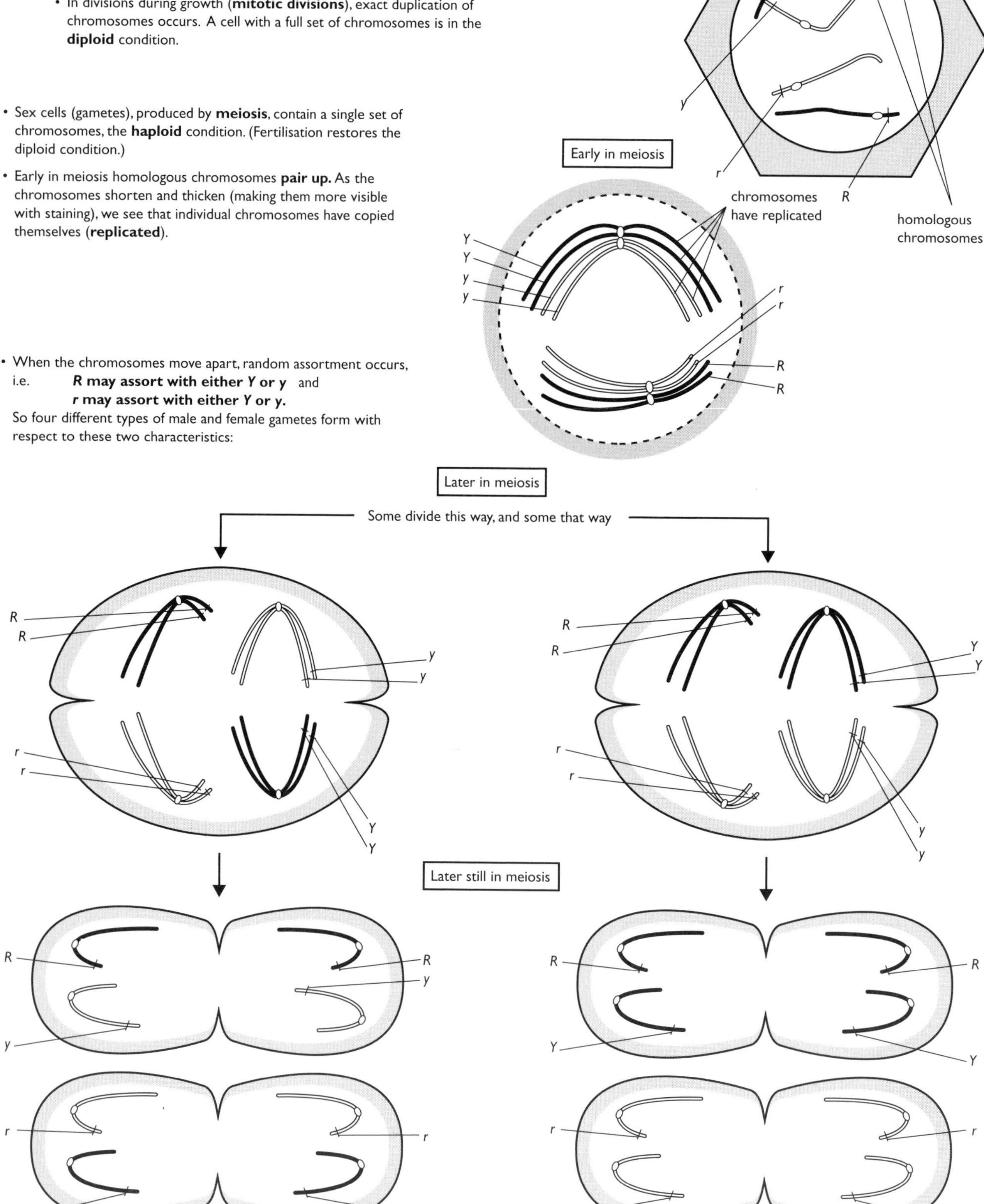

• Where very many gametes are formed they occur in the following proportions: $\frac{1}{4}RY : \frac{1}{4}Ry : \frac{1}{4}rY : \frac{1}{4}ry$.
• Then random fertilisations between these gametes will produce the ratio of progeny (9 : 3 : 3 : 1) of the dihybrid cross.

Probability and chance in Mendelian crosses

The progeny produced in a dihybrid cross experiment do not exactly agree with the prediction we make from Mendel's explanation. For example, in Figure 2.18 (page 12) the 556 seeds produced do not exactly fit the 9:3:3:1 ratio.

What can go 'wrong'?

- More pollen grains of one type than the others may succeed in fertilising eggs cells.
- If few progeny survive (for example, owing to browsing/predation) then the sample may be too small to be representative.

Do the observed values differ significantly from the expected outcome?

- A simple statistical test, the chi-squared test (χ^2), is used to estimate the probability that differences between the observed and the expected results are due to chance.

Figure 2.21 The chi-squared test of Mendel's dihybrid cross.

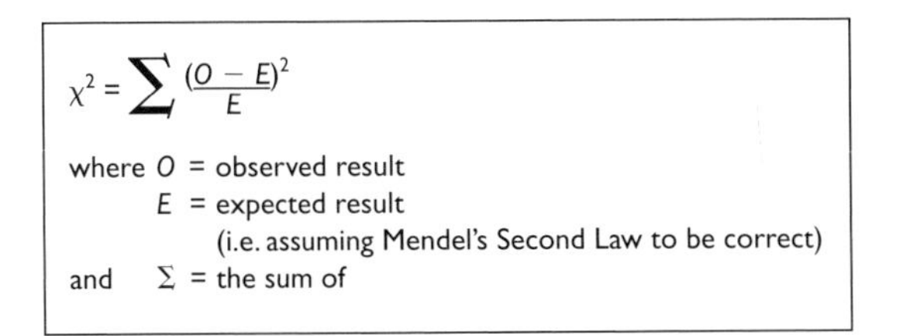

The chi-squared test of Mendel's dihybrid cross shown in Figure 2.18, page 12:

Category	Predicted	O	E	O – E	(O – E)^2	$\frac{(O-E)^2}{E}$
round yellow	9	315	312.75	2.25	5.062	0.016
round green	3	108	104.25	3.75	14.062	0.135
wrinkled yellow	3	101	104.25	−3.25	10.562	0.101
wrinkled green	1	32	34.75	−2.75	7.562	0.218
	total =	556			Σ =	0.47

Thus $\chi^2 = 0.47$

There were four categories, and therefore only three degrees of freedom (i.e. for any one condition there are three alternatives).

Values of χ^2 for three degrees of freedom (taken from statistical tables):

Probability	0.99	0.95	0.9	0.7	0.5	0.3	0.1	0.05	0.01	0.001
df = 3	0.115	0.35	0.58	0.71	1.39	3.66	6.25	7.82	11.34	16.27

This value (0.47) lies between a probability of 0.95 and 0.90. This means that a deviation of this size is due to chance.

It can be expected 90–95% of the times the experiment is carried out.

There is no significant deviation between the observed (O) and the expected (E) results.

9 The observed results of one of Mendel's monohybrid crosses are given in Figure 2.3 (page 5). Is the difference between these values (O) and the results to be expected (E) due to chance; that is, is the deviation between the observed and expected result an insignificant one?

Note that the formula for χ^2 in cases where there are only two categories is:

$$\chi^2 = \frac{\{(O - E) - 0.5\}^2}{E}$$

As there are only two categories there is only one degree of freedom (df). Values of χ^2 for one degree of freedom (taken from statistical tables) are:

Probability	0.99	0.95	0.5	0.3	0.1	0.01	0.001
df = 1	0.00016	0.004	0.455	1.074	2.71	6.635	10.83

Drosophila and the dihybrid cross

Drosophila melanogaster (the vinegar fly) was first selected by an American geneticist called Thomas Morgan in 1908 to investigate Mendelian genetics in an animal. Morgan was awarded a Nobel Prize in 1933, for he had shown:

- that Mendel's 'factors' are linear sequences of genes on chromosomes (the Chromosome Theory of Inheritance);
- the relative positions of genes on chromosomes (page 22);
- sex chromosomes and sex linkage (pages 23–24);
- crossing over, the exchange of genes between chromosomes, resulting from chiasmata formed during meiosis (page 20).

Drosophila occurs around rotting vegetable materials as a **common form** (originally called the 'wild type'*) and as various naturally occurring **mutants**. *Drosophila* has four pairs of chromosomes, and a generation time of about 14 weeks. One female produces hundreds of offspring. These flies are relatively easily handled, can be cultured on a sterilised artificial medium in glass bottles and can be temporarily anaesthetised for setting up cultures and sorting progeny.

No, no, Gregor! God will find a purpose for them some day!

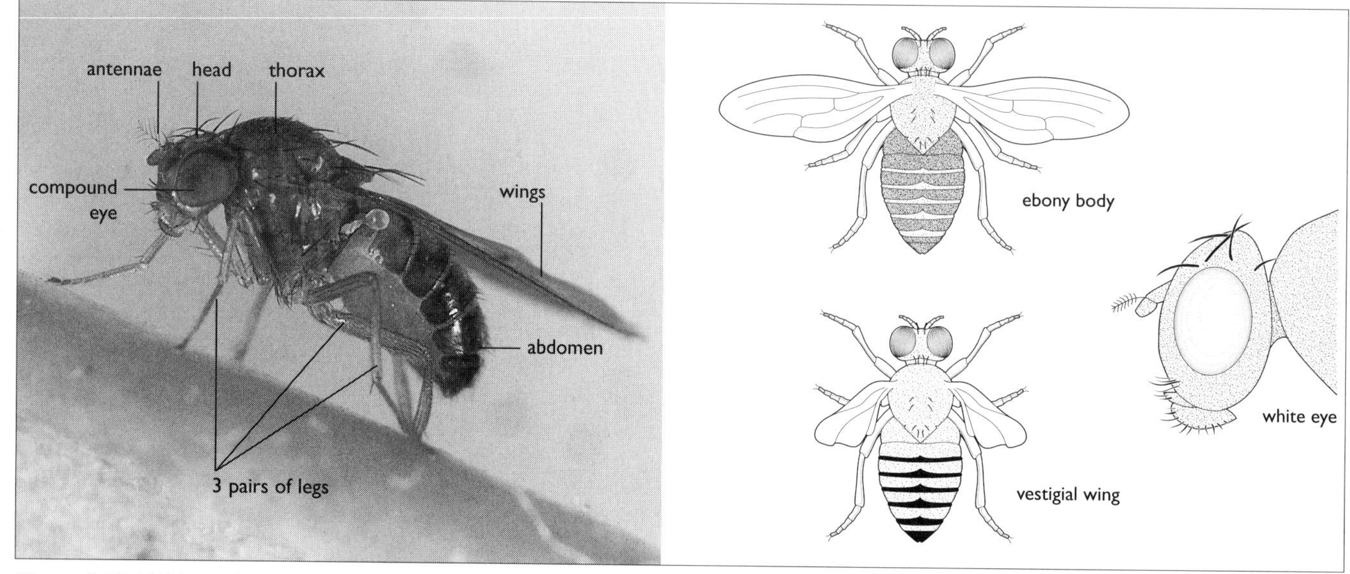

Figure 2.22 Wild type *Drosophila* and some common mutants.

The **dihybrid cross** can be shown in *Drosophila*, for example by crossing normal flies (wild type) with flies homozygous for vestigial wing and ebony body.

10 What is meant by the term 'mutant'?

*Some sources represent 'wild type' as ++, but this has been replaced by the usual upper case (for dominant) and lower case (recessive) letters used in representing crosses.

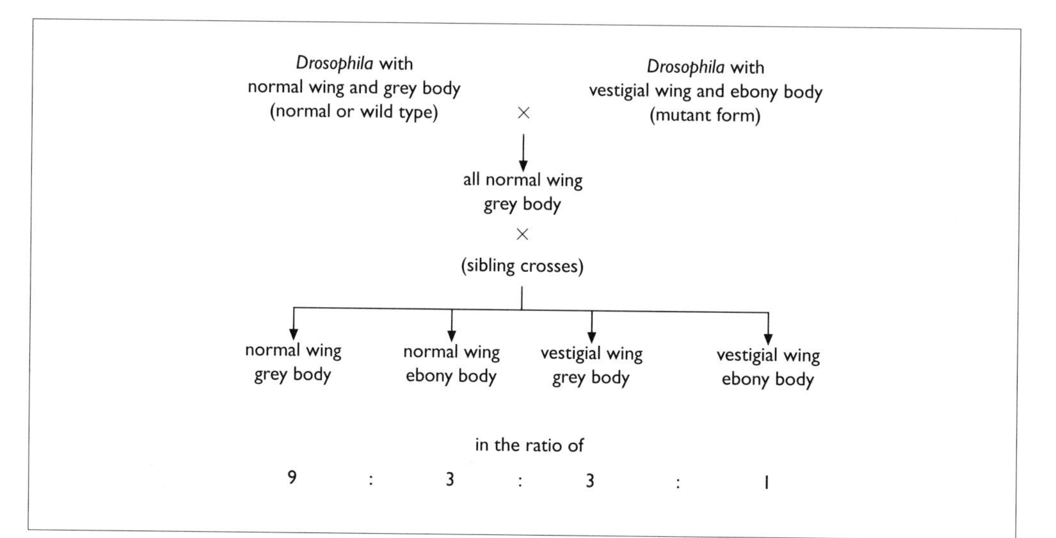

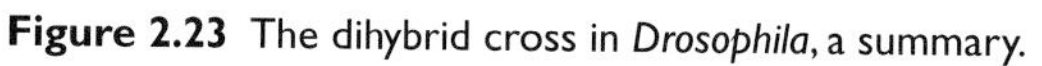

Figure 2.23 The dihybrid cross in *Drosophila*, a summary.

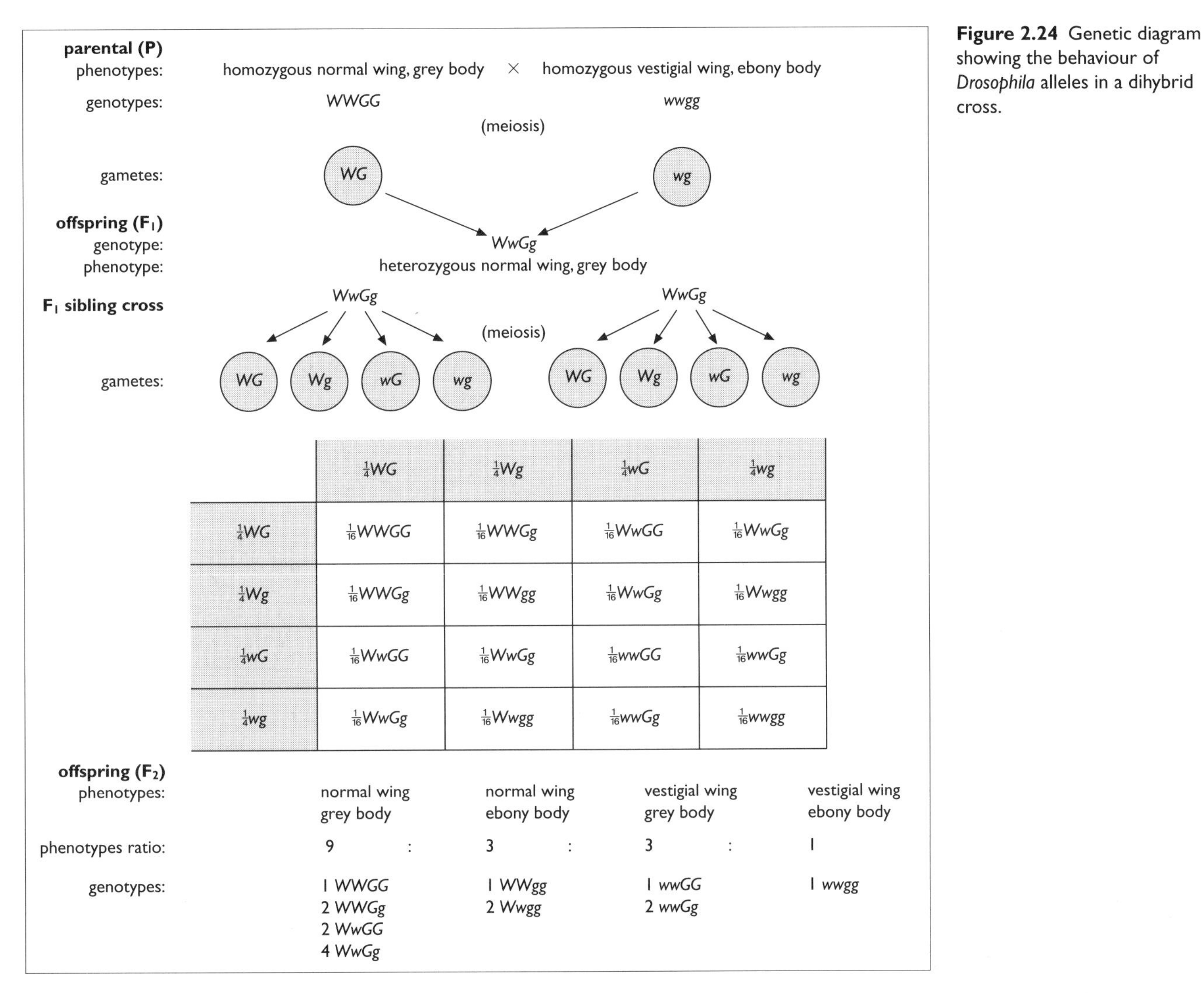

Figure 2.24 Genetic diagram showing the behaviour of *Drosophila* alleles in a dihybrid cross.

The dihybrid test cross

The test cross makes it possible to distinguish the genotypes of heterozygotes and homozygous dominants involved in the dihybrid cross.

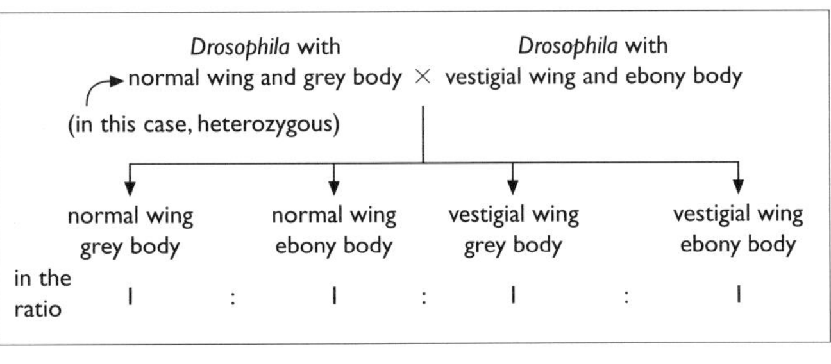

Figure 2.25 Dihybrid test cross in summary.

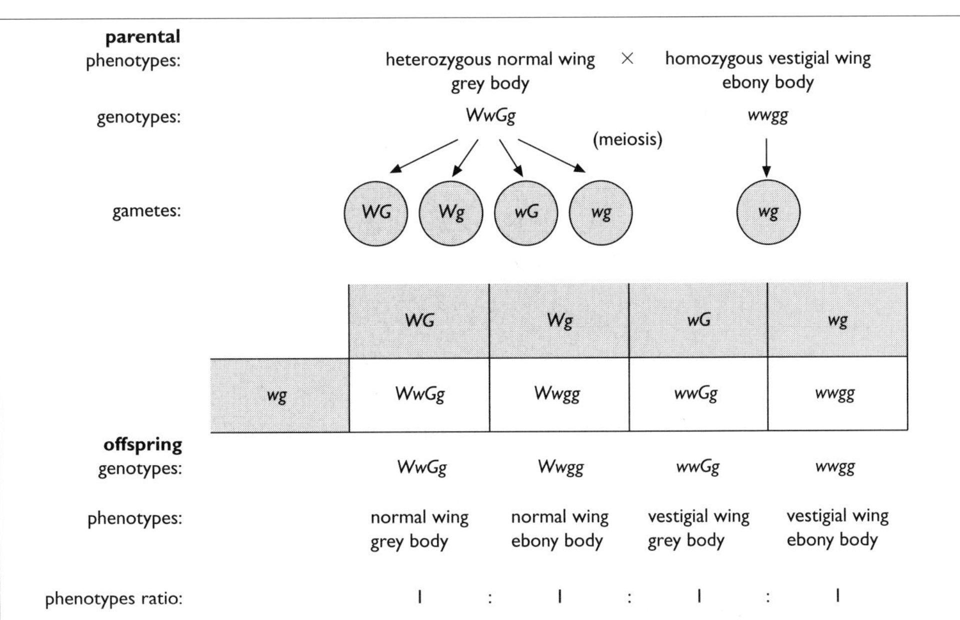

Figure 2.26 Genetic diagram of the dihybrid test cross.

Genetics since Mendel

Gregor Mendel created the basis of modern genetics because he worked with statistically significant samples, checked that 'parent' organisms bred true (that is, were homozygous) and restricted individual experiments to one, two (or a very few) contrasting characteristics that he observed carefully. He succeeded, too, through the application of probability theory to his numerical results. **He was lucky** to have chosen contrasting characteristics controlled by single genes, and his pairs of contrasting characters happened to be located on different chromosomes. Mendel had sufficient strength of character to develop his original concept of 'factors' in cells, and to continue laborious experimentation despite the total absence of understanding of his achievements in his lifetime.

Since Mendel's work (which was rediscovered in 1900), the following concepts have been added, extending the basis of modern genetics:

- **'factors' are genes** located on chromosomes in the nuclei of cells. Chromosomes are replicated in mitotic division and halved in number in meiotic division, typically in gamete formation (see 'chromosome theory', pages 6 and 14);
- **linkage:** many genes are linked together (and tend to be inherited together) because they occur on the same chromosome (page 19);
- **'crossing over':** this is exchange between adjacent chromatids of homologous pairs early in meiosis, which may give rise to new combinations of characters (page 20);
- **sex linkage:** in organisms where one of the pairs of chromosomes determines gender, then the other genes on the sex chromosomes are sex linked (page 24);
- **multiple alleles:** more than two alleles of a gene may exist, although only two occur in any one diploid organism (page 28);
- **polygenes:** many characteristics of organisms are controlled by a combination of genes, often located on different chromosomes (page 30);
- **environmental effects:** the appearance of an organism (phenotype) is determined by the genetic constitution (genotype) interacting with the effects of the environment (page 34);
- **mutations:** these are abrupt changes in the structure, arrangement or quantity of the material of the gene (DNA) that influence the characteristics of the organism and that may be potentially inheritable (page 36).

The **rediscovery of Mendel's work** was made by Hugo de Vries (1848–1935), a Dutch physiologist who became a geneticist.

- Early in his research de Vries worked on water relations of cells and coined the term 'plasmolysis'.
- Later, at the University of Amsterdam, he studied inheritance in the evening primrose *Oenothera lamarckiana*, and, by 1900, had discovered the same 'Laws' as Mendel.
- He searched the literature for other examples, and he came across Mendel's published papers.
- He went on to discover occasional, sudden, single variations in *Oenothera*, which he called **'mutations'**.
- He argued that mutations were a means by which new species could arise, so he also played a key part in the establishment of Darwin's theory of evolution (page 67).

Figure 3.1 The 'evening primrose' plant. Working with this plant, de Vries rediscovered Mendelian ratios, and then discovered 'mutations'.

Linkage

There are many thousands of genes per cell, but relatively few chromosomes. Animal cells typically have more, short chromosomes; plant cells have fewer, longer chromosomes.

Table 3.1 Number of chromosomes per diploid cell – some examples.

Garden pea (*Pisum sativum*)	14	Human (*Homo sapiens*)	46
Meadow buttercup (*Ranunculus acris*)	14	Mouse (*Mus musculus*)	40
Dandelion (*Taraxacum officinale*)	24	Crayfish (*Astacus pallipes*)	200

1 Why is it that the number of chromosomes in diploid cells is always even?

So we visualise a chromosome as a linear series of a very large number of genes, linked together. Genes on the same chromosome are very likely to be inherited together.

offspring
genotypes: 1 *AABB*, 2 *AaBb* : 1 *aabb*
phenotypes ratio: 3 : 1

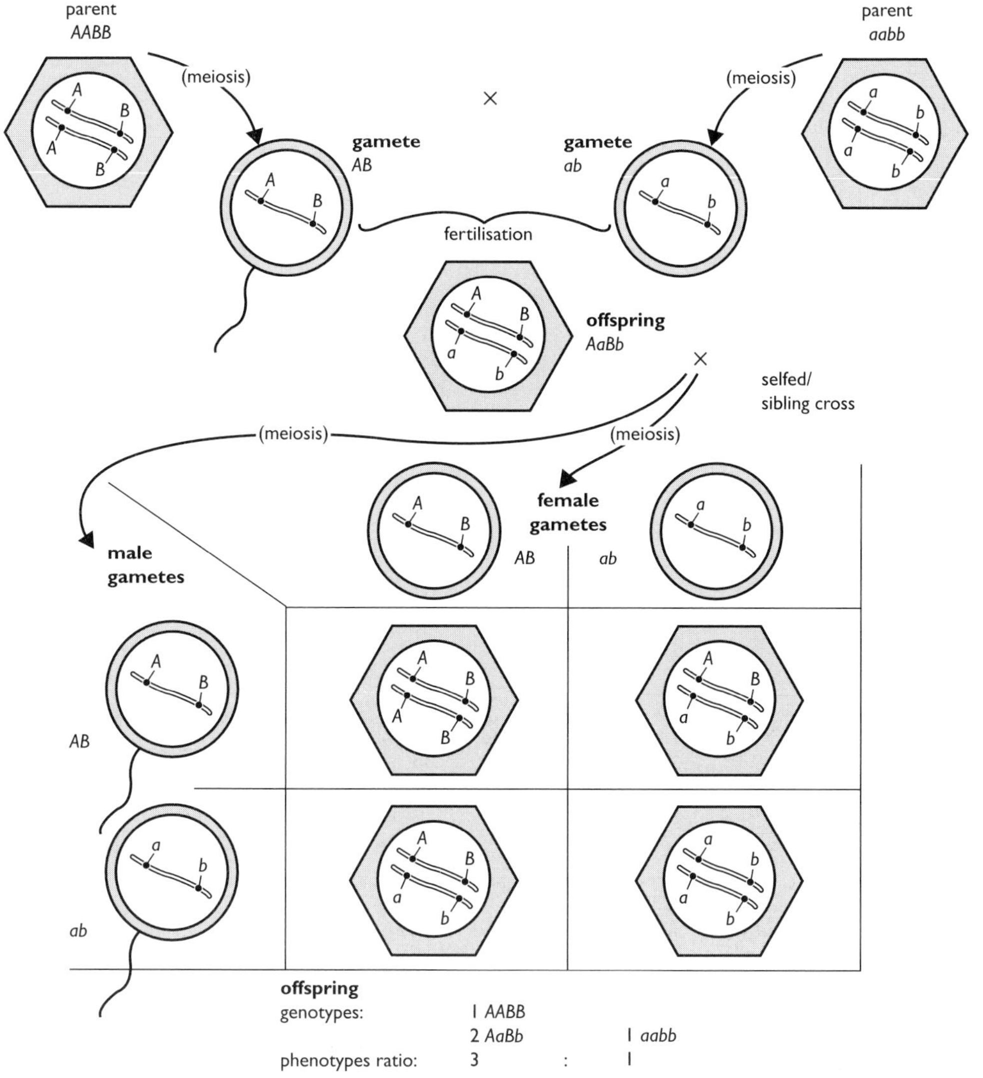

Figure 3.2 The inheritance of genes on the same chromosome. Linkage ensure that no *AAbb* or *aaBB* genotypes are formed.

An **example of linkage** in the sweet pea is the inheritance of flower colour (purple/red) and shape of pollen (elongated/rounded). Because the genes concerned are on the same chromosome, these characteristics tend to be inherited together (and the dihybrid ratio of 9 : 3 : 3 : 1 is **not** obtained).

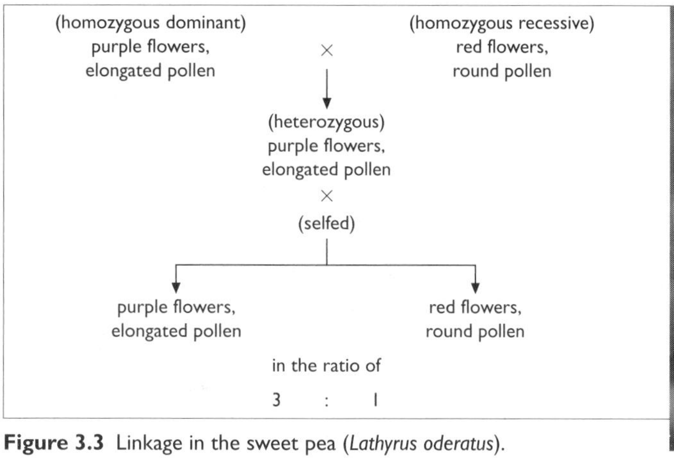

(homozygous dominant) purple flowers, elongated pollen × (homozygous recessive) red flowers, round pollen

↓

(heterozygous) purple flowers, elongated pollen

× (selfed)

purple flowers, elongated pollen | red flowers, round pollen

in the ratio of

3 : 1

Figure 3.3 Linkage in the sweet pea (*Lathyrus oderatus*).

Crossing over

Crossing over is the exchange of segments between adjacent chromatids of homologous pairs early in meiosis, which may give rise to new combinations of characteristics. Almost every pair of homologous chromosomes shows crossing over during meiosis.

> **2** What is **a)** the mechanical, and **b)** the genetic significance of chiasmata in meiosis?

Figure 3.4 What happens in meiosis.

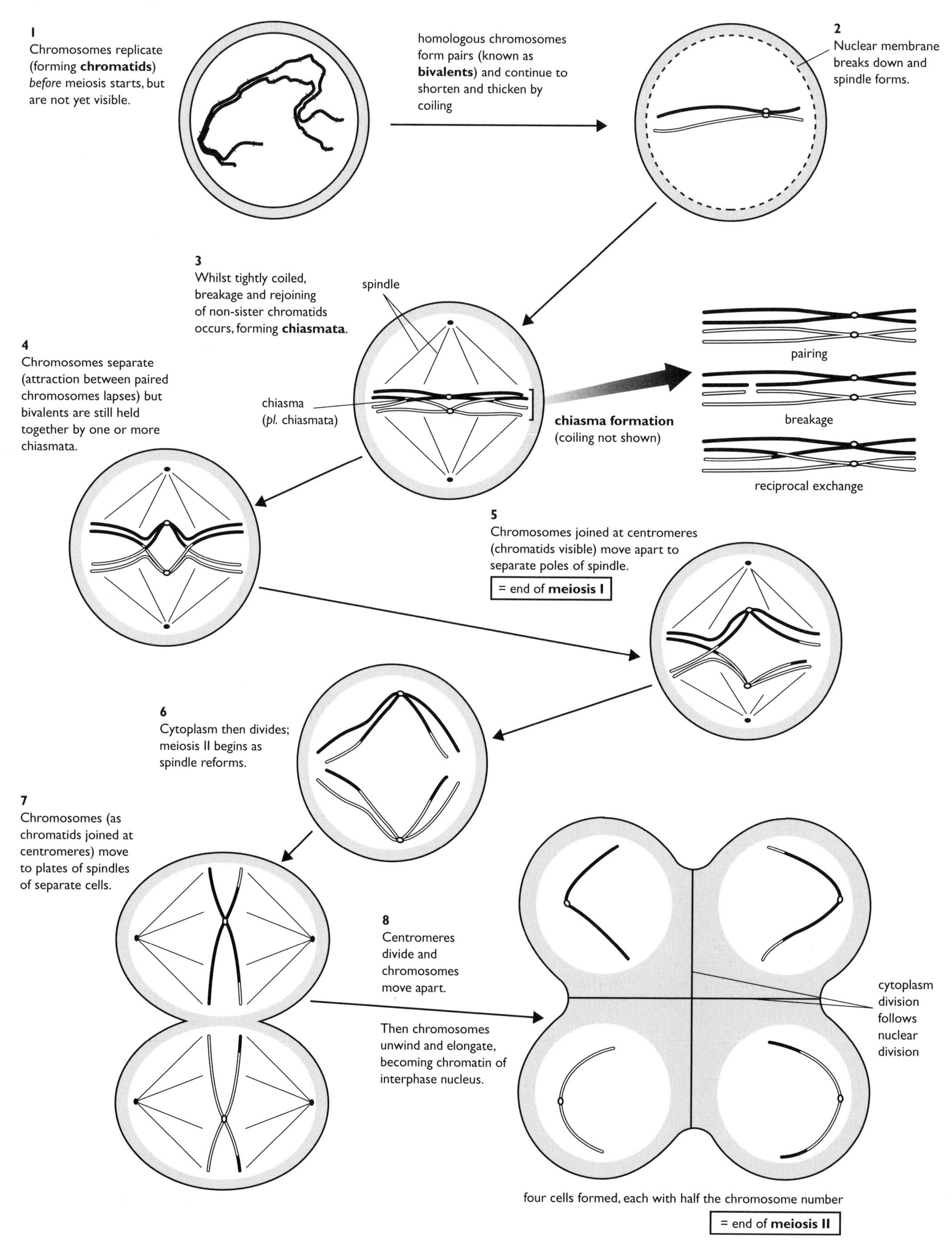

The **outcome of crossing over** is that both 'parental types' and 'recombinant types' normally appear among the offspring of crosses where contrasting characters are controlled by genes on the ***same*** chromosome. This is illustrated in *Drosophila* in Figure 3.7 (page 22). Therefore, the sweet pea cross shown in Figure 3.3 (page 19) does not show the whole story. In addition to 'parental types' a few purple-flowered plants with round pollen grains, and some red-flowered plants with elongated pollen grains ('recombinant' types) also appear in the progeny. Why this occurs is shown in Figure 3.6 below.

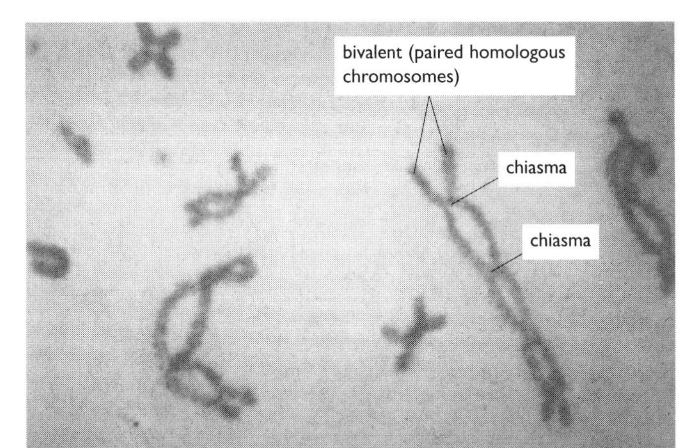

Figure 3.5 Chromosomes late in prophase of meiosis I.

Figure 3.6 Crossing over in the sweet pea.

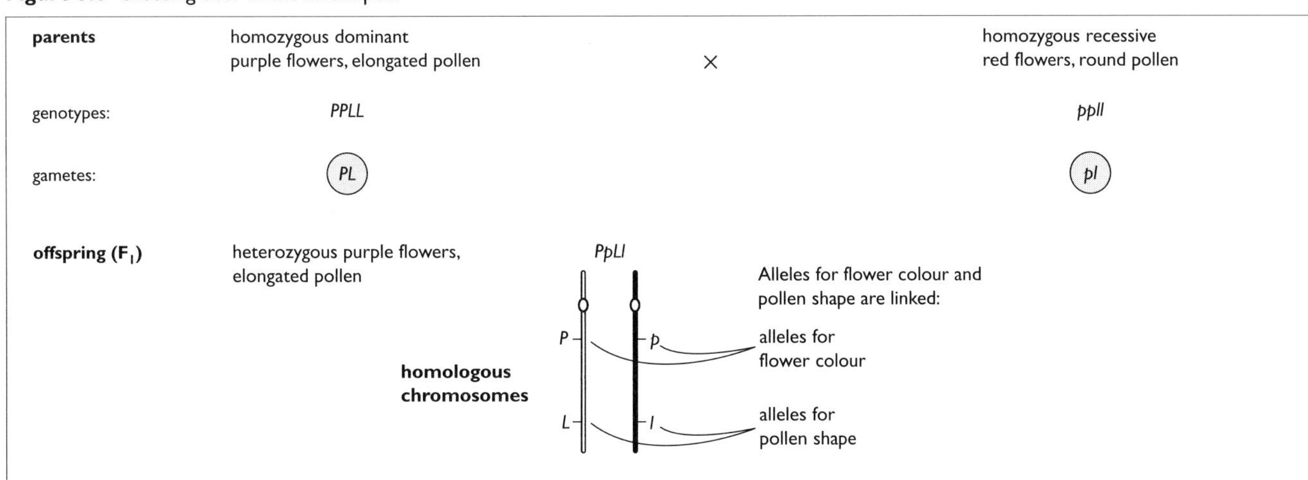

When the F_1 progeny are selfed, the progeny formed depends on whether chiasmata occur **between** the linked alleles, or **elsewhere**.

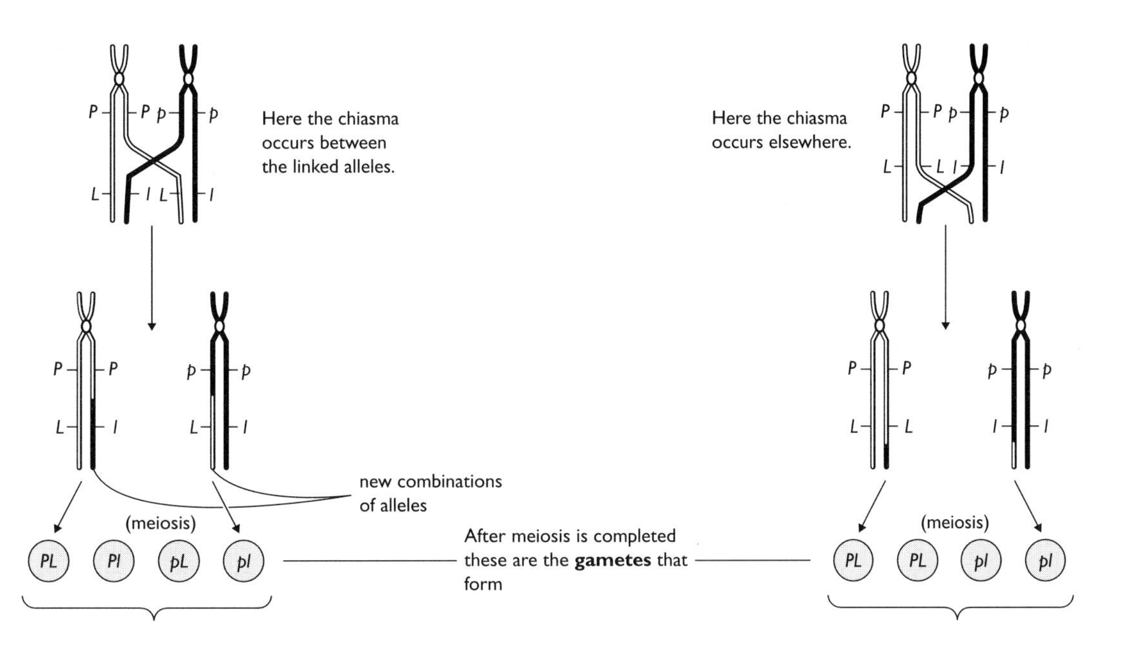

The progeny produced from these gametes, if selfed, will be:
parental types
PPLL, *PpLl* (purple flowers, elongated pollen)
and *ppll* (red flowers, round pollen)
and **recombinant types**
PPll, *Ppll* (purple flowers, round pollen)
ppLL, *ppLl* (red flowers, elongated pollen)

The progeny produced from these gametes, if selfed, will be:
parental types
PPLL, *PpLl* (purple flowers, elongated pollen)
and *ppll* (red flowers, round pollen)

most progeny are of this type

Figure 3.7 Linkage and crossing over in *Drosophila*.

In a **test** cross between (male) homozygous recessive *Drosophila* flies with ebony body and curled wing and (female) heterozygous flies with grey body and straight wing:

parental

phenotypes: ebony body, curled wing (homozygous) × grey body, straight wing (heterozygous)

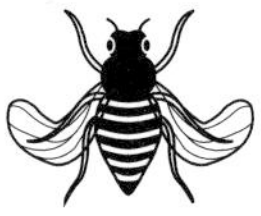

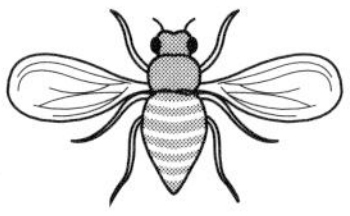

genotypes: *ggss* × *GgSs*

(meiosis) (meiosis)

gametes: *gs* — *GS*, *Gs*, *gS*, *gs*

This is what was expected:

	GS	*Gs*	*gS*	*gs*
gs	*GgSs*	*Ggss*	*ggSs*	*ggss*

offspring

phenotypes:	grey straight	grey curled	ebony straight	ebony curled
phenotypes ratio:	1 :	1 :	1 :	1

But this is what happened:

Offspring	Phenotypes	Genotypes	Numbers obtained
1 parental types: 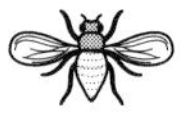	grey body, straight wing	*GgSs*	536
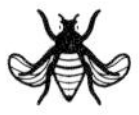	ebony body, curled wing	*ggss*	481
2 recombinant types: 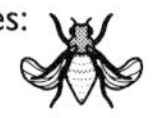	grey body, curled wing	*Ggss*	101
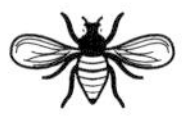	ebony body, straight wing	*ggSs*	152

Note: the **majority of the offspring were parental types**, so the genes for body colour and wing shape must be on the same chromosomes, i.e. **linked**; however, **crossing over** between these genes has occurred.

Gene mapping by cross-over value

The frequency of recombination is the **cross-over value**:

$$\frac{\text{number of recombinant individuals produced}}{\text{total number of offspring}} \times 100$$

Crossing over is more likely to occur between genes that are more widely spaced. It is possible to 'map' the relative positions of genes using the data of cross-over values; two genes whose alleles give a cross-over value of 15% are said to be 15 units apart.

3 In the above test cross, which of the gametes formed by the parent of genotype *GgSs* may lead to recombinant offspring?

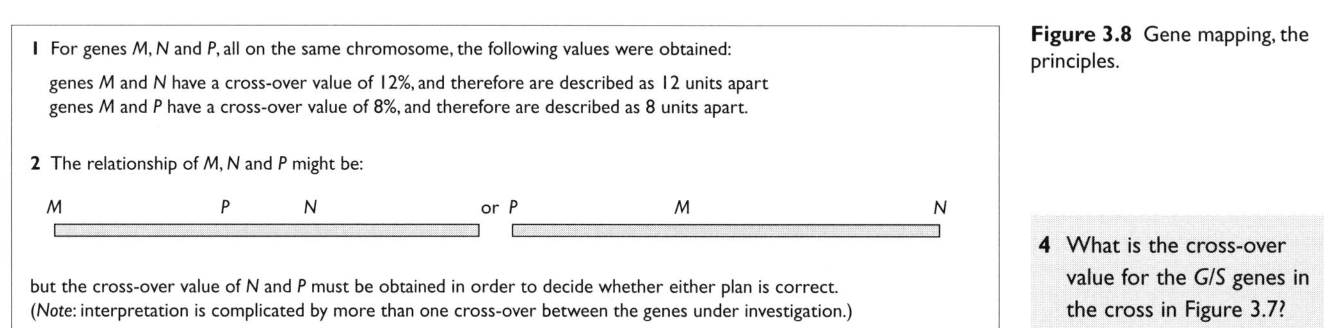

Figure 3.8 Gene mapping, the principles.

4 What is the cross-over value for the *G/S* genes in the cross in Figure 3.7?

Sex chromosomes and sex determination

In many organisms the gender (male or female) of individuals is determined by specific chromosomes, known as the **sex chromosomes**. For example, in humans there is one pair of sex chromosomes (either XX or XY chromosomes) along with the 22 other pairs (known as **autosomal chromosomes**). The undifferentiated gonad in the very young human embryo will develop into an ovary unless 'instructed' otherwise. This is what happens where the sex chromosomes are XX. However, in an embryo with XY, the presence of a gene on the Y chromosome triggers development of the gonad tissue into a testis. This 'switch' occurs about 7–8 weeks into the growth of an embryo. Subsequently, many other genes, mostly present on autosomal chromosomes, control the detailed differentiation of male or female characteristics of the fetus.

5 In humans, equal numbers of X and Y bearing sperms are produced, yet slightly more boys than girls are born. What explanations for this can you suggest?

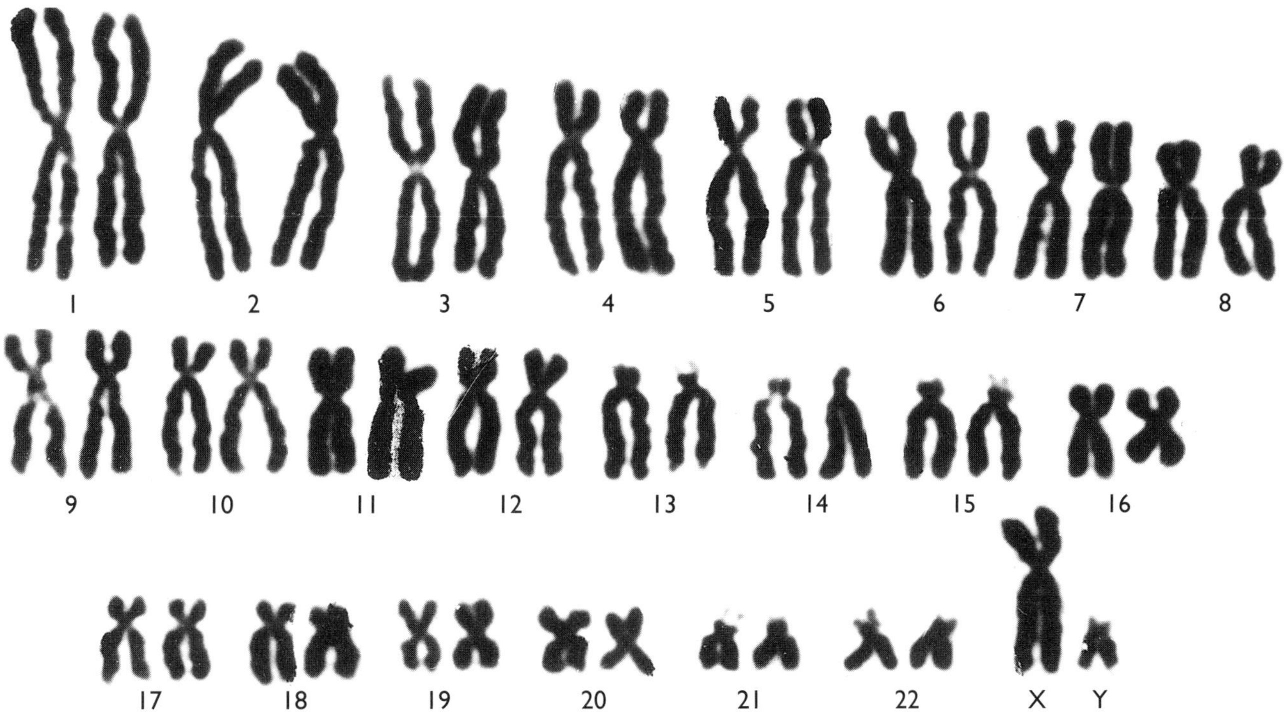

1 2 3 4 5 6 7 8

9 10 11 12 13 14 15 16

17 18 19 20 21 22 X Y

Figure 3.9 Human chromosomes as homologous pairs (bivalents), arranged in order of length.

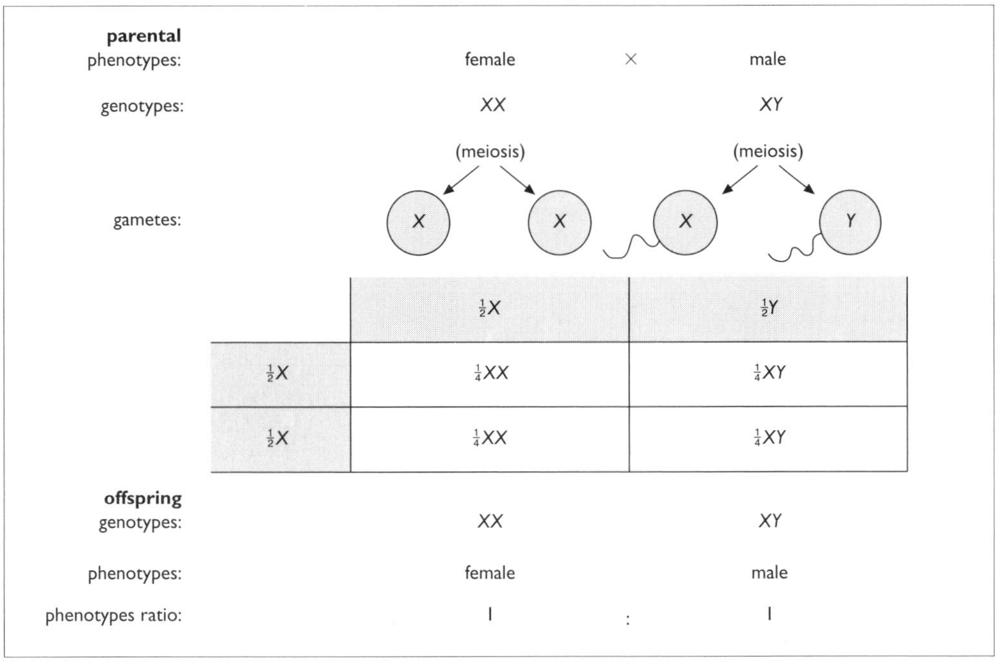

parental
phenotypes: female × male

genotypes: XX XY

(meiosis) (meiosis)

gametes: X X X Y

	$\frac{1}{2}$X	$\frac{1}{2}$Y
$\frac{1}{2}$X	$\frac{1}{4}$XX	$\frac{1}{4}$XY
$\frac{1}{2}$X	$\frac{1}{4}$XX	$\frac{1}{4}$XY

offspring
genotypes: XX XY

phenotypes: female male

phenotypes ratio: 1 : 1

Figure 3.10 X and Y chromosomes and the determination of sex.

Sex is determined differently in many organisms, but an X/Y system is the rule in mammals, and it is common to most other vertebrates, many insects, some other non-vertebrate groups, and in those flowering plants where the sexes are separate. In birds and butterflies, the males are XX and the females XY (or XO, where O = absent).

Sex linkage

Only a very small part of the X and Y chromosomes of humans can and do pair up during meiosis (that is, have **complementary alleles**). In fact the bulk of each sex chromosome contains genes that have no corresponding alleles on the other type of sex chromosome. Thus, the short Y chromosome carries genes specific for male sex determination and sperm production, including the 'male' gene coding for the testis determining factor (TDF) that switches development of embryonic gonad tissue to testes early in embryonic development. Meanwhile the X chromosome carries an assortment of genes, very few of which are concerned with sex determination.

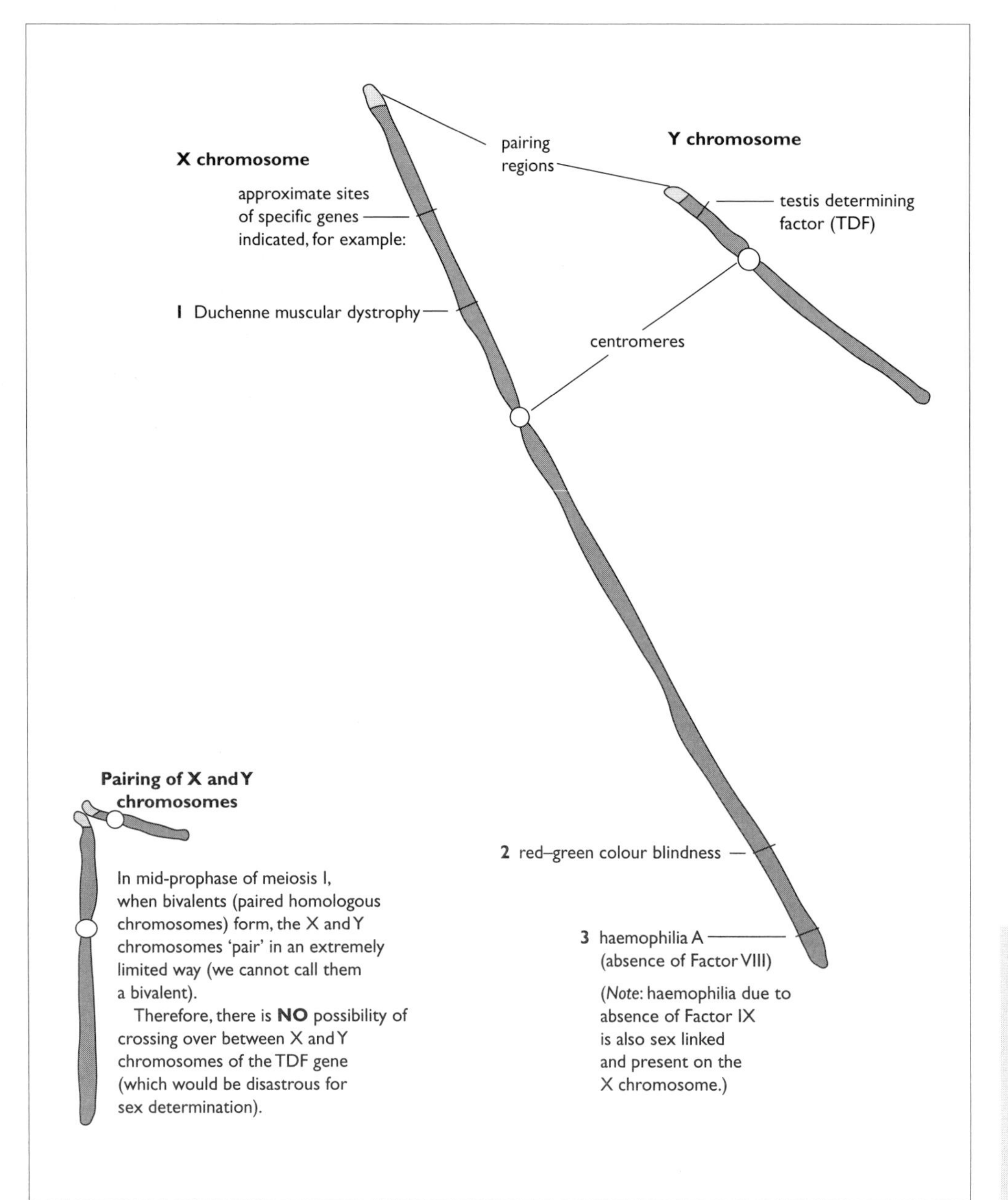

Figure 3.11 The human X and Y chromosomes, and the extent to which they 'pair'.

Sex-linked genes are the unpaired genes located on the sex chromosomes that are inherited with the sex of the individual. The inheritance of these sex-linked genes is different from the inheritance of genes of the autosomal chromosomes. For example, ***in a female*** a single recessive gene may be masked by a dominant allele of the other X chromosome, as with autosomal chromosomes. Examples of important (but fortunately rare) recessive genes on the X chromosome are the alleles for red–green colour blindness, for Duchenne muscular dystrophy and for haemophilia. However, ***in a male*** the same recessive genes on the sole X chromosome will be expressed. So, all these recessive conditions are extremely rare in females, but are found to varying extents in males. Similarly, the unpaired alleles of Y chromosomes are all expressed in the male (but these are concerned with male structures and functions).

6 Eye colour in *Drosophila* is a sex-linked characteristic. Whilst the normal condition is red eyes, a small proportion of flies are found to have white eyes (that is, a recessive condition). Using the symbols X^R and X^r for the alleles for eye colour, compare the ratio of offspring to be expected when a red-eyed female (homozygous) is crossed with a white-eyed male, and a white-eyed female (homozygous) with a red-eyed male, and the subsequent sibling crosses of the progeny are carried out.

Red–green colour blindness

A red–green colour blind person sees the colours green, yellow, orange and red as the same colour. The condition afflicts about 8% of males, but only 0.4% of females. It is helpful for those who are red–green colour blind to recognise it. The condition is detected by means of multi-coloured test cards such as the Ishihara test card series.

Figure 3.12 Detection and inheritance of red–green colour blindness. Why it is impossible to have a 'carrier' male.

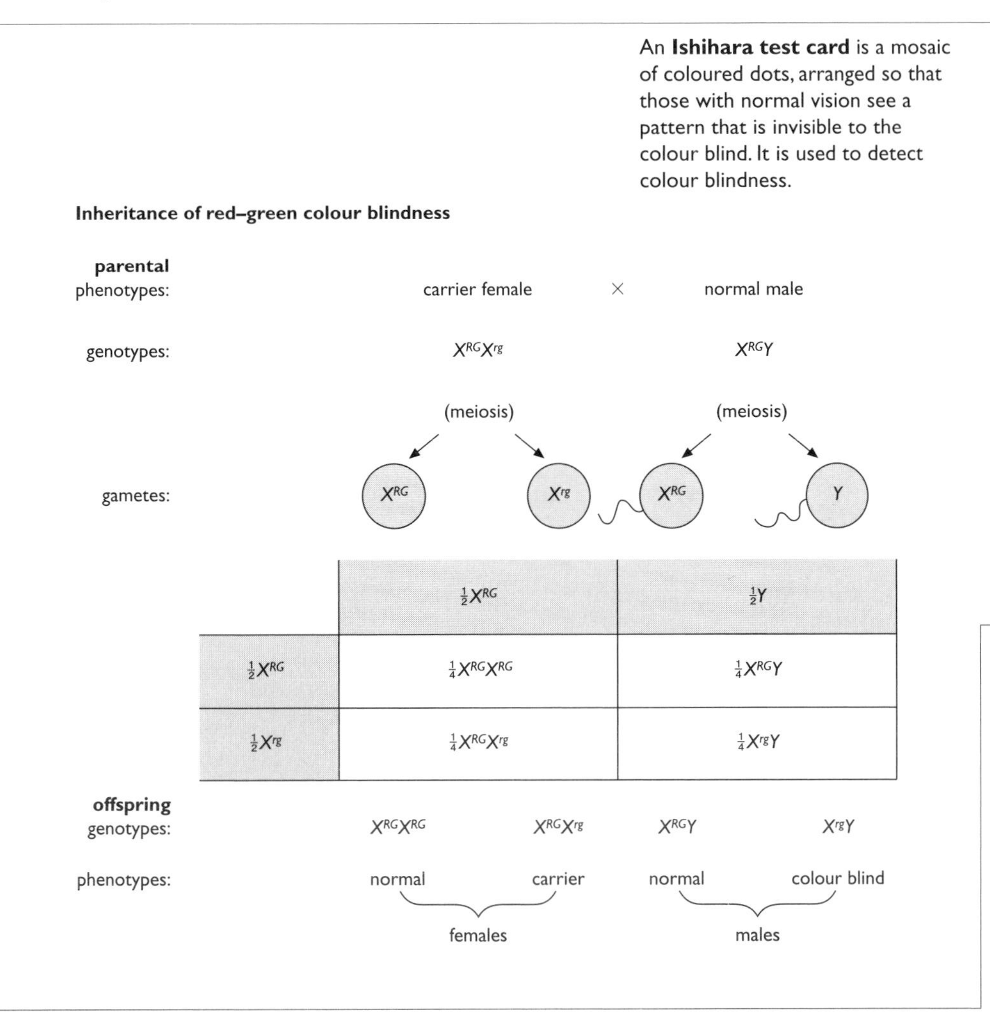

	$\frac{1}{2}X^{RG}$	$\frac{1}{2}Y$
$\frac{1}{2}X^{RG}$	$\frac{1}{4}X^{RG}X^{RG}$	$\frac{1}{4}X^{RG}Y$
$\frac{1}{2}X^{rg}$	$\frac{1}{4}X^{RG}X^{rg}$	$\frac{1}{4}X^{rg}Y$

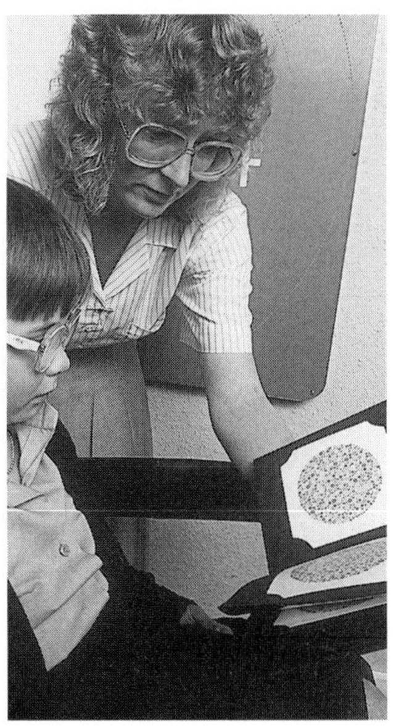

7 How is the genetic constitution of a female who is red–green colour blind represented? Why is it impossible to have a 'carrier' male?

Duchenne muscular dystrophy

Duchenne muscular dystrophy (with only extremely rare exceptions) affects only boys. The condition results from a defect in a muscle protein called dystrophin. In effect, muscle tissue is progressively replaced by fibrous tissue. The disease is named after the doctor who first studied muscular dystrophies, working in Paris over a hundred years ago. Typically, affected boys show signs of difficulty in walking at age 1–3 years, and between 8 and 11 years become unable to walk. By the late teens or early twenties muscular weakness is serious enough to be life threatening.

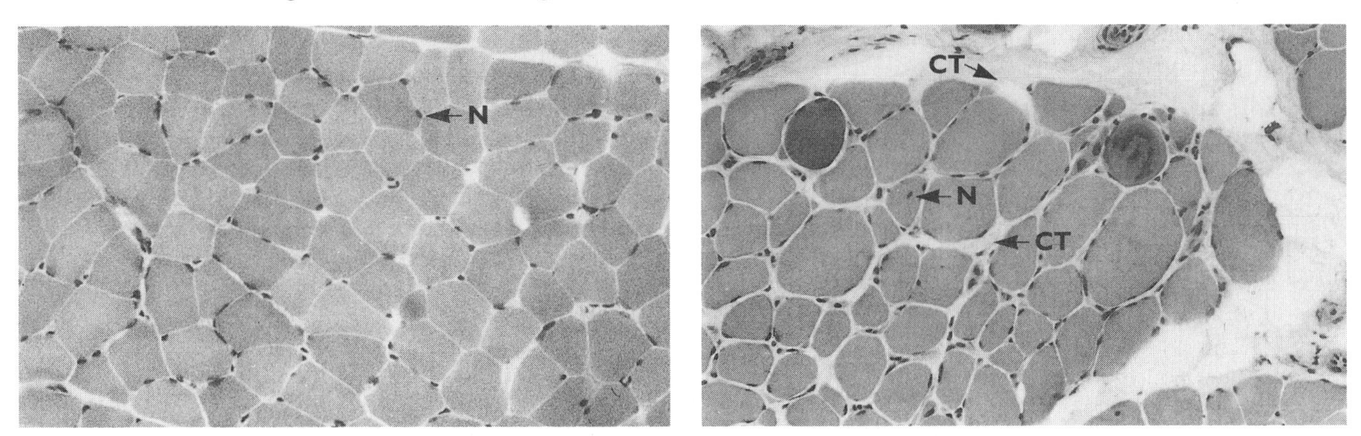

Figure 3.13 Transverse section of healthy voluntary muscle (left) and of Duchenne affected muscle (right) (N = nucleus, CT = connective tissue). There is an increased amount of connective tissue between muscle blocks in Duchenne muscular dystrophy, and nuclei often appear in the centres of fibres rather than at the periphery.

Haemophilia

In the closed circulation system of a mammal, blood is pumped through a continuous system of tubes (arteries, capillaries and veins) at relatively high pressure, by the action of the heart. Where a break occurs, there is a risk of uncontrolled bleeding. This is normally overcome by the blood-clotting mechanism that causes a gap to be plugged.

Haemophilia is a rare, genetically determined, condition of frequent, excessive bleeding. This may occur at the minor haemorrhages in our circulation that happen as we move about, or from larger breaks that may occur at our joints, or when we have minor knocks or more serious cuts in our skin. This bleeding in haemophiliacs is due to the inability of their blood to clot normally. One form of haemophilia (haemophilia A) is due to a shortfall in a blood protein called Factor VIII; another form (haemophilia B) is due to a shortfall in a blood protein called Factor IX. Today, haemophilia is effectively treated by the administration of the clotting factor that the patient lacks.

8 Another potential defect of blood is to clot too readily, but this is not a sex-linked genetic defect. What are the dangers to the body of clot formation in intact blood vessels?

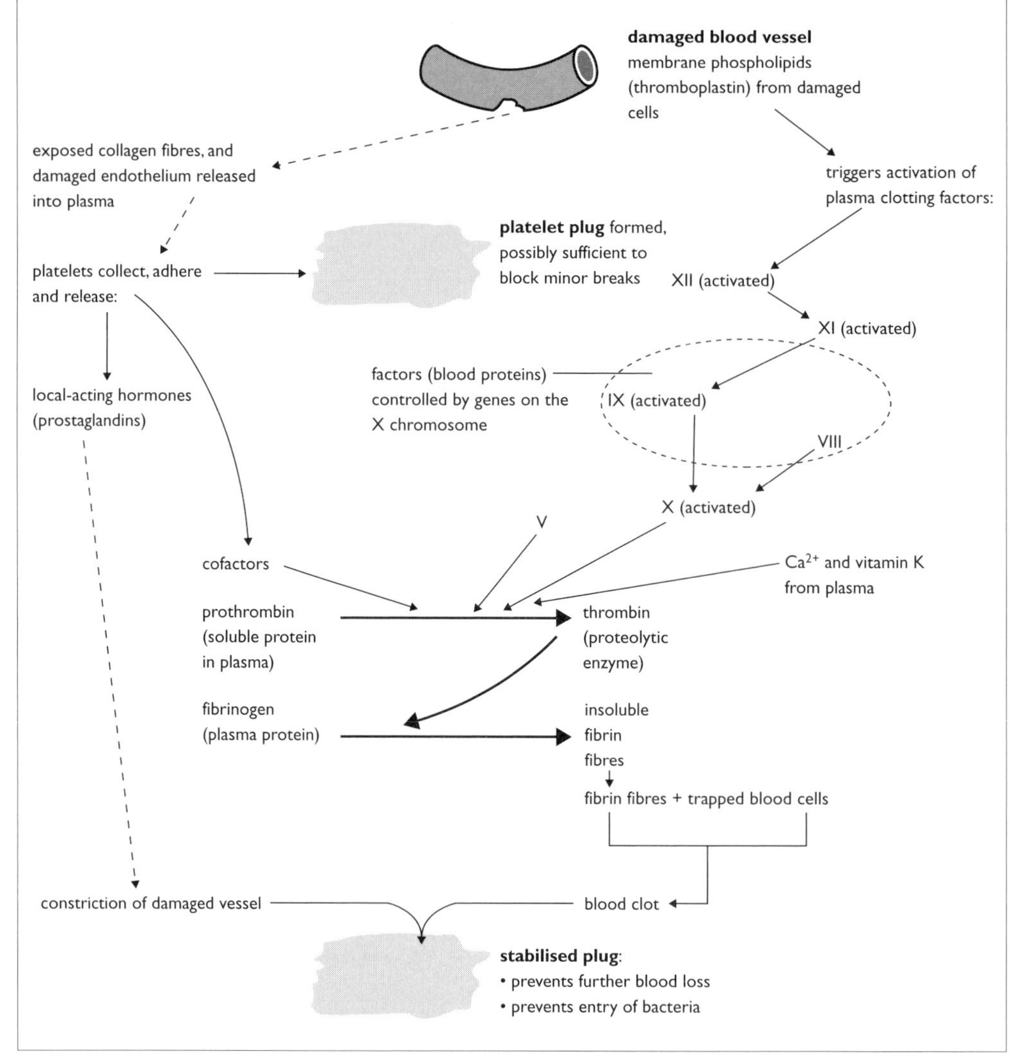

Figure 3.14 The blood-clotting mechanism.

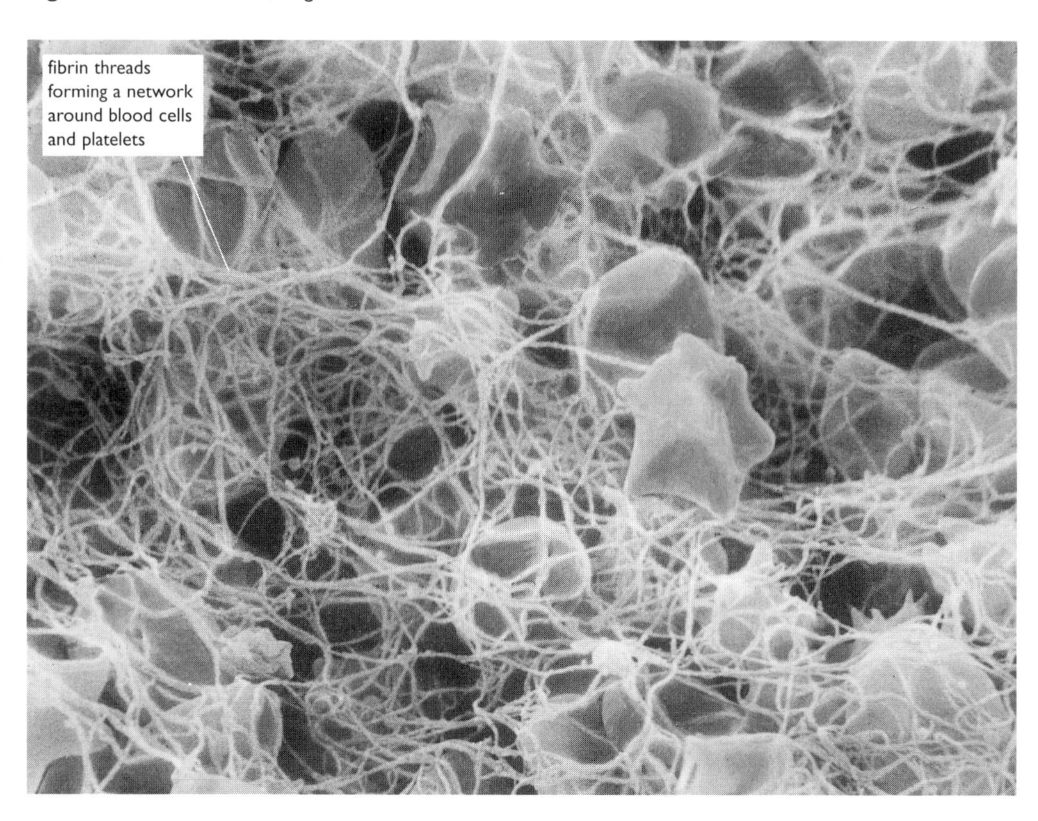

Figure 3.15 SEM of part of a blood clot.

Haemophilia is a sex-linked condition; the genes controlling production of blood Factors VIII and IX are located on the X chromosome. Haemophilia is caused by a **recessive allele** on the single X chromosome of a male (X^hY), so haemophilia is largely a disease of the male. A female with an X chromosome with the recessive allele (X^HX^h) is described as a 'carrier' in that, partnered by a normal male, there is a 50% chance that her offspring may be a carrier female child or afflicted male child. For a female to have the disease herself, she must be homozygous for the recessive gene (X^hX^h), but this condition is usually fatal *in utero* (typically resulting in a natural abortion).

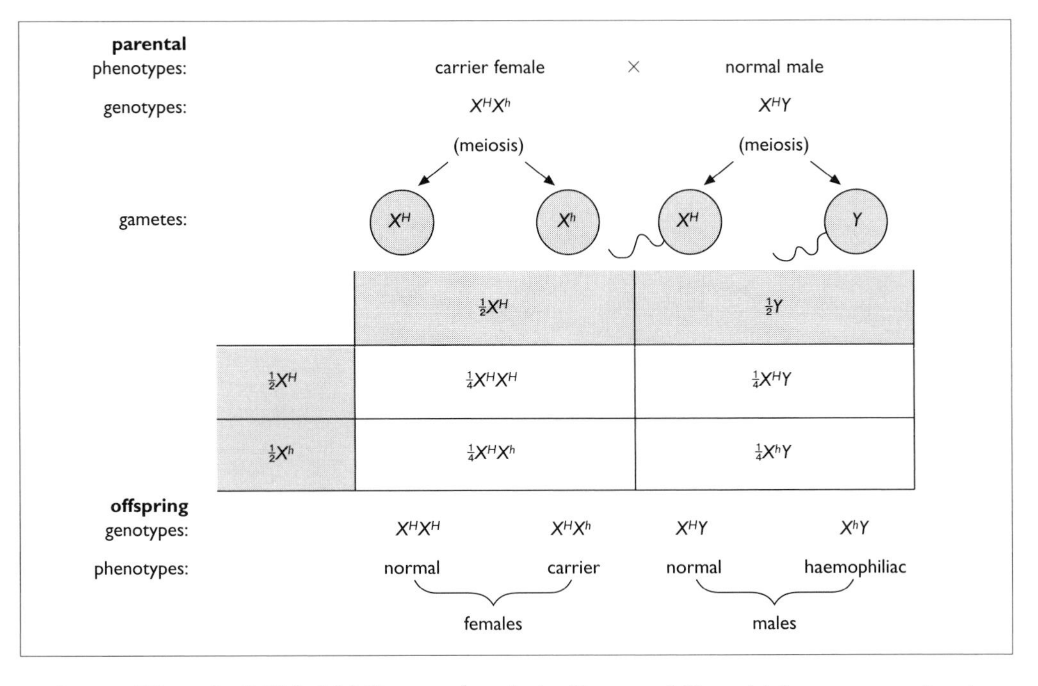

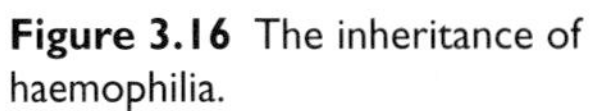
Figure 3.16 The inheritance of haemophilia.

Information about haemophilia can be obtained from the Haemophilia Society, 123 Westminster Bridge Road, London SE1 7HR.

Queen Victoria (1819–1901) was a 'carrier' of haemophilia, which was transmitted to three of her nine children and to at least seven of her grandchildren. There was no history of haemophilia in her mother's or her father's families, so most probably, a mutation (page 36) occurred prior to her conception in one of her parents, or her natural father was a male member of the court at that time, who was a haemophiliac. The transmission of this 'royal' haemophilia, which had political and social ramifications over the past 150 years, particularly in Russia and Spain, is well documented. You can read about it in the book by Professor WT Potts (1995) *Queen Victoria's Gene; Haemophilia and the Royal Family*, published by Sutton, Stroud.

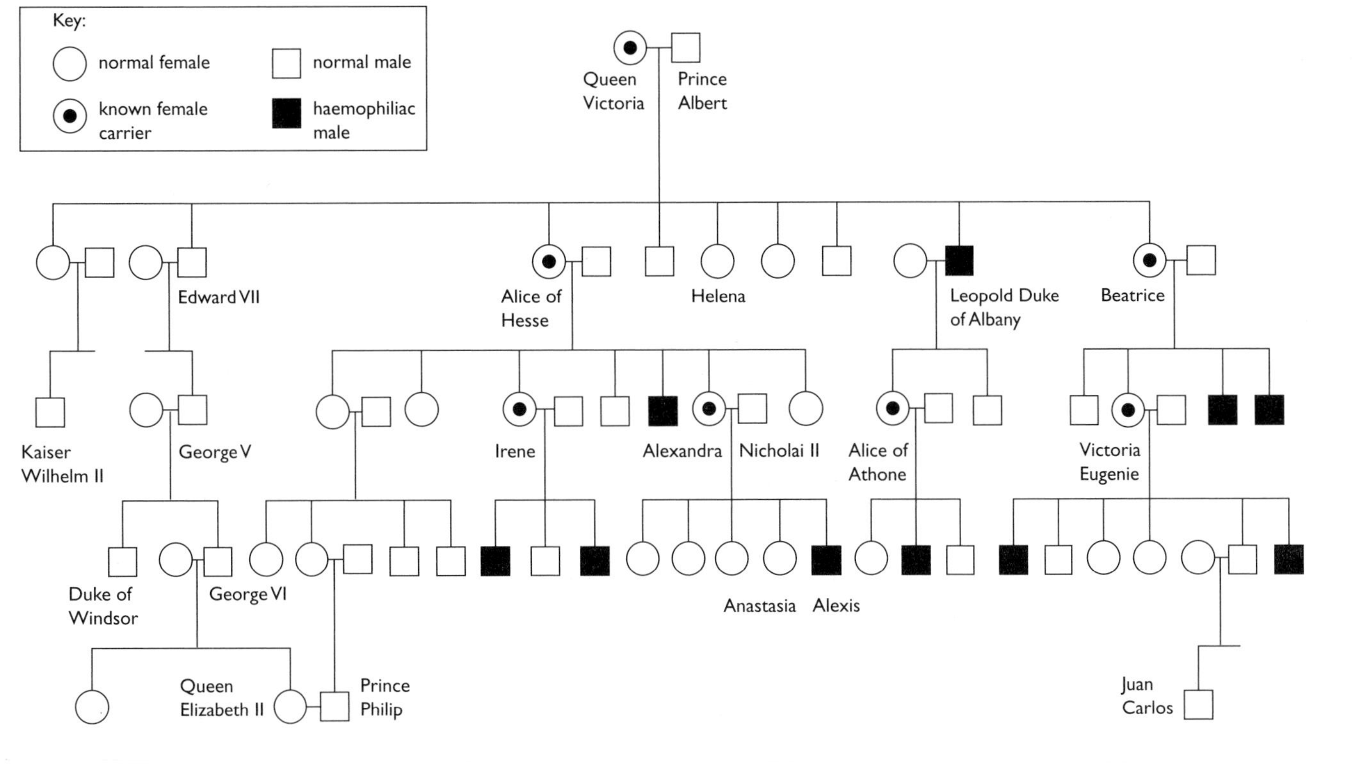

Figure 3.17 Queen Victoria and her heirs, a celebrated case!

Multiple alleles

The genes introduced so far exist in two forms (two alleles), like the 'height' gene of the garden pea, which exists as tall or dwarf alleles. Not all genes are like this. In fact very many genes exist as more than two alternatives. One good example of such **multiple alleles** involves those controlling the ABO blood group system of humans. Our blood is of group A, B, AB or O, and this is determined by some combinations of the alleles we represent by the symbols: I^A, I^B and I^O. In each individual only two of these three alleles exist, but they are inherited in a Mendelian fashion.

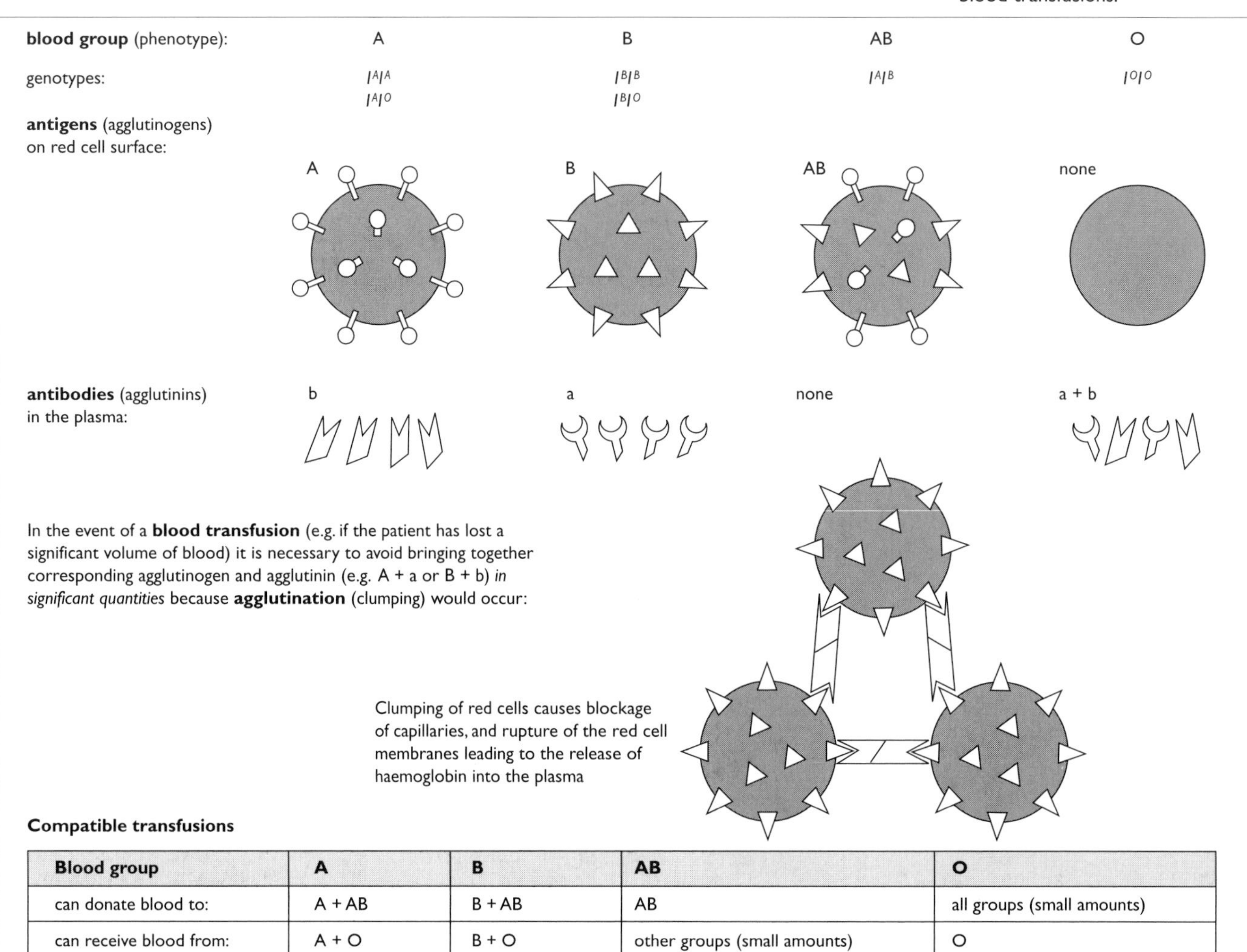

Compatible transfusions

Blood group	A	B	AB	O
can donate blood to:	A + AB	B + AB	AB	all groups (small amounts)
can receive blood from:	A + O	B + O	other groups (small amounts)	O

Figure 3.18 The ABO blood group system and compatible blood transfusions.

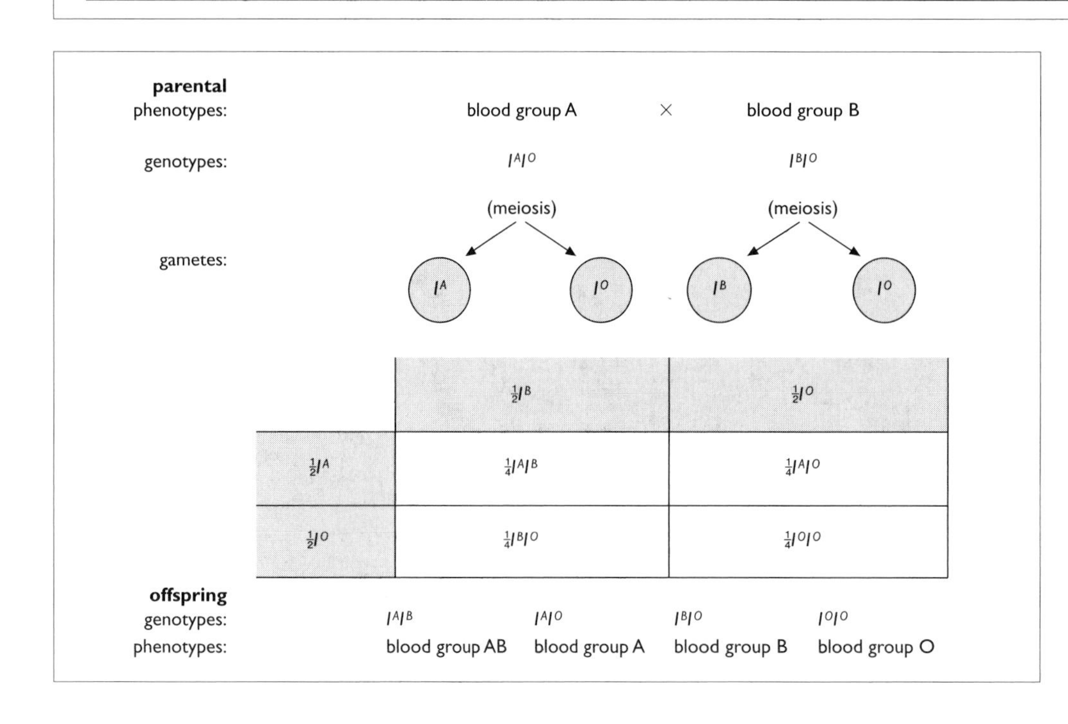

Figure 3.19 An example of inheritance of blood groupings A, B, AB and O.

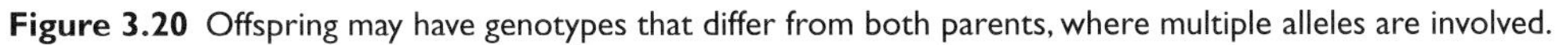

Figure 3.20 Offspring may have genotypes that differ from both parents, where multiple alleles are involved.

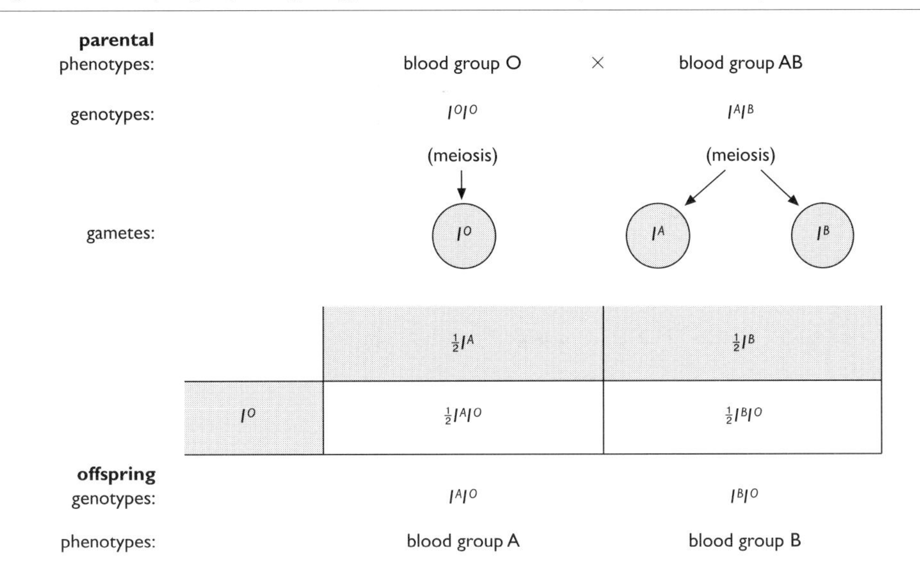

Multiple alleles are common

For simplicity, we often study the inheritance of two specific alleles of a gene, as this shows us the pattern of inheritance, and allows us to investigate linkage to other genes. In fact, most genes have more than two alleles; multiple alleles are the norm.

9 There are many different, genetically determined blood group systems that can be detected on the surface of red cells, but only two systems are considered important in routine blood transfusions. In addition to ABO, the second system is one we share with a species of monkey. What is that system called, and how many types of allele do you anticipate it involves?

Figure 3.21 Coat colour in the rabbit.

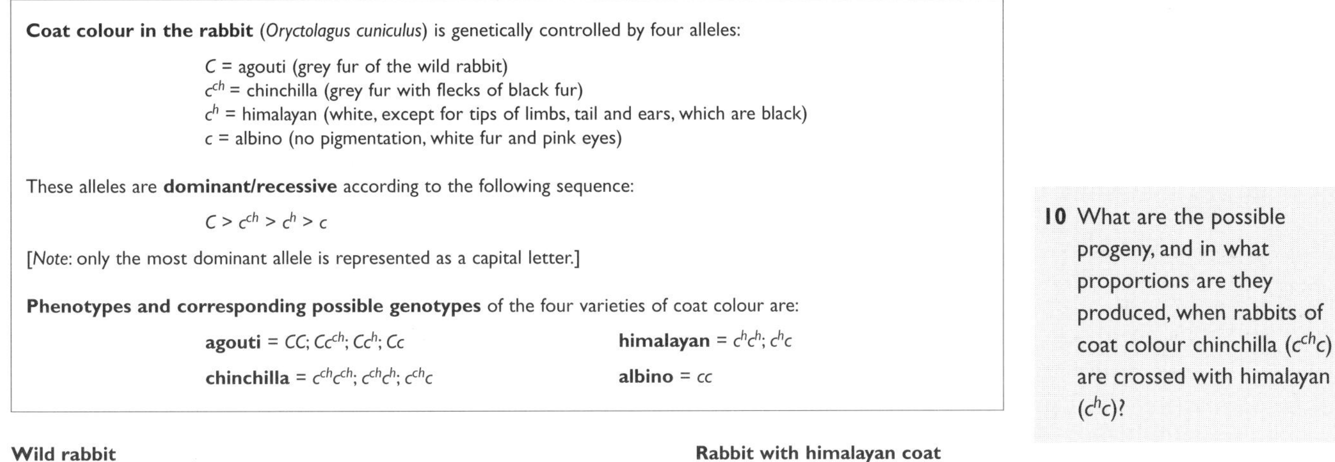

Coat colour in the rabbit (*Oryctolagus cuniculus*) is genetically controlled by four alleles:

C = agouti (grey fur of the wild rabbit)
c^{ch} = chinchilla (grey fur with flecks of black fur)
c^h = himalayan (white, except for tips of limbs, tail and ears, which are black)
c = albino (no pigmentation, white fur and pink eyes)

These alleles are **dominant/recessive** according to the following sequence:

$C > c^{ch} > c^h > c$

[*Note*: only the most dominant allele is represented as a capital letter.]

Phenotypes and corresponding possible genotypes of the four varieties of coat colour are:

agouti = CC; Cc^{ch}; Cc^h; Cc **himalayan** = c^hc^h; c^hc

chinchilla = $c^{ch}c^{ch}$; $c^{ch}c^h$; $c^{ch}c$ **albino** = cc

10 What are the possible progeny, and in what proportions are they produced, when rabbits of coat colour chinchilla ($c^{ch}c$) are crossed with himalayan (c^hc)?

Wild rabbit

Rabbit with himalayan coat

Polygenes

We began the story of modern genetics with Mendel's investigation of the inheritance of height in the garden pea (page 4), where one gene with two alleles gave tall or dwarf plants. This clear-cut difference in an inherited characteristic is an example of **discontinuous variation**, sometimes called discrete (that is, there is no intermediate form, and no overlap between the two phenotypes).

In fact very few characteristics of organisms are controlled by a single gene. Mostly, characteristics of organisms are controlled by a number of genes, known as multiple genes or **polygenes**. These are often (but not necessarily) located on different chromosomes. Many features of humans, including height, are controlled by polygenes. Any one of our genes for height individually causes relatively little difference in the phenotype, but particular combinations may give us very tall or quite short adults, and every sort of intermediate height, too.

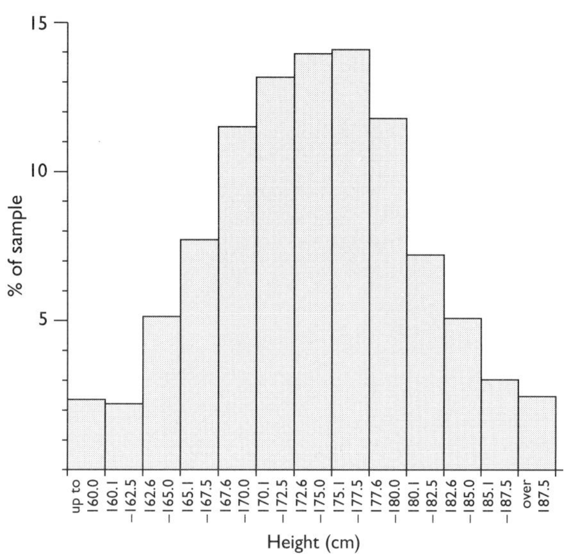

Figure 3.22 Frequency histogram of the heights of adult males in the UK population (a sample of 4500 individuals).

In fact the number of genes controlling a characteristic does not have to be large before the variation in a phenotype becomes more or less continuous among a large group of offspring. Characteristics controlled by polygenes show **continuous variation**. Nevertheless, the individual genes concerned are inherited in accordance with Mendelian laws.

11 What types of variation in the offspring do you expect when **a)** many genes control one characteristic, and **b)** one gene controls one characteristic?

Interactions of alleles and genes

The picture of genetic control is further complicated by the fact that some alleles and genes interact, producing new or modified characteristics among offspring. Once each case is explained, our understanding of the control of inherited characteristics (genetics) is extended. Some of the cases are important ecologically, economically or medically.

1 Interactions between alleles of a single gene take alternative forms

a) **Co-dominance** – both alleles are expressed, for example **MN blood group of humans**. Our MN blood group is due to the presence of special proteins, called antigens, on the surface of our red cells. There are two alleles involved, resulting in three possible phenotypes: M phenotype (*MM* genotype), N phenotype (*NN* genotype), or MN phenotype (*MN* genotype). Thus, both alleles contribute equally to the phenotype when present, rather than one being dominant and the other recessive.

MN antigens are additional to those of the ABO system (page 28). Unlike the ABO system, there are no natural antibodies in the plasma. This means: i) there are no problems arising from blood transfusions; ii) in order to 'type' a blood sample for MN grouping, you need to inject human red cells into another mammal (for example, a rabbit) and then extract the specific antibodies produced.

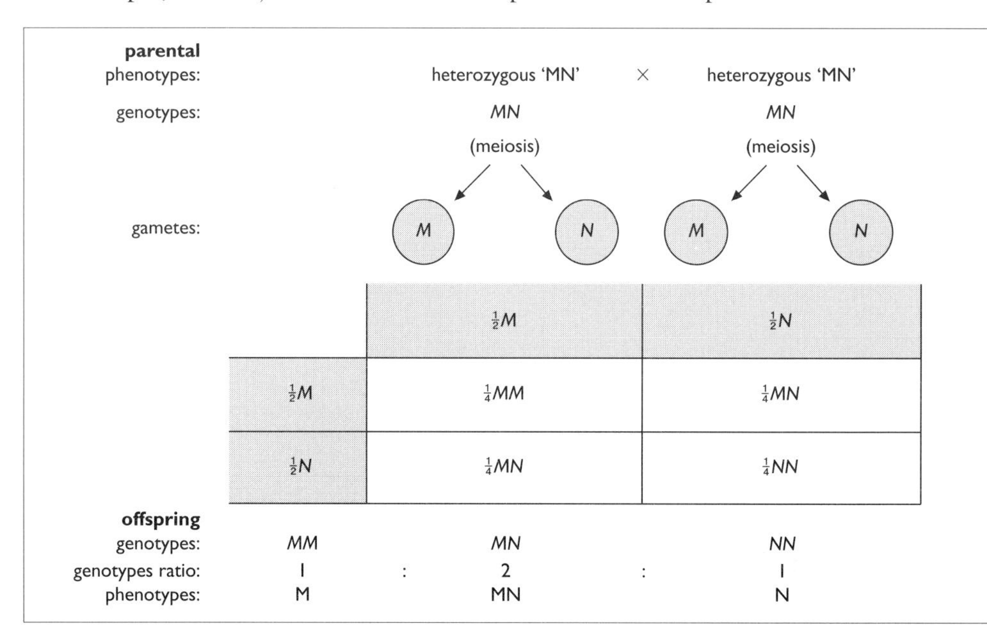

Figure 3.23 Example of MN blood group inheritance.

b) **Incomplete dominance** – an intermediate phenotype results, for example, **plumage pigmentation in the domestic fowl.** In the domestic fowl (*Gallus gallus domesticus*), strains that have black feathers (known as 'Andalusian fowls') have a pigment, melanin. The strain that has all white feathers produces no melanin. The offspring of a cross of these two strains include slate blue fowl, due to partial development of pigmentation.

12 In *Antirrhinum*, homozygous red-flowered (*RR*) × homozygous white-flowered (*rr*) gives F_2 offspring in the ratio of 1 red (*RR*) : 2 pink (*Rr*) : 1 white (*rr*) (rather than the expected 3 red : 1 white). What offspring and what ratio do you anticipate when a pink-flowered *Antirrhinum* is crossed with a white-flowered plant? Show your reasoning as a genetic diagram.

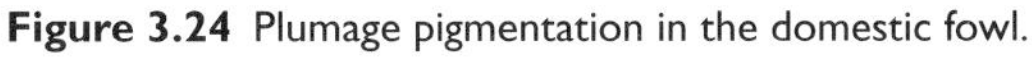
Figure 3.24 Plumage pigmentation in the domestic fowl.

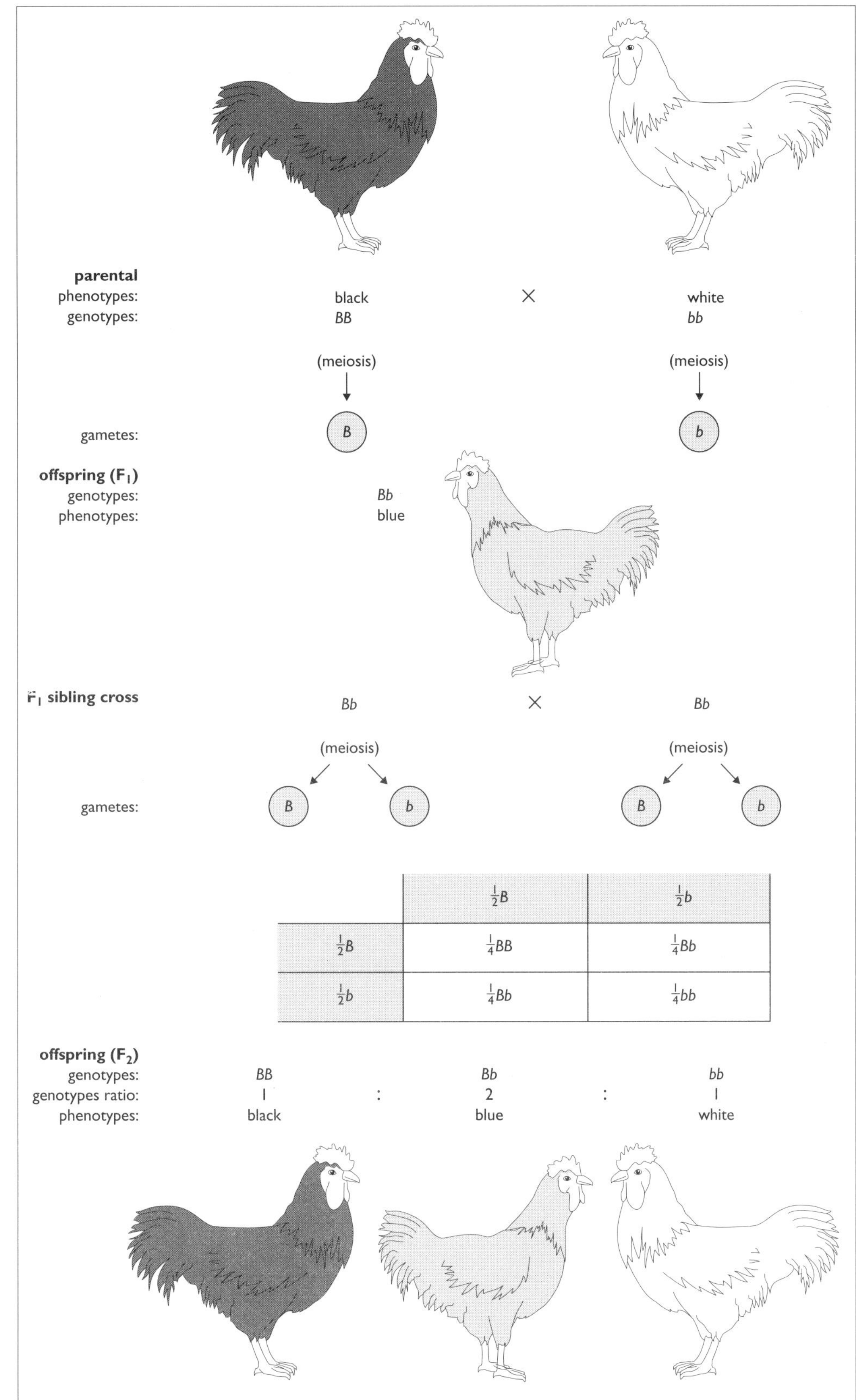

	$\frac{1}{2}B$	$\frac{1}{2}b$
$\frac{1}{2}B$	$\frac{1}{4}BB$	$\frac{1}{4}Bb$
$\frac{1}{2}b$	$\frac{1}{4}Bb$	$\frac{1}{4}bb$

2 Interactions between genes

a) **'Simple' gene interaction** – the interaction of the alleles of two genes produces four phenotypes, for example, **comb form in the fowl (*Gallus gallus domesticus*).**

The 'comb' is a red fleshy crest on the head of the domestic fowl. There are distinct forms of the crest, controlled by two independent genes (that is, occurring on separate chromosomes), known as *P* (or *p*) and *R* (or *r*). These genes interact according to whether they are present as dominant or recessive alleles. This is simple gene interaction in that:

one or two dominant *P* alleles, with recessive *r* alleles, gives **'pea comb'**;
one or two dominant *R* alleles, with recessive *p* alleles, gives **'rose comb'**.

However, dominant *P* and dominant *R* alleles together gives **'walnut comb'** and interaction between the recessive alleles alone gives **'single comb'**.

> **13** The genotypes of two pairs of breeding fowl are:
> **a)** *PpRr* × *ppRr*;
> **b)** *PPrr* × *ppRR*.
> What are the phenotypes of these parent birds, and which of the two pairs produces offspring that are:
> i) walnut comb only;
> ii) all four comb types?

Figure 3.25 Comb types of the domestic fowl.

Pea comb (*PPrr*, *Pprr*)

Rose comb (*ppRR*, *ppRr*)

Walnut comb (*PPRR*, *PpRR*, *PPRr* or *PpRr*)

Single comb (*pprr*)

b) **Complementary genes** – the interaction of the alleles of two genes produces an effect different from the effect either gives separately, for example, **white/purple petal colour in sweet pea (*Lathyrus odoratus*).**

Here two independent genes are involved, one (symbol *P*) producing a colourless forerunner or precursor molecule in the cells of the petals, and the other gene (symbol *C*) triggering the conversion of the precursor into a purple pigment. In the presence of either the alleles *pp* (that is, no precursor formed) or the alleles *cc* (that is, no conversion enzymes formed), the petals remain white.

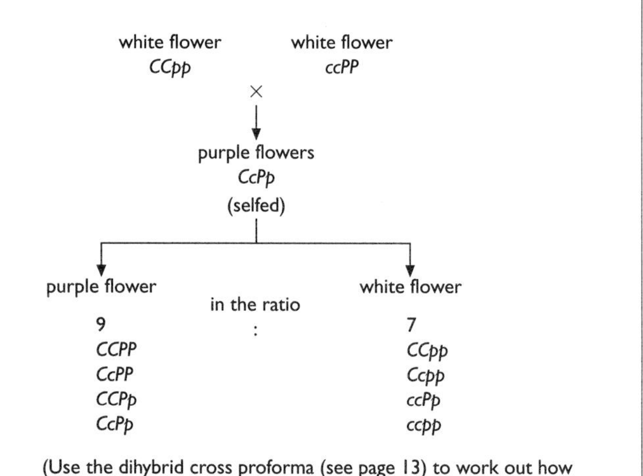

Figure 3.26 Complementary gene action in the sweet pea.

c) **Epistasis** – one gene totally inhibits the expression of another, independent gene, for example, **shell banding of the snail, *Cepaea nemoralis*.**

Banding occurs in various forms. One gene determines the absence/presence of bands (unbanded [*BB* or *Bb*] is dominant to banded [*bb*]). The other gene determines the number and position of bands (mid-banded [*MM* or *Mm*] is dominant to five-banded [*mm*] and is only expressed in the presence of *bb*).

The coloration of the shell is also genetically controlled, independently of banding. Shells may be brown, pink or yellow. There is good evidence that these variable features together help to conceal snails from predators (for example, the thrush) in different habitats, so they are seen as **cryptic camouflage**.

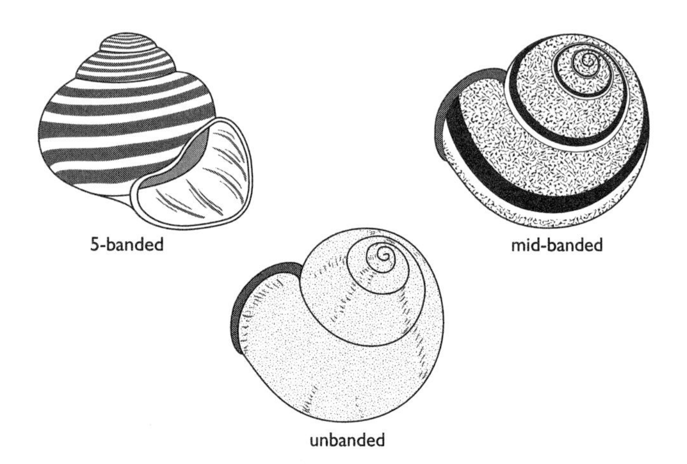

Figure 3.27 Banding of the shell of *Cepaea nemoralis*.

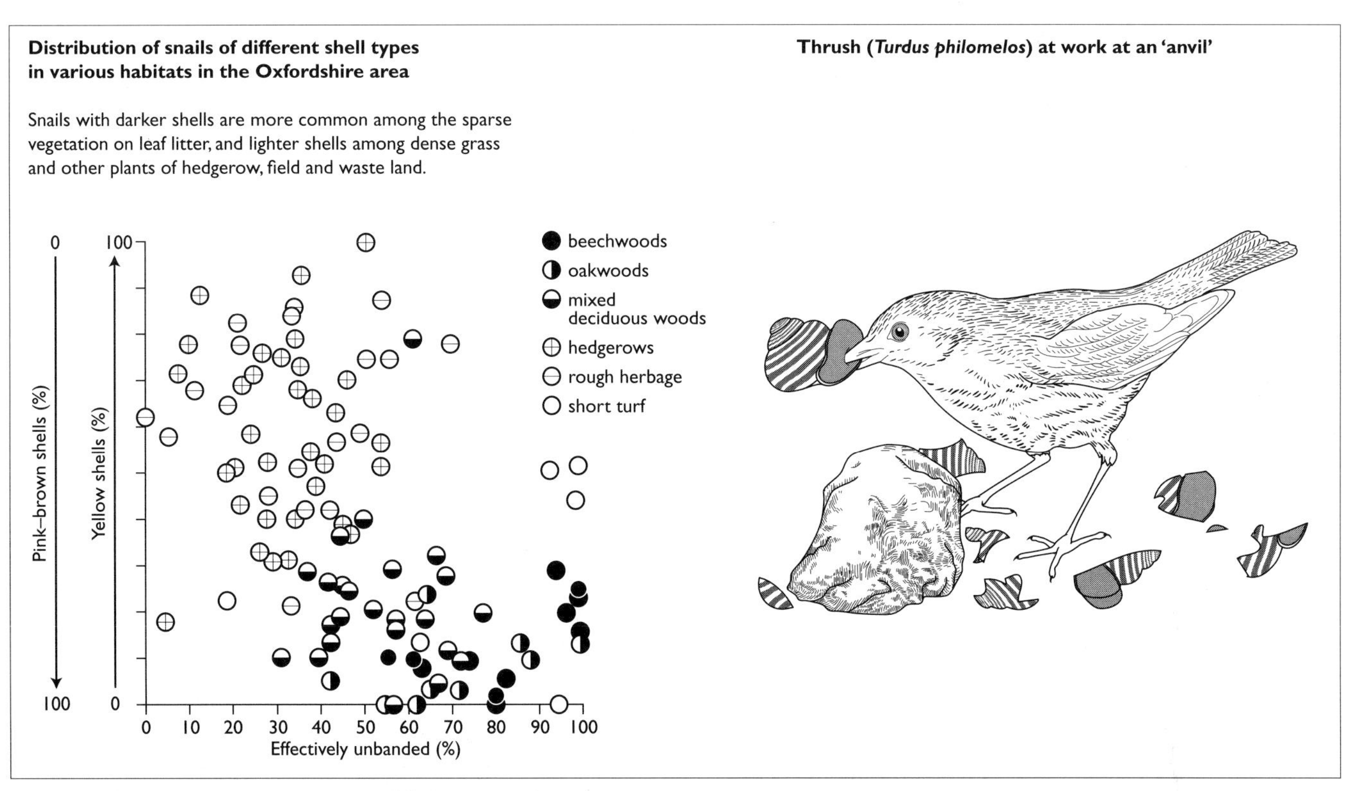

Figure 3.28 Distribution and predation of *Cepaea nemoralis.*

d) **Pleiotropy** – a single gene gives multiple effects, for example, **the cystic fibrosis transmembrane regulator gene.**

A single gene (we call it the *CF* gene) codes for the protein that fits into cell membranes and functions in the transport of Cl^- ions. In epithelial cells throughout the body, where ions and water are transported from the blood plasma or tissue fluid to the outside, the proper functioning of this protein is crucial.

The *CF* gene may undergo a mutation (page 36) to an inactive form, from time to time, and the bearer becomes a 'carrier' of a single *cf* allele. About 1 in 20 Caucasians are carriers; most are unaware of this. If two carriers reproduce there is a possibility that one or more of their children will inherit double recessive *cfcf* alleles. Cystic fibrosis is the most common genetic disorder in the UK.

14 How are the data in the graph above interpreted as evidence for effective cryptic camouflage?

Further information is available from The Cystic Fybrosis Trust, 11 London Road, Bromley BR1 1BY.

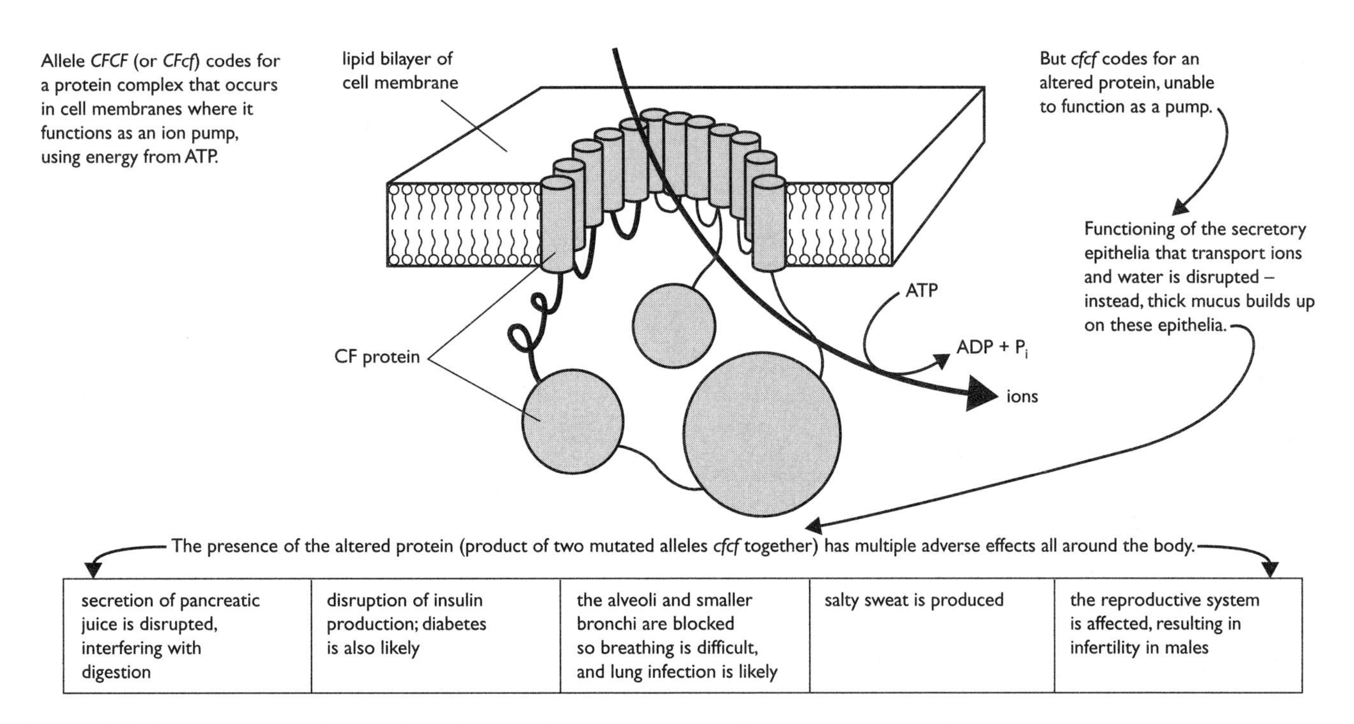

Figure 3.29 The protein coded by the *CF* gene *in situ*, and the consequences of inheriting two copies of the (mutant) recessive *cf* gene.

Environmental effects

If plants of a tall variety of a pea are deprived of nutrients in the growing phase of development, full size may not be reached. A 'tall' plant may appear to be dwarf. This interaction of the inherited instructions in the genes with the conditions of the environment is a clash of **'nature vs nurture'**. As the majority of organisms fail to survive to reproduce we might say that in all these cases, 'nurture' overtakes 'nature'. However, in organisms that do survive to reproduce, the environment critically influences phenotype in many cases.

Temperature sex determination (TSD) in reptiles

Genetic sex determination (for example, the XY/XX system of mammals) is discussed on page 23. In contrast to this, in many species of reptiles (but not in all) it is the temperature of incubation of fertilised eggs that determines their gender. TSD was noticed because the ratio of the sexes varied erratically in many species of reptile. Then, experiments with the eggs of alligators, artificially incubated at various temperatures, established the role of temperature. This was backed up by field observations. As is typical of most reptiles, the alligator deposits its eggs in warm conditions (for example, piles of rotting vegetation) rather than incubating them in nests, as birds do. Relatively low temperatures give female alligators and higher temperatures, male alligators. Lizards show this same pattern; turtles show the reverse pattern. The temperature at which a shift in sex ratio occurs varies with species, too.

***Alligator mississippiensis* in a typical habitat. Eggs are laid on drier surrounding land, where rotting vegetation has collected**

Data from a laboratory experiment on the incubation of eggs at different temperatures

	Temperature of egg incubation (°C)					
	26	28	30	32	34	36
Number of eggs used at the start	50	100	100	100	100	50
% of the total used that died	86	4	3	2	6	86
Females produced as a % of living offspring	100	100	100	86.7	0	0
Males produced as a % of living offspring	0	0	0	13.3	100	100

Figure 3.30 The alligator, *Alligator mississippiensis*, and the effects of temperature of incubation on gender.

15 Today, relatively few organisms exhibit TSD; most have evolved some form of genetic sex determination. Speculate on the possible influences of TSD in the extinction of the dinosaurs, *assuming that early reptiles exhibited this type of gender control.*

Diet and phenotype in the honey bee

In a colony of honey bees (*Apis mellifera*) there are three phenotypes (**workers**, **drones** and **queen**), but only two genotypes. The drones are the community's males, and they develop from unfertilised eggs. The queen and the workers develop from fertilised eggs, and they differ only in the diet (an environmental factor) fed in their larval stage.

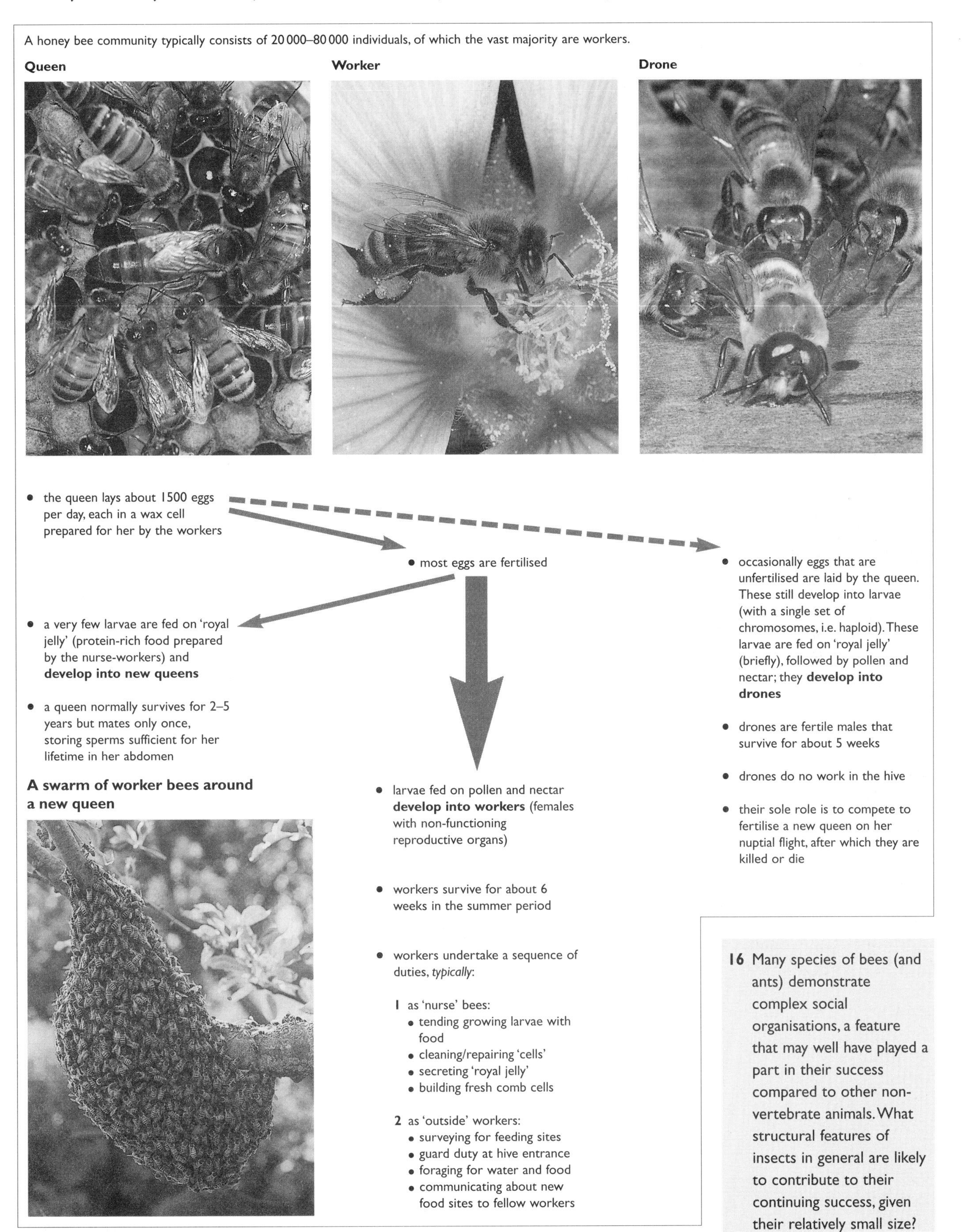

Figure 3.31 Workers, drones and queen bees and their roles.

16 Many species of bees (and ants) demonstrate complex social organisations, a feature that may well have played a part in their success compared to other non-vertebrate animals. What structural features of insects in general are likely to contribute to their continuing success, given their relatively small size?

Mutation

A mutation is a sudden change in the genetic information of an organism that may be heritable, arising from a change in structure, arrangement or quantity of the DNA of the chromosomes. Mutation events occur randomly and spontaneously, and can result in a marked difference in the characteristics of an organism.

- Mutations that occur in the reproductive organs (ovaries, testes, anthers or embryo sac), producing changes to the genes present in the gametes, may be passed to offspring.
- Mutations in the other cells of the body (the soma) are not transmitted to the next generation in sexual reproduction (but may be transmitted by vegetative propagation/budding).

Chromosome mutations involve a change in the structure or number of chromosomes. The types of chromosome mutation are defined in Table 3.2.

Table 3.2 Classification of chromosome mutations.

Euploidy – an alteration in the number of *whole sets of chromosomes*. An organism with more than two sets of chromosomes is called a polyploid. Polyploids are largely restricted to plants and (some) animals that reproduce asexually (the sex determination mechanism of vertebrates prevents polyploidy).

Autopolyploids have additional set(s) of chromosomes *from the same species*, typically formed if the spindle fails in meiosis, causing diploid gametes to be formed; for example, the cultivated potato *Solanum tuberosum* ($2n = 48$), related to the smaller, wild *Solanum brevidens* ($2n = 24$).

Allopolyploids have additional set(s) of chromosomes *from a different species*. The additional set(s) are most likely not to be homologous, so the new individual is sterile, unless the chromosome number is doubled by mitosis in the polyploid cell; for example, polyploid cord grass (see Figure 3.32) and modern bread wheat (see Figure 3.33).

Aneuploidy – an alteration to *part of the chromosome set*. This can occur when part of one chromosome is deleted, duplicated, or broken and rejoined, inverted, on to a different chromosome. It can also occur when one chromosome of the full set is duplicated; for example, **Down's syndrome**, a genetic disorder caused by the addition of a third chromosome number 21, causing congenital heart defects, defects in the eyes, neurological impairment, mental retardation, immune system deficiencies, and an increased risk of developing leukaemia. Chromosome 21 carries approximately 1.5% of the total genes of a human, about 1500 genes.

17 Why may sets of chromosomes from different species, brought together in a new hybrid, be unlikely to form gametes by meiosis (that is, tend to create a sterile hybrid)?

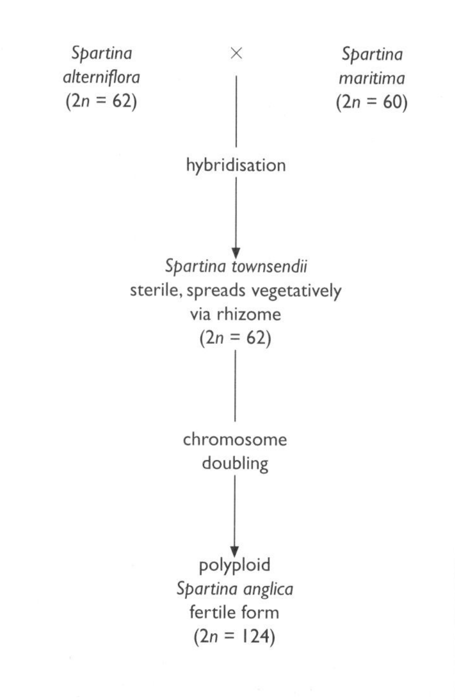

Figure 3.32 Polyploid cord grass (*Spartina anglica*).

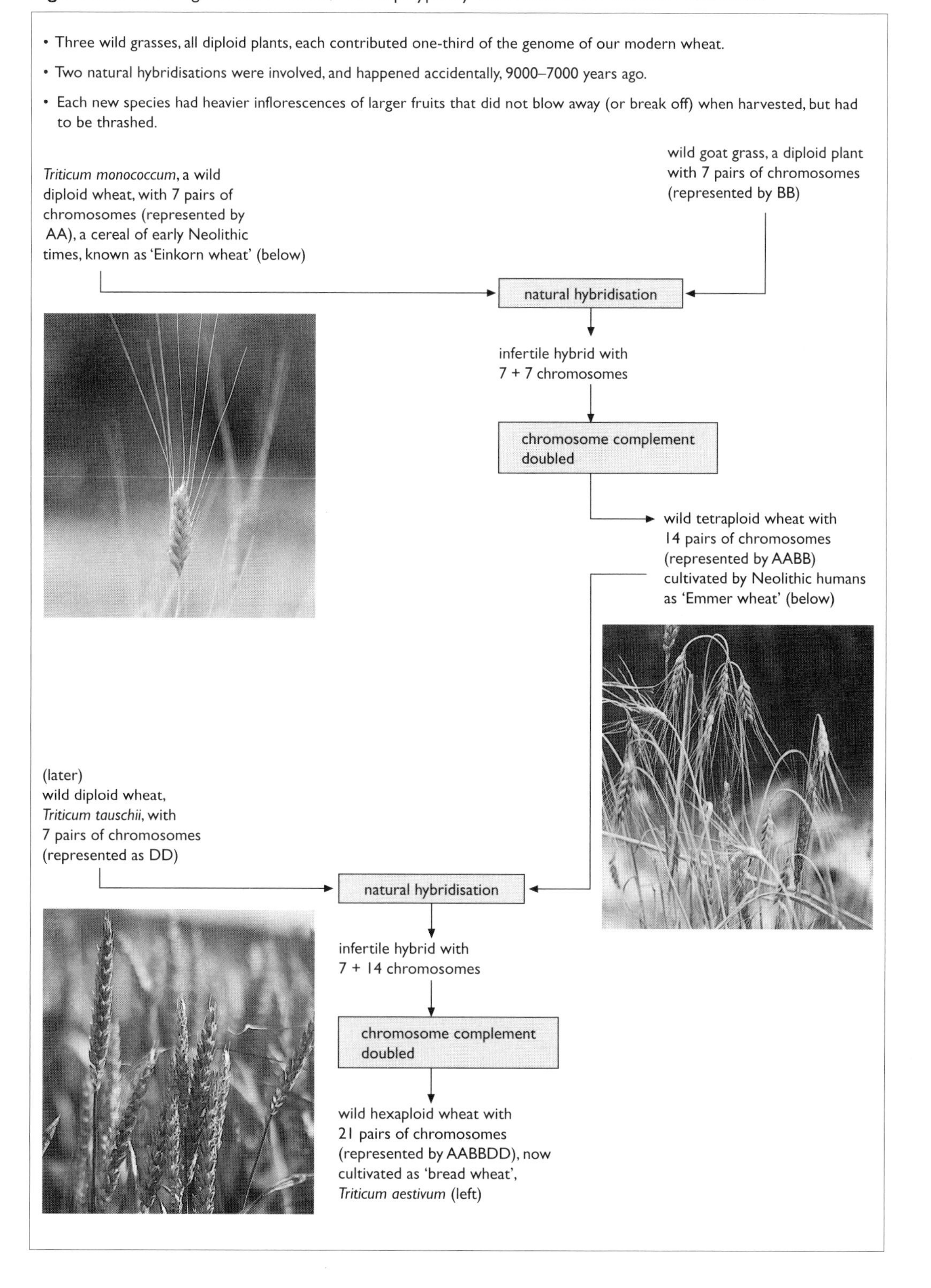

Figure 3.33 The origin of bread wheat; natural polyploidy at the time of the Neolithic revolution.

Gene mutations involve a change in the structure of a gene. Today we think of a gene as a short length of the DNA of a chromosome (page 40). An abrupt change in the chemical structure of a gene may cause a changed characteristic.

Experimental evidence of how genes work in controlling characteristics originally came from studies of the effects of mutations. Very soon after the term 'gene' was first used for a Mendelian 'factor' (by a Danish biologist, W Johannsen, in 1909, long before the chemistry of the gene was understood), it was suggested that genes might work by controlling enzymes (for example, from studies of human metabolic disorders like phenylketonuria, page 39).

GW Beadle and EL Tatum, working at Stamford University, USA, used changes in specific enzymes of metabolism that they induced in the bread mould fungus, *Neurospora*, to show that each gene controls the activity of a single enzyme. They later shared a Nobel Prize for this work (Figure 3.34).

Figure 3.34 A summary of Beadle and Tatum's 'one gene–one enzyme' experiment.

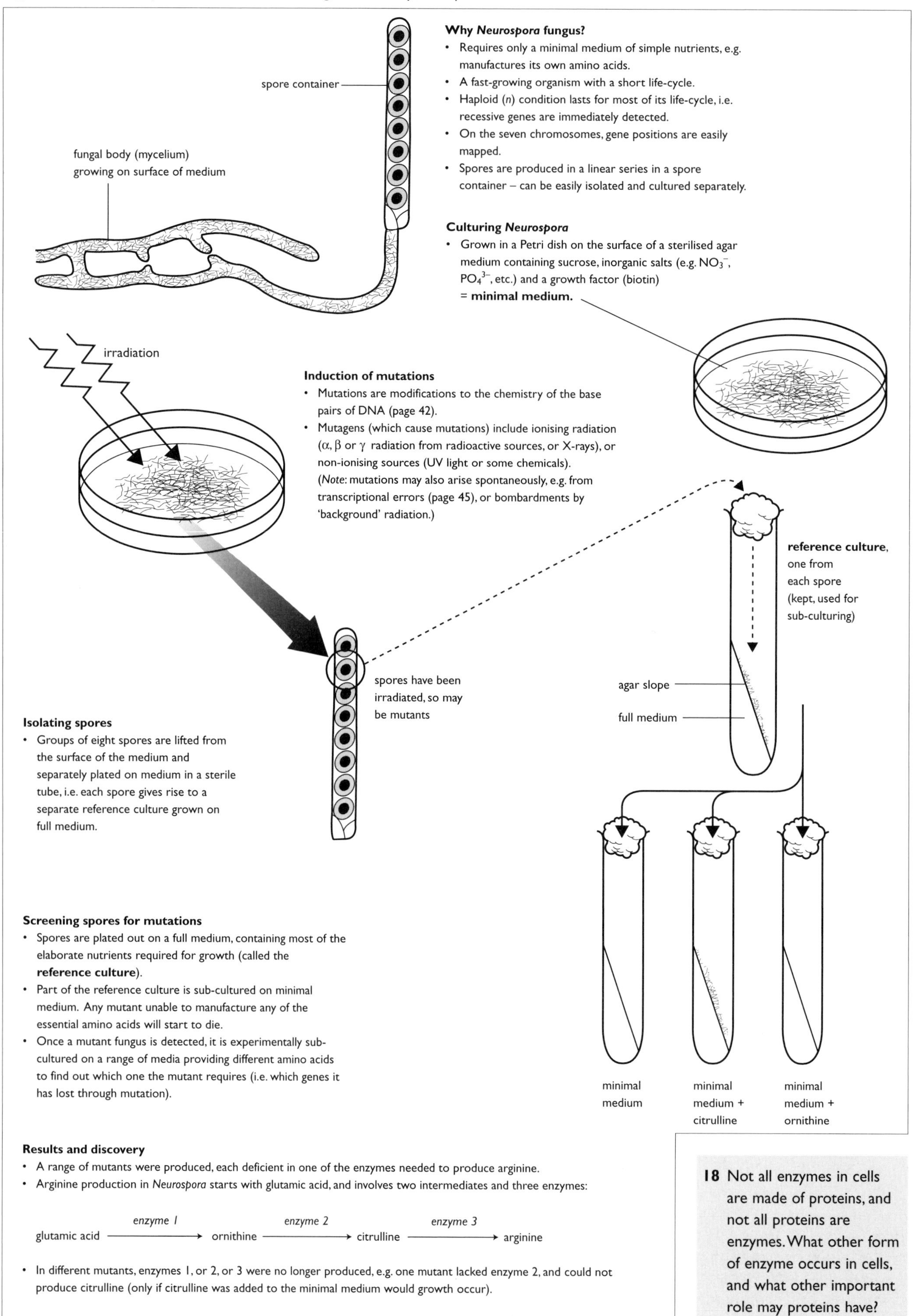

18 Not all enzymes in cells are made of proteins, and not all proteins are enzymes. What other form of enzyme occurs in cells, and what other important role may proteins have?

Sickle-cell anaemia, a disease triggered by a gene mutation

Sickle-cell anaemia is a genetically transmitted disease of the blood caused by an abnormal form of haemoglobin. The normal β haemoglobin gene (*Hb*) is replaced by a sickle-cell haemoglobin gene (Hb^S) as a result of a mutation. People with a single mutant gene ($HbHb^S$) have **sickle-cell trait**; those with a double dose of the mutant gene (Hb^SHb^S) have **sickle-cell anaemia**.

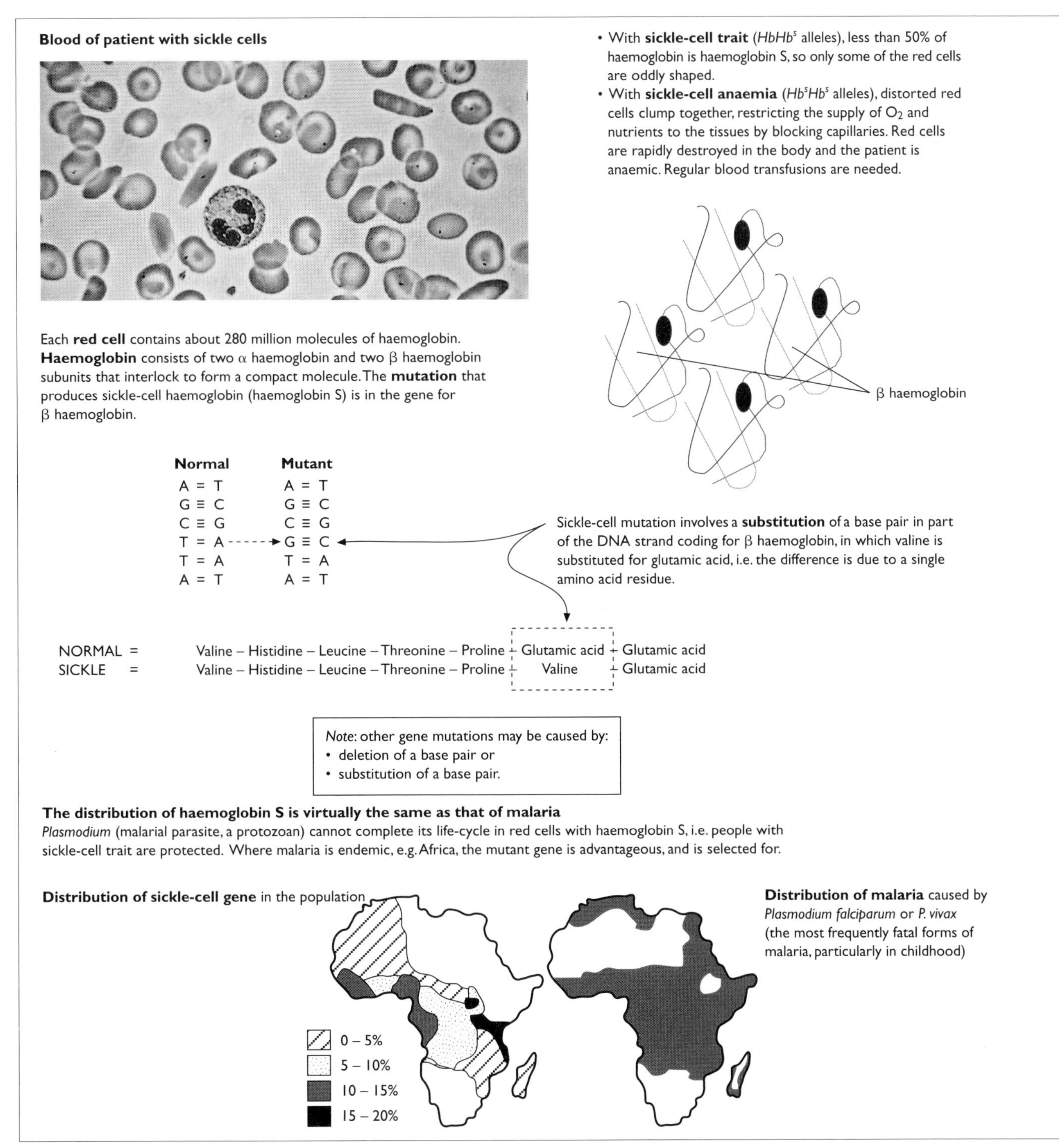

Figure 3.35 Sickle-cell mutation, cause and consequences.

Phenylketonuria (PKU), a dangerous metabolic disorder

The disease PKU is due to the absence of a metabolic enzyme that converts the amino acid phenylalanine (for example, released in protein digestion) to the amino acid tyrosine. If phenylalanine accumulates in the body it causes severe mental retardation. We now know the PKU gene arises as a mutation. Investigation of errors in metabolism like PKU showed that they were inherited as simple (single-gene), recessive Mendelian characteristics. These discoveries led to the hypothesis that genes work via enzymes. (Today, the adverse effects of this mutation are avoided by a selected diet.)

4 Genetics and cell biology

Today, genetics is a major component of the **cell biology revolution**, along with biochemistry, cytology (study of cell ultrastructure) and microbiology. Developments in electron microscopy, analytical chemistry (for example, spectroscopy, chromatography, X-ray crystallography, ultracentrifugation) and enzymology have enabled us to study the ways cells are structured and how they function at the molecular level. Central to this is the way DNA in the chromosomes, the hereditary material, controls and directs all aspects of cellular activity.

Figure 4.1 The chemical composition and physical structure of a chromosome.

The chemistry of a chromosome

DNA	27%
protein	67%
RNA	6%

The structure of the chromosomes

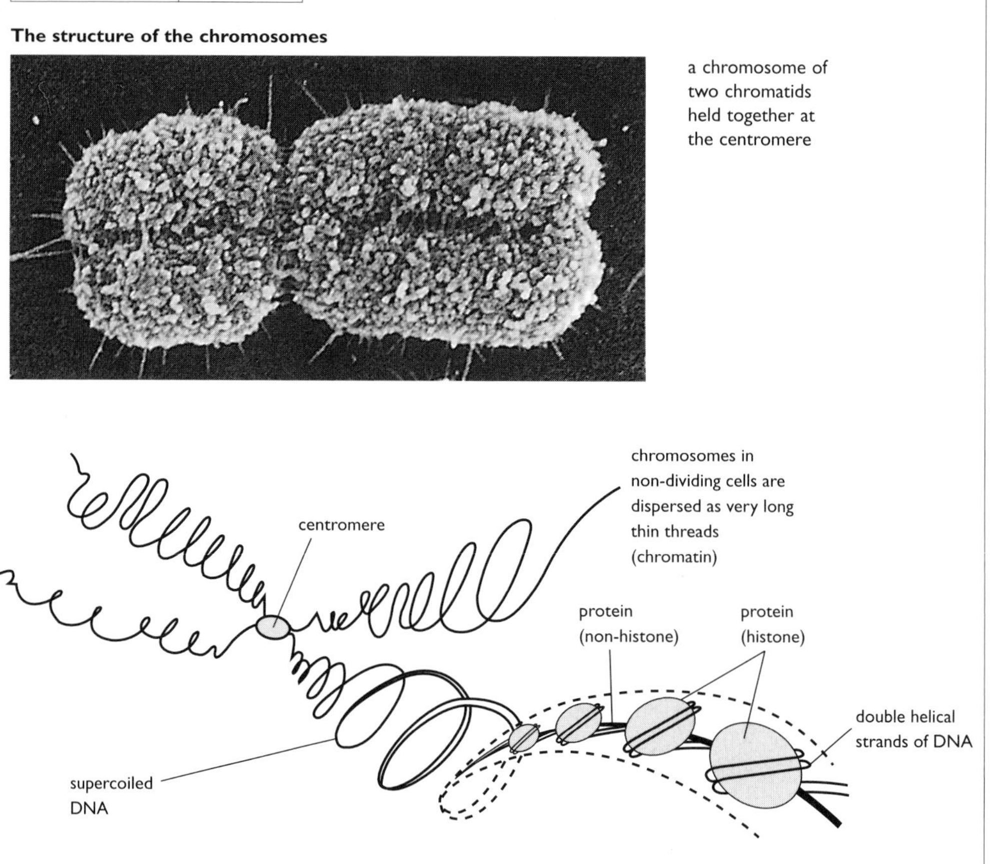

Issue 1: How do we know that DNA is the hereditary material?

DNA was discovered as a biochemical as long ago as 1897, but its role was not guessed. The first steps to this came in 1928, from experiments with the bacterium causing pneumonia in mice (and humans). A microbiologist called Griffith discovered something we call **'transformation'** in bacteria. He did not know what caused it.

Figure 4.2 TEM of *Streptococcus pneumoniae*.

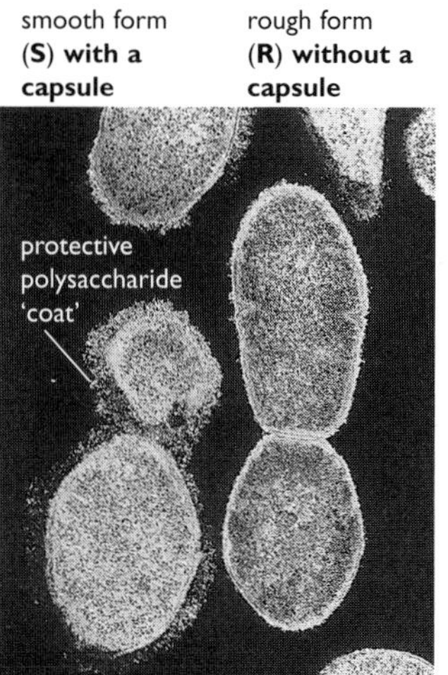

Figure 4.3 Using mice to discover the virulence of **R** and **S** forms.

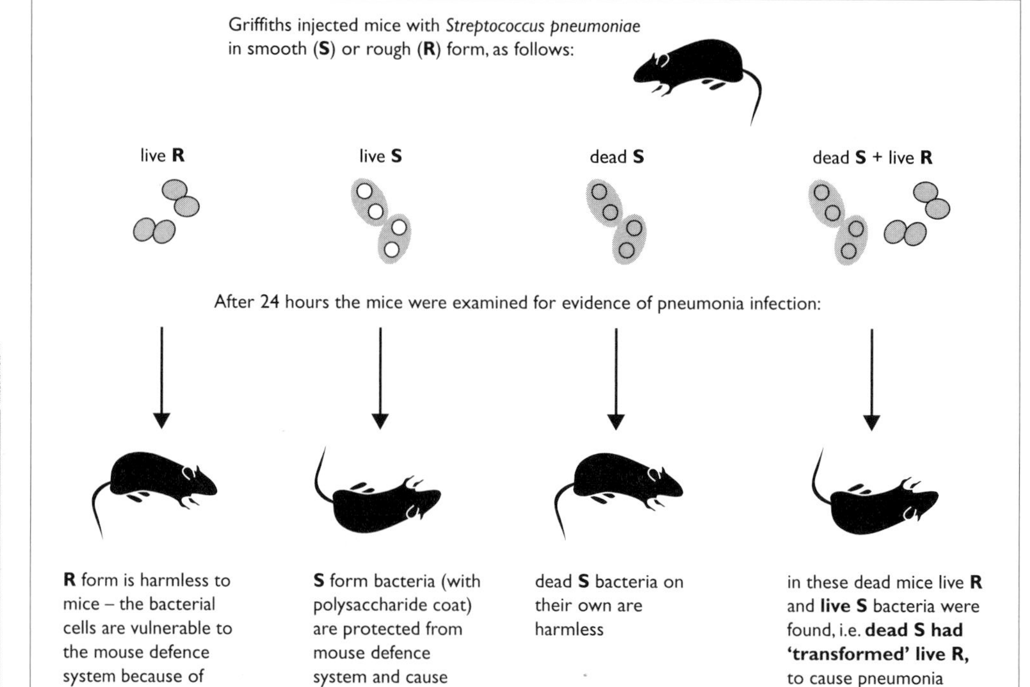

Then, Avery, Macleod and McCarty (1944) showed that the **transforming substance is DNA**. Remember, the DNA of bacteria (prokaryotes) exists as a double strand of DNA in the form of a ring.

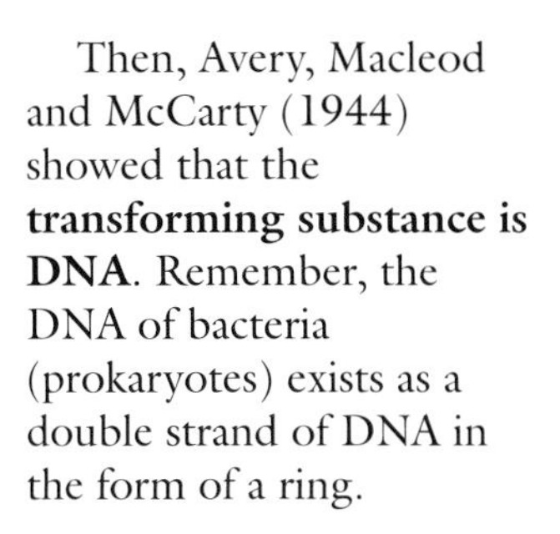

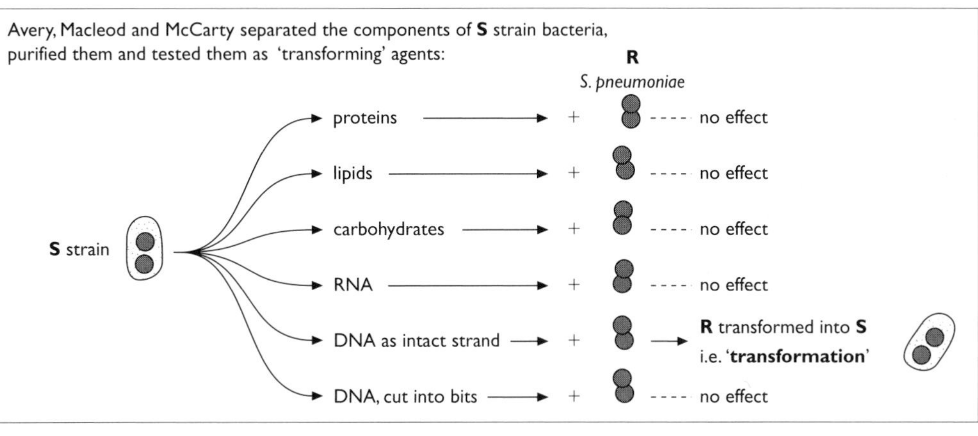

Figure 4.4 Purified, intact DNA could 'transform' **R** strain *S. pneumoniae*.

1 Explain the difference between a stable and a radioactive isotope.

Using a **bacteriophage** and **radioactive isotopes**, DNA was confirmed as the genetic material, by Alfred Hershey and Marsha Chase (1952). A bacteriophage is a virus that attacks bacteria.

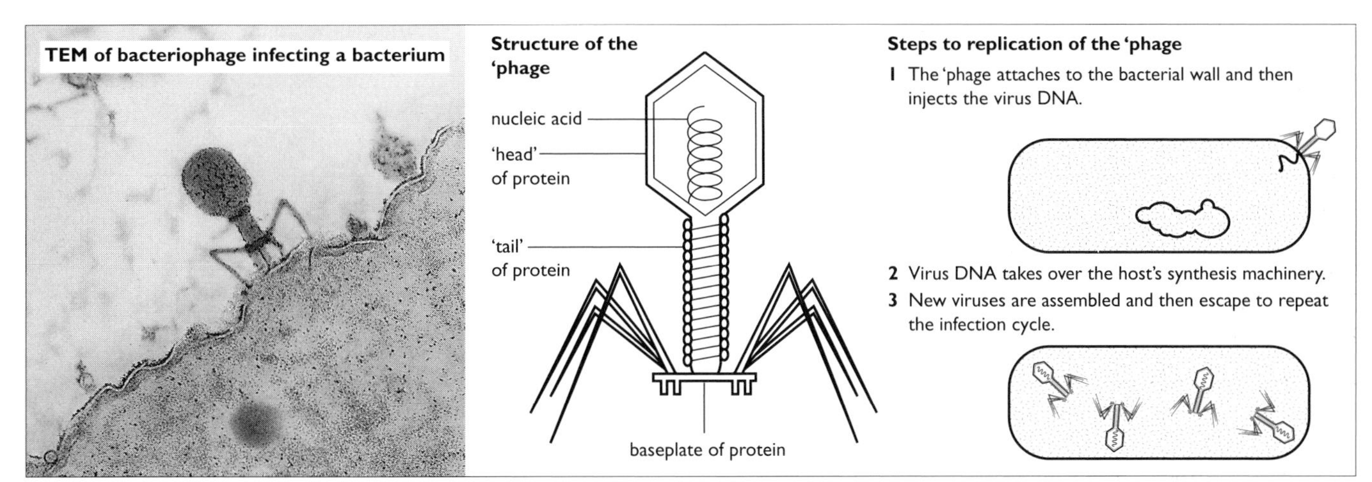

Figure 4.5 How a bacteriophage parasitises a bacterium.

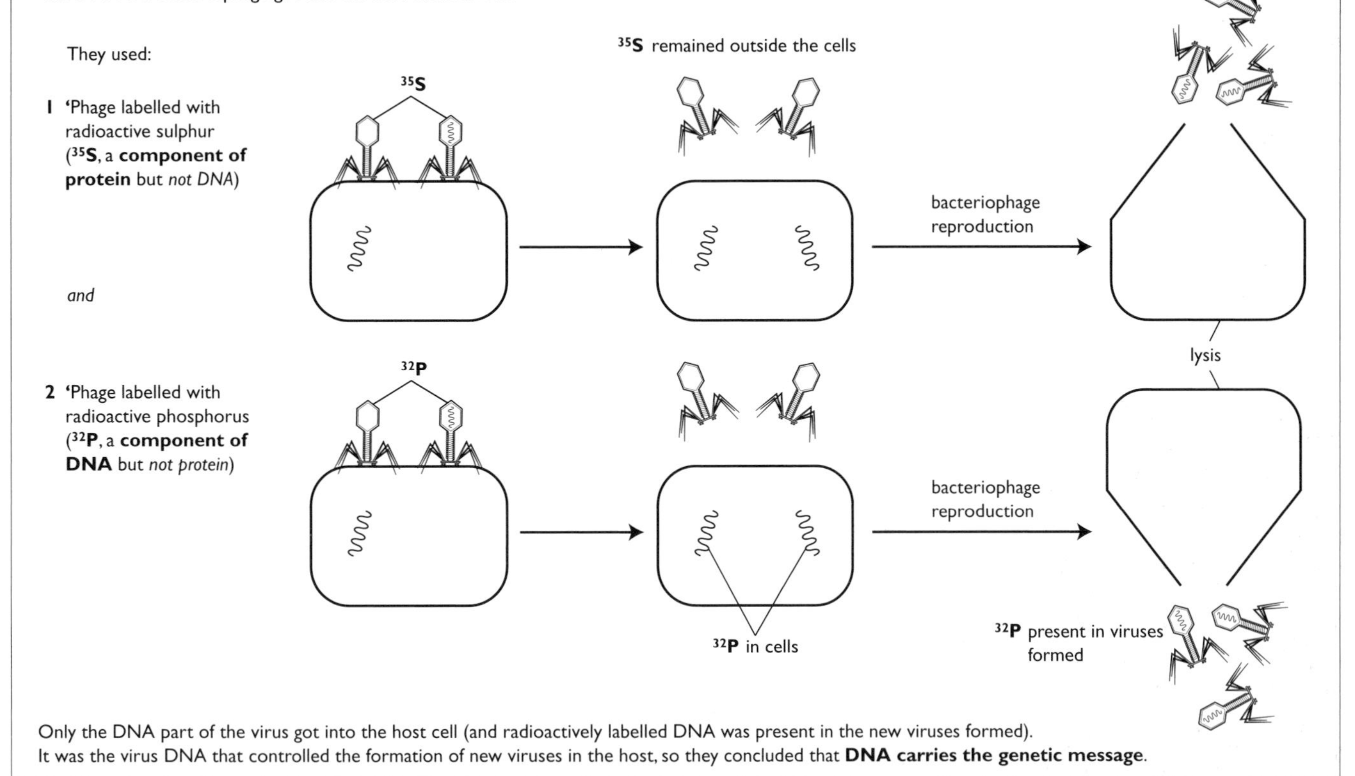

Figure 4.6 How Hershey and Chase proved that DNA was the genetic material.

Issue 2: What is the structure of DNA?

When X-rays are passed through crystalline DNA they are scattered in a way that produces a distinctive pattern on photographic film. Mathematical analysis of the pattern discloses the arrangement of atoms within the DNA molecule. By this technique it was established that DNA:

- is a long thin molecule, of diameter 2 nm;
- is a helix, with a complete twist every 3.4 nm;
- has ten nitrogenous bases to each 'twist';
- consists of two strands.

Dr Rosalind Franklin was a major contributor in this field, but she died of cancer before the Nobel Prize was awarded for the discovery of DNA structure in 1962.

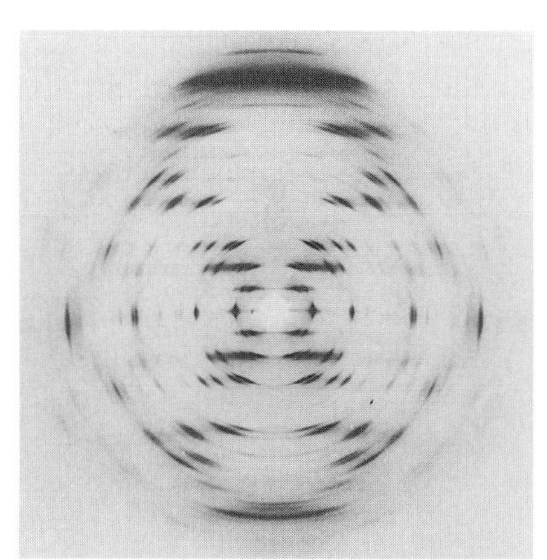

Figure 4.7 Rosalind Franklin and Maurice Wilkins, working at Kings College, London, in an uneasy partnership, produced and analysed X-ray diffraction patterns of crystalline DNA (1952–1953). This is an X-ray photograph of DNA in the β form taken by Rosalind Franklin late in 1952.

Figure 4.8 The structure of DNA, proposed by Francis Crick and Jim Watson, at the Cavendish Laboratory, Cambridge, 1953.

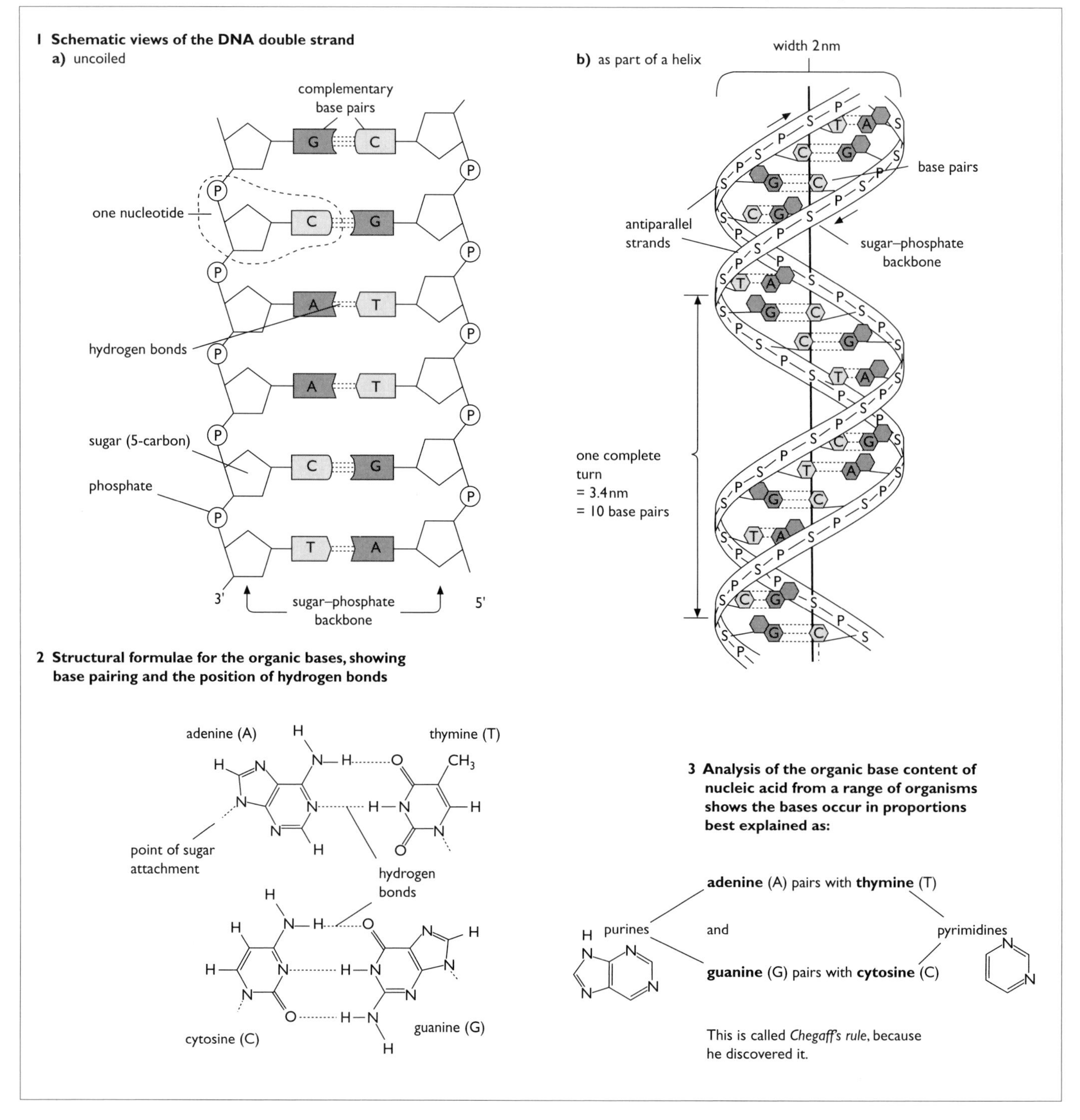

A fascinating account of the discovery of DNA can be read in Francis Crick (1988) *'What Mad Pursuits – A Personal View of Scientific Discovery'*, Penguin Books, London.

When and how DNA replication occurs

Chromosomes separate during mitosis of cell division, but the replication of DNA itself occurs altogether earlier in the cycle of cell growth and division. DNA must accurately replicate if genetic information is to be available for transmission to daughter cells and from generation to generation in reproduction.

Figure 4.9 The timing of replication in the process of mitosis and cell division.

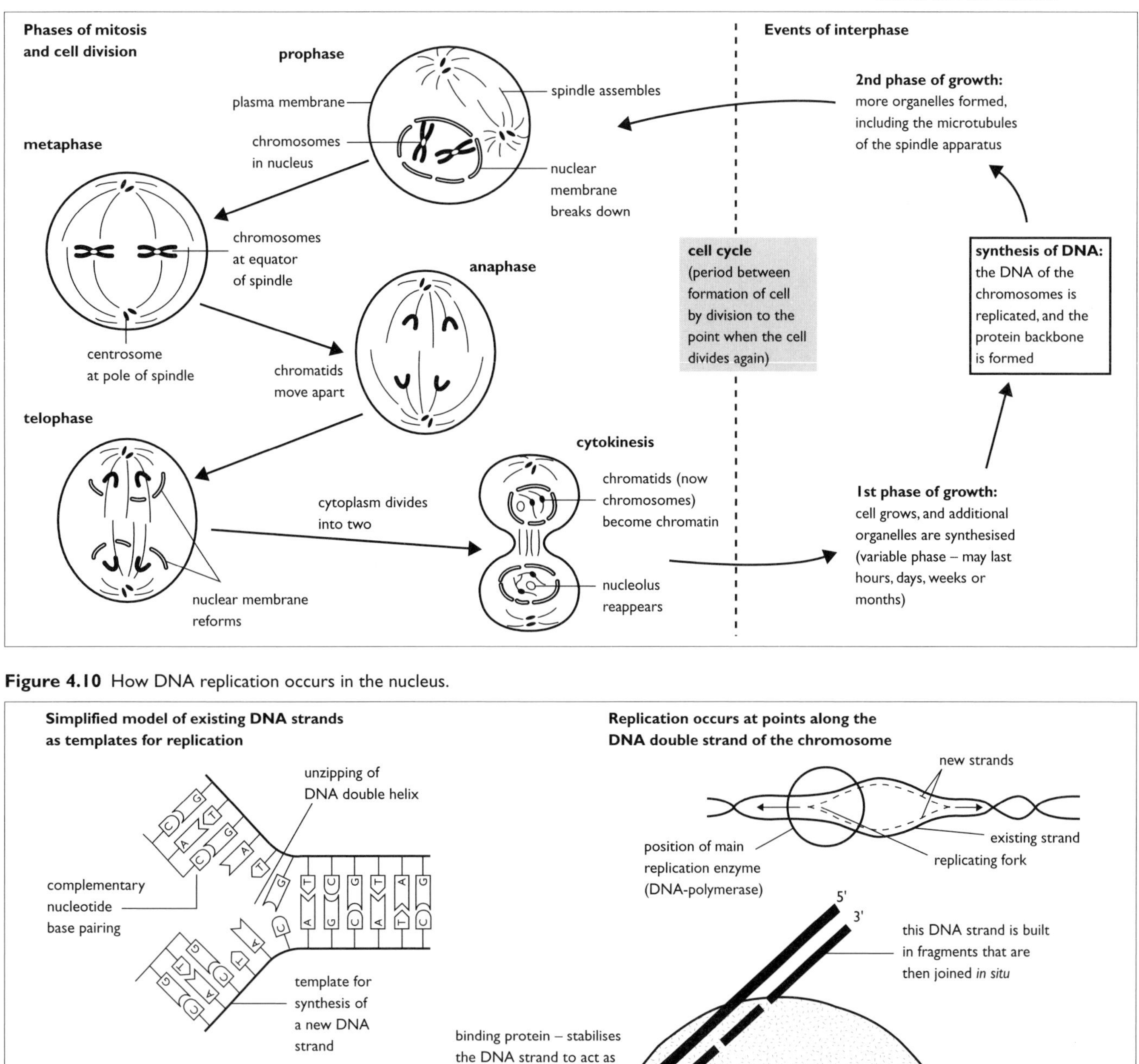

Figure 4.10 How DNA replication occurs in the nucleus.

Today the enzyme machinery of **DNA replication** (Figures 4.10 and 4.11) is known, but when Watson and Crick first published their ideas about DNA structure (*Nature*, 25th April, 1953), the biological implications were speculations:

> *'It has not escaped our notice that the specific pairing we have postulated (i.e. A & T; C & G) immediately suggests a possible copying mechanism for the genetic material.'*

The mechanism had yet to be established. For example, do the DNA double strands 'unzip' and act as templates for a new strand (known as **'semi-conservative' replication**)?

2 What is the chemical composition of a nucleotide, and how do individual nucleotides relate to the structure of a strand of DNA?

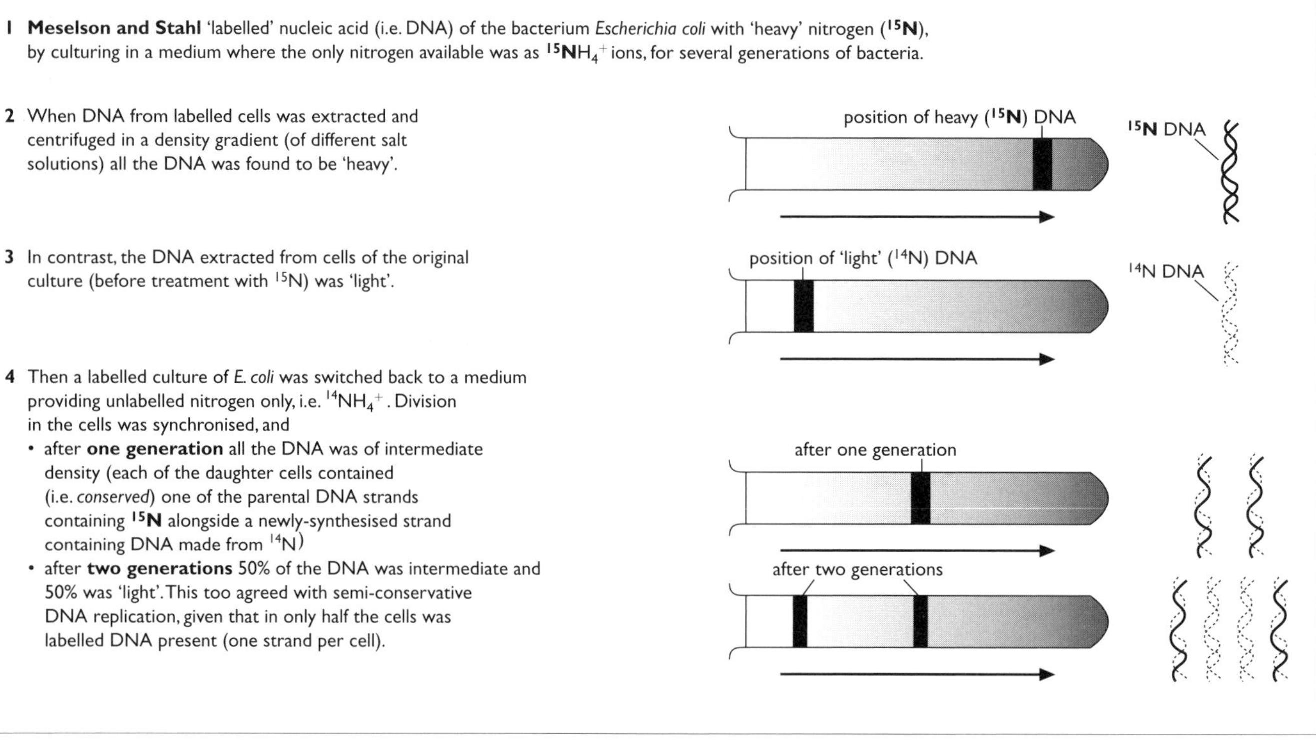

Figure 4.11 DNA replication is 'semi-conservative'.

Issue 3: How can DNA contain 'information'?

The sugar–phosphate 'backbone' of DNA escapes suspicion of having an 'information' role because of its uniform composition. In DNA, the backbone is of alternating deoxyribose (five-carbon sugar) and phosphate (and in RNA, of ribose and phosphate).

To the sugar is also attached an organic base (**adenine [A], thymine [T], cytosine [C] or guanine [G]). Some combination of these bases must be a 'word' or unit of information.**

As the role of the gene is to control protein synthesis, and proteins are made of amino acids condensed together, information in DNA must code for the amino acids from which proteins are synthesised. So **how many bases code for an amino acid?**

Figure 4.12 The potential dictionary from doublet and triplet codes.

Some 20 amino acids make up the proteins of living things, so it is this number of amino acids that must be coded by the four bases of nucleic acid. Organic bases are represented by their first letter, i.e. **A**denine, **T**hymine, **G**uanine and **C**ytosine.
Possible codes are:

doublet				**triplet**			
AA	AG	AC	AT	AAA	AAG	AAC	AAT
GA	GG	GC	GT	AGA	AGG	AGC	AGT
CA	CG	CC	CT	ACA	ACG	ACC	ACT
TA	TG	TC	TT	ATA	ATG	ATC	ATT
				GAA	GAG	GAC	GAT
				GGA	GGG	GGC	GGT
				GCA	GCG	GCC	GCT
				GTA	GTG	GTC	GTT
				CAA	CAG	CAC	CAT
				CGA	CGG	CGC	CGT
				CCA	CCG	CCC	CCT
				CTA	CTG	CTC	CTT
				TAA	TAG	TAC	TAT
				TGA	TGG	TGC	TGT
				TCA	TCG	TCC	TCT
				TTA	TTG	TTC	TTT

So, the number of amino acids that can be coded with a **doublet code** is **16**, and with a **triplet code** is **64**.

Thus, **a triplet code is essential**, but has spare capacity, that is, two or more triplets might code for the same amino acid.

This arrangement is known as a **degenerate code**.

The triplet code has been deciphered experimentally. We can now predict the amino acid sequence of polypeptides when these are made, using DNA (or mRNA, see page 46) in which the sequence of bases is known. This type of experiment is conducted outside cells (using extracted ribosomes and the protein synthesis enzymes). The polypeptides formed are then analysed for their composition and sequence of amino acids.

3 What is the connection between a polypeptide and a protein?

Figure 4.13 Francis Crick's 'frame-shift' evidence for a triplet code.

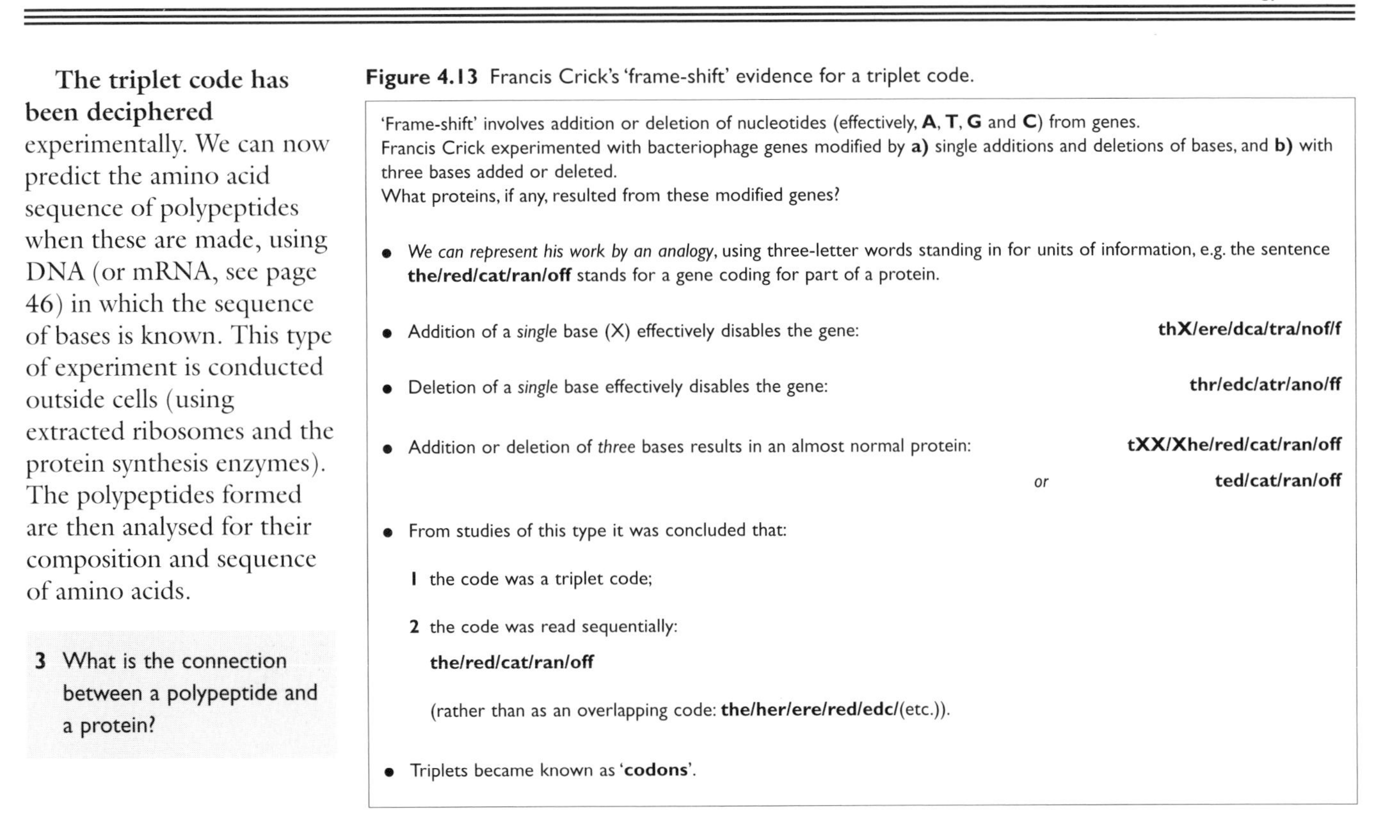

'Frame-shift' involves addition or deletion of nucleotides (effectively, **A**, **T**, **G** and **C**) from genes.
Francis Crick experimented with bacteriophage genes modified by **a)** single additions and deletions of bases, and **b)** with three bases added or deleted.
What proteins, if any, resulted from these modified genes?

- *We can represent his work by an analogy*, using three-letter words standing in for units of information, e.g. the sentence **the/red/cat/ran/off** stands for a gene coding for part of a protein.
- Addition of a *single* base (X) effectively disables the gene: **thX/ere/dca/tra/nof/f**
- Deletion of a *single* base effectively disables the gene: **thr/edc/atr/ano/ff**
- Addition or deletion of *three* bases results in an almost normal protein: **tXX/Xhe/red/cat/ran/off** *or* **ted/cat/ran/off**
- From studies of this type it was concluded that:

  1 the code was a triplet code;

  2 the code was read sequentially:

  the/red/cat/ran/off

  (rather than as an overlapping code: **the/her/ere/red/edc/**(etc.)).
- Triplets became known as '**codons**'.

Figure 4.14 The 20 amino acids of proteins and the genetic code.

Genetic code in circular form

The genetic code is more or less **universal**, a codon codes for the same amino acids in all living things.

This listing of codons is of mRNA (page 46).
In RNA uracil (U) replaces thymine (T).

Read the code radially, from the centre, e.g. serine is coded by UCU, UCC, UCA or UCG.

In addition, some codons stand for 'START' and some for 'STOP', signalling the end of a peptide/protein chain.

Amino acid abbreviations:

alanine	Ala
arginine	Arg
asparagine	Asn
aspartic acid	Asp
cysteine	Cys
glutamine	Gln
glutamic acid	Glu
glycine	Gly
histidine	His
isoleucine	Ile
leucine	Leu
lysine	Lys
methionine	Met
phenylalanine	Phe
proline	Pro
serine	Ser
threonine	Thr
tryptophan	Trp
tyrosine	Tyr
valine	Val

Issue 4: How is the information in the code used in protein synthesis?

The central dogma of microbiology implies a one-way flow of information in the cell (but see Figure 5.7, page 51). The actual steps to protein synthesis are illustrated on page 46.

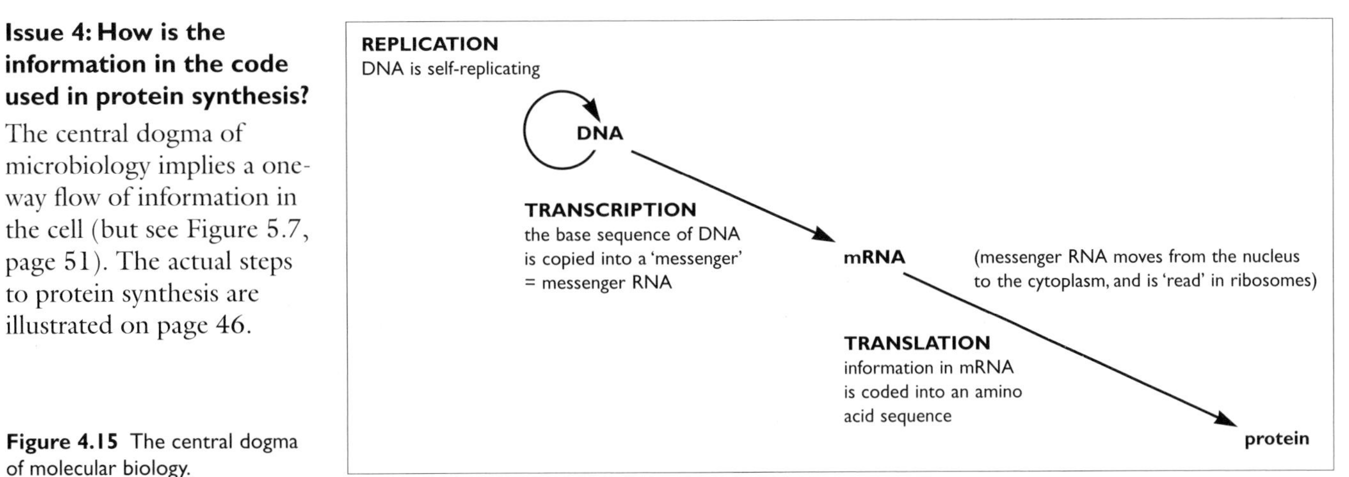

Figure 4.15 The central dogma of molecular biology.

Protein synthesis occurs in the cytoplasm, directed by the DNA of the nucleus. A second type of nucleic acid is involved, **ribonucleic acid (RNA)**.

RNA differs importantly from DNA in that it exists as a single strand (DNA exists as a double strand), and the base uracil (**U**) replaces thymine (**T**). Of course, the RNA 'backbone' contains a different sugar (ribose).

Messenger RNA (**mRNA**) takes the coded message from the chromosomes to the ribosomes (built of rRNA and protein) in the cytoplasm. Here 'active sites' for protein synthesis are maintained. In the cytoplasm, transfer RNA (**tRNA**) makes the link between amino acids and their codons. There is at least one type of tRNA for each of the 20 amino acids.

Step One: Transcription is the transfer of the coded message of a gene from DNA to the cytoplasm, via mRNA.

> **4** How does the form and position of DNA in bacteria differ from that of the eukaryotic cell?

Step Two: Amino acid activation involves the attachment of an amino acid to the tRNA that encodes for it, using energy from ATP. Unique tRNA molecules exist for each of the 20+ amino acids.

> **5** What is the potential evolutionary significance of an universal genetic code?

Figure 4.16 Transcription in the eukaryotic nucleus.

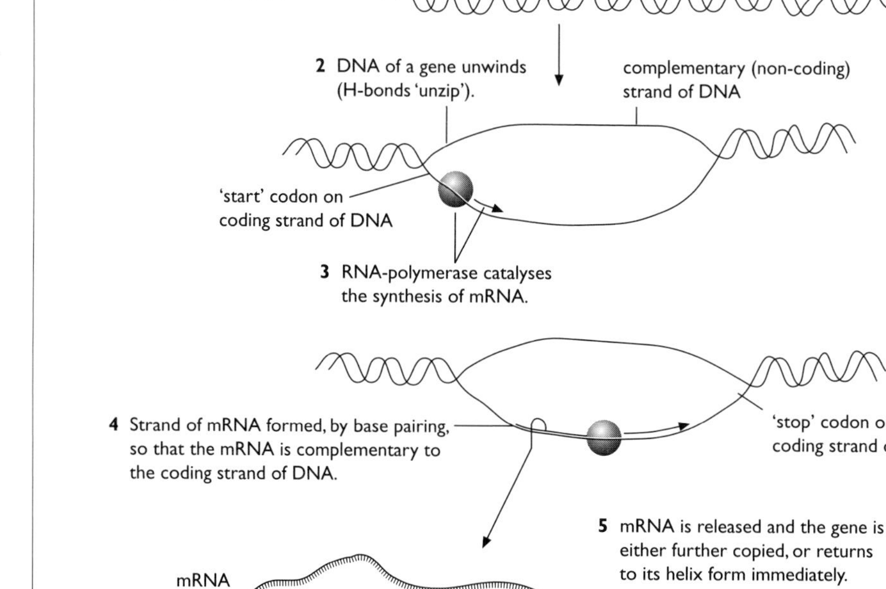

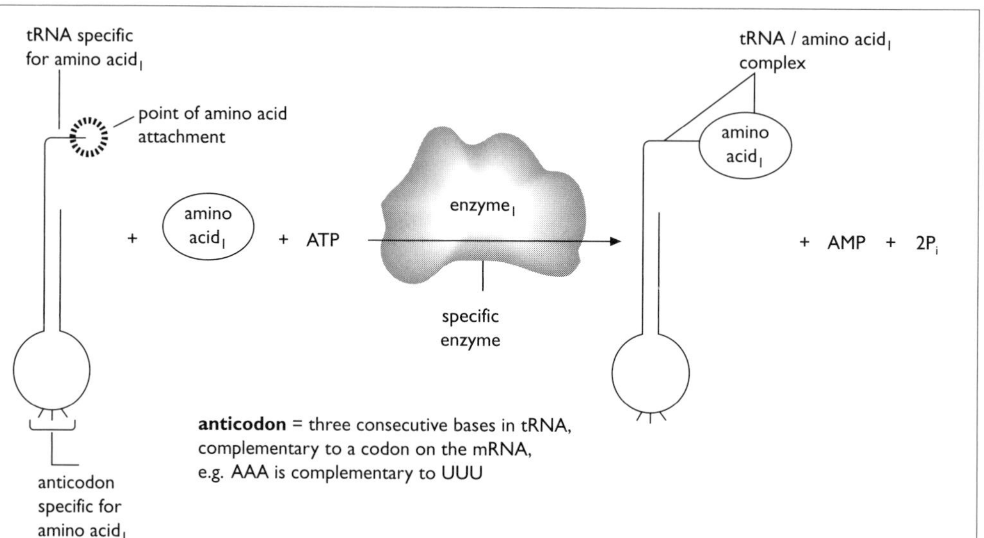

Figure 4.17 Amino acid activation.

Step Three: Translation occurs in the ribosomes. Here anticodons of tRNA match codons of mRNA, to assemble amino acids in the sequence required for a specific protein. The amino acids are then combined to form protein (Figure 4.18).

The roles and fates of proteins in cells are summarised in Figure 4.19.

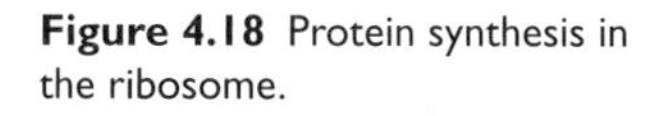

Figure 4.18 Protein synthesis in the ribosome.

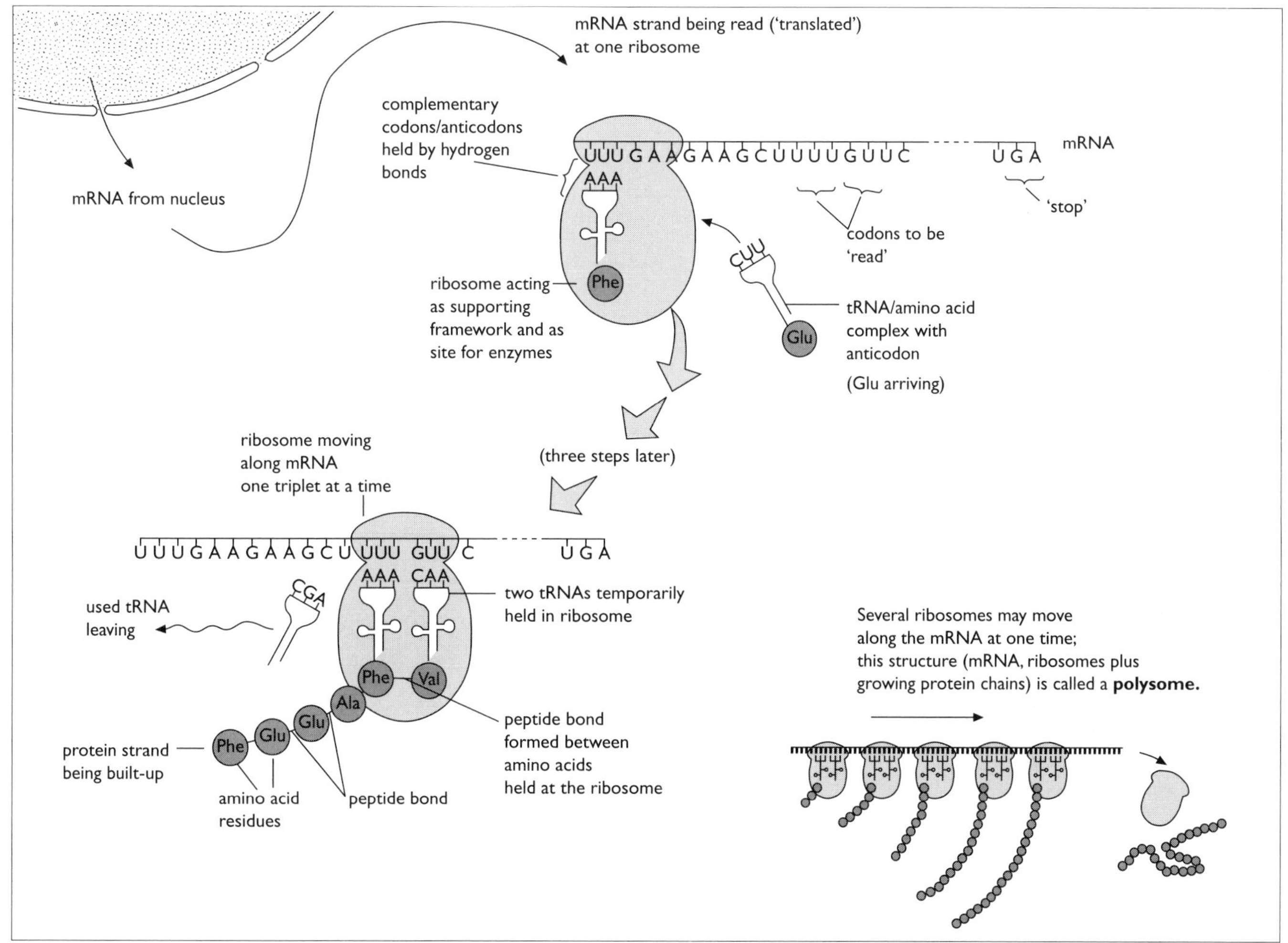

Figure 4.19 Roles and fates of cell proteins.

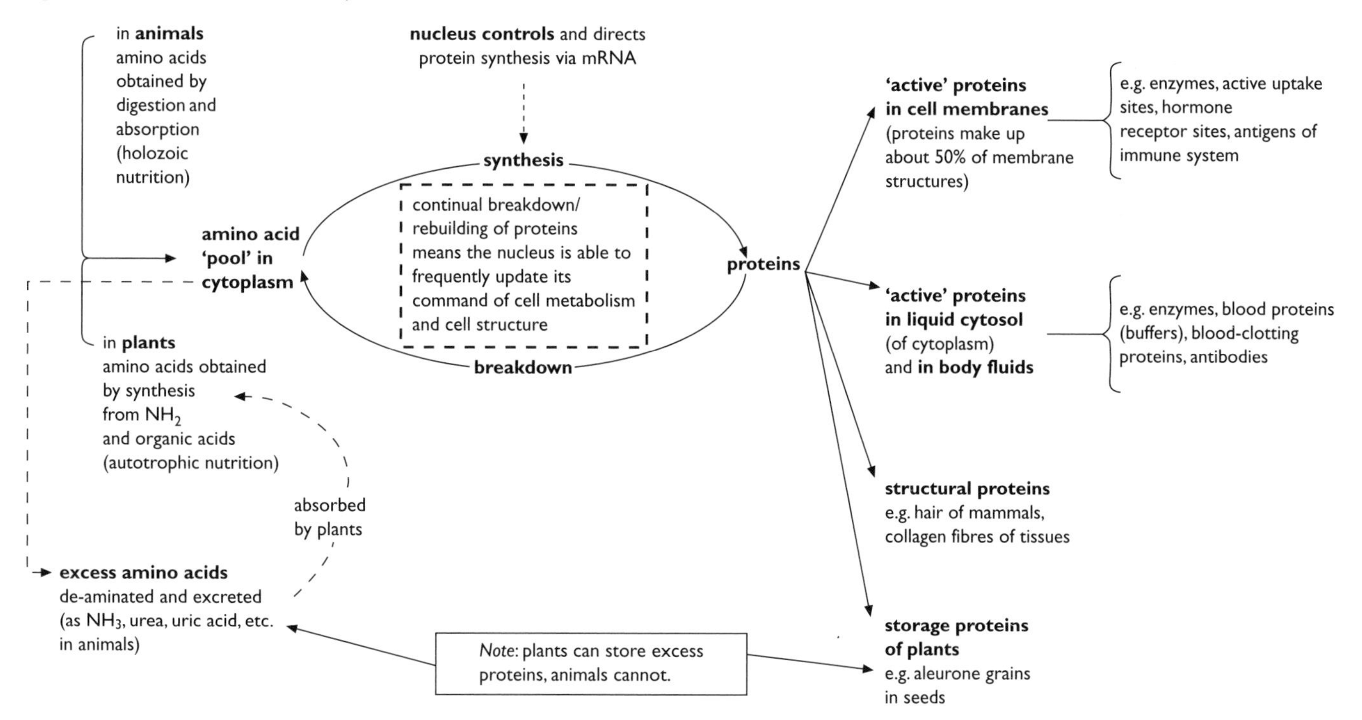

(In effect, most of our proteins are 'an army of workers' on behalf of our genes, endlessly available for 'reconstruction'.)

5 Genetic engineering

Genetic engineering occurs when genes from one organism are transferred to the complement of genes (genome) of another unrelated organism, by artificial means. The process is also known as **recombinant DNA technology**. The outcomes are new varieties of organism, mostly but not exclusively microorganisms. The results have important applications in biotechnology, pharmaceuticals production, medicine, gene therapy, forensic science, agriculture and horticulture. This is currently the **fastest growing branch of modern genetics**, from which there have already been revolutionary products, and about which there are both high hopes and concerns about ethical and environmental issues.

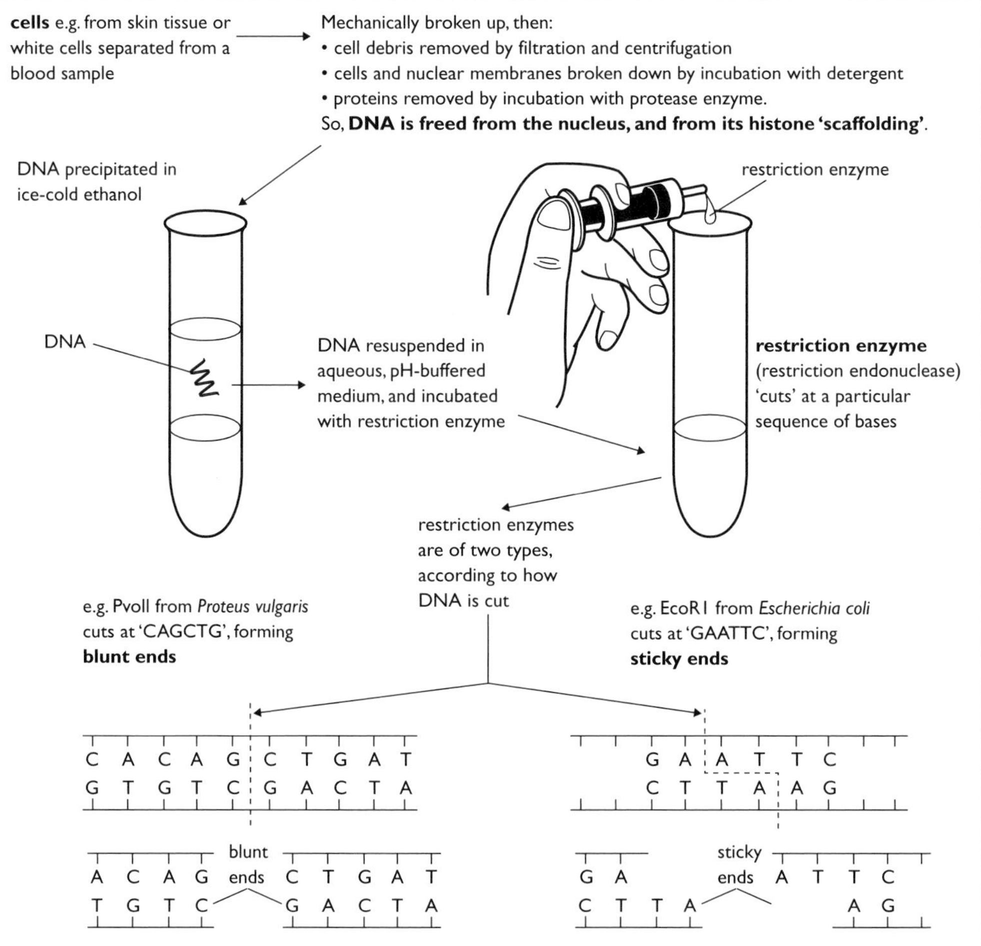

Figure 5.1 Isolating and cutting DNA.

Unpacking the 'tool-kit' for gene manipulation

First, DNA double strands containing the gene to be exploited (for example, part of an animal or plant chromosome) are **'sliced' into fragments**, using restriction endonuclease enzymes. These enzymes occur naturally in bacteria, as a defence against DNA injected by invading viruses. Genetic engineers work to isolate and exploit these enzymes, of which many types exist.

With the DNA in manageable fragments, the next step is to **sort out the pieces**. (The identification of the fragment with the required gene comes later, see Figure 5.5, page 50.)

1 Restriction endonuclease enzyme cuts DNA strands into fragments of differing length at the restriction sites, one of which will contain the **required gene.**

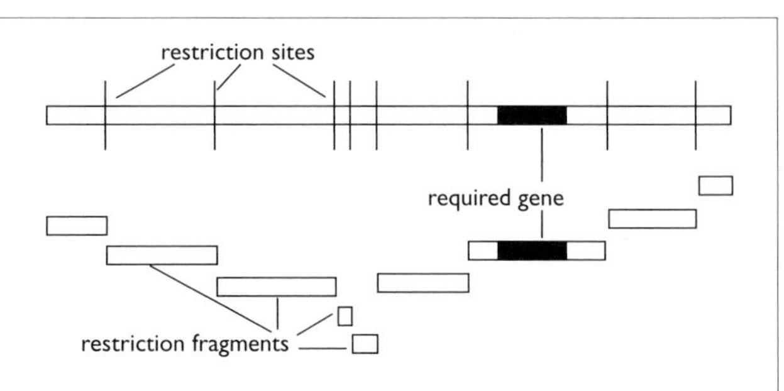

2 DNA fragments are separated by **gel electrophoresis**, using an agar gel (agarose gel):

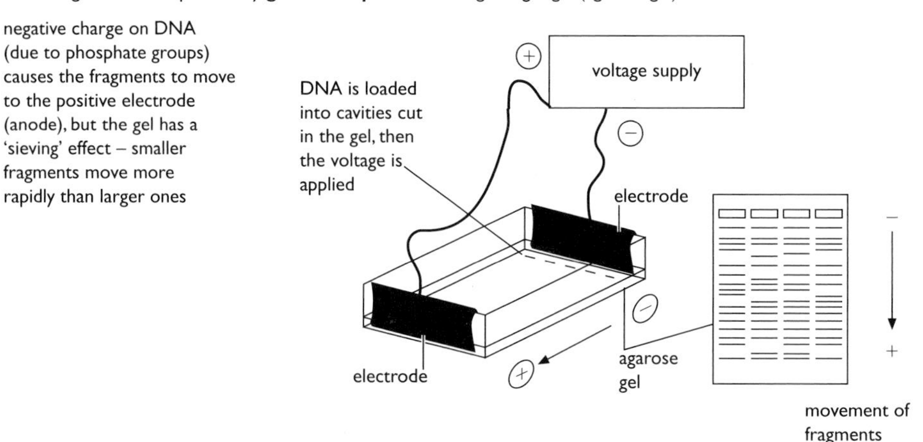

3 Methods used to **detect the position of fragments** include adding a dye.

4 Alternative methods of detecting DNA fragments, using radioactively labelled gene probes, involve 'Southern blotting' (see Figure 5.14, page 55).

Figure 5.2 Separating the DNA fragments.

Then, **cloning of the isolated gene** occurs, in order to produce many working copies. Typically this is done by adding the gene into a **bacterial plasmid**, and then inserting the modified plasmid into a bacterium that can be conveniently and safely cultured.

1 What features of their DNA make bacteria more useful than eukaryotes for recombinant DNA technology?

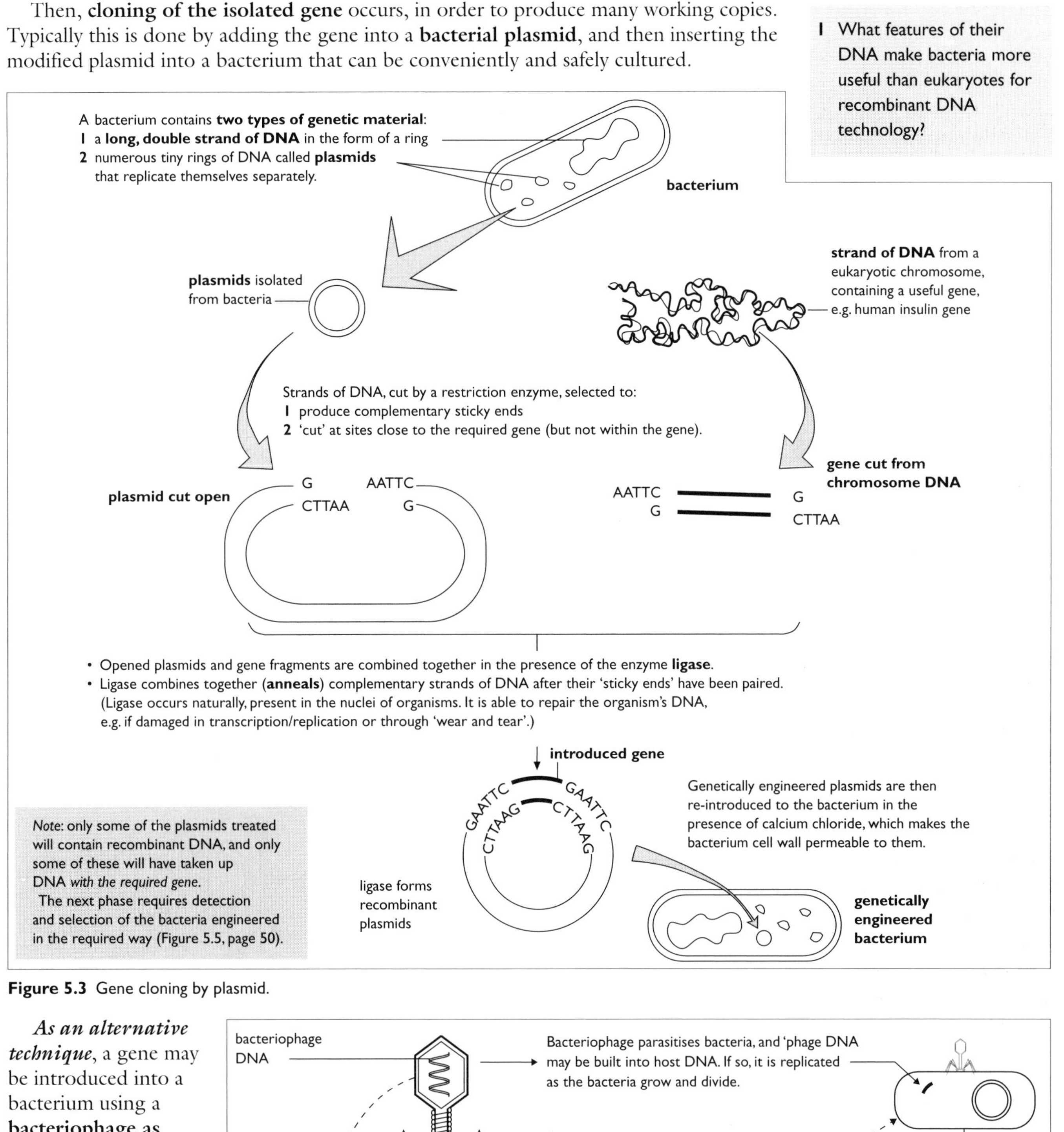

Figure 5.3 Gene cloning by plasmid.

As an alternative technique, a gene may be introduced into a bacterium using a **bacteriophage as vector**. This mechanism is most useful in attempts to clone larger genes (longer lengths of double-stranded DNA).

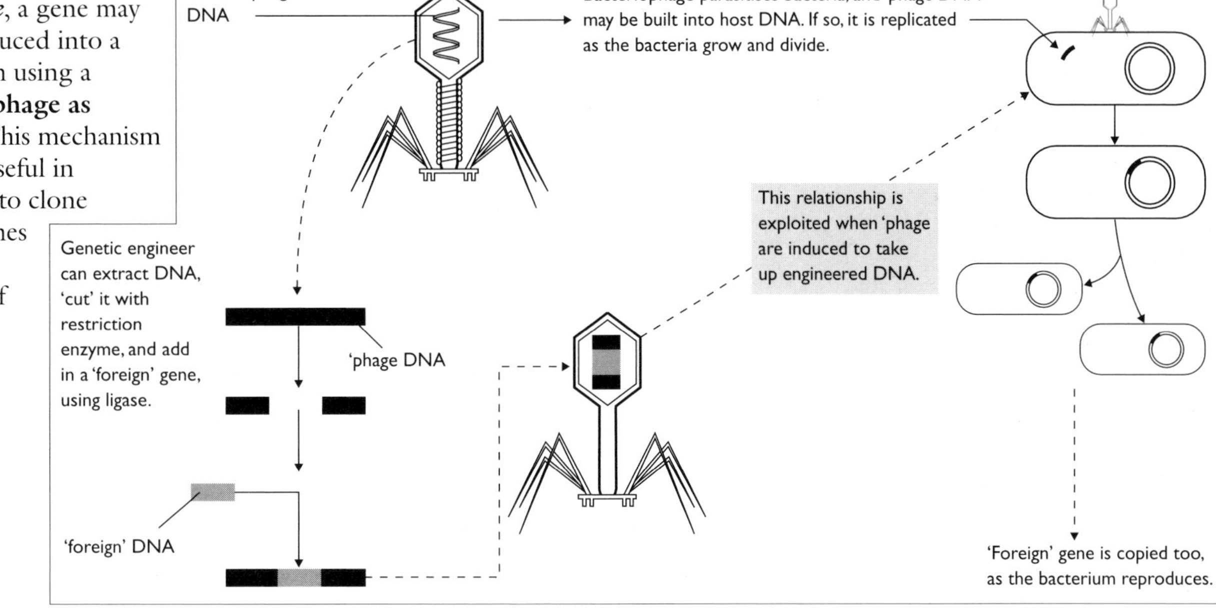

Figure 5.4 Bacteriophage as vector.

The **identification and selection** of engineered bacteria are necessary prior to cloning, to ensure that only the genetically modified cells are used. In this way a significant amount of the engineered gene's 'product' is formed. To be selective, plasmids that contain genes for resistance to specific antibiotics (as a group they are known as **R-plasmids**) are used, in the procedures summarised in Figure 5.5.

2 By what mechanism might a gene for resistance to an antibiotic actually work?

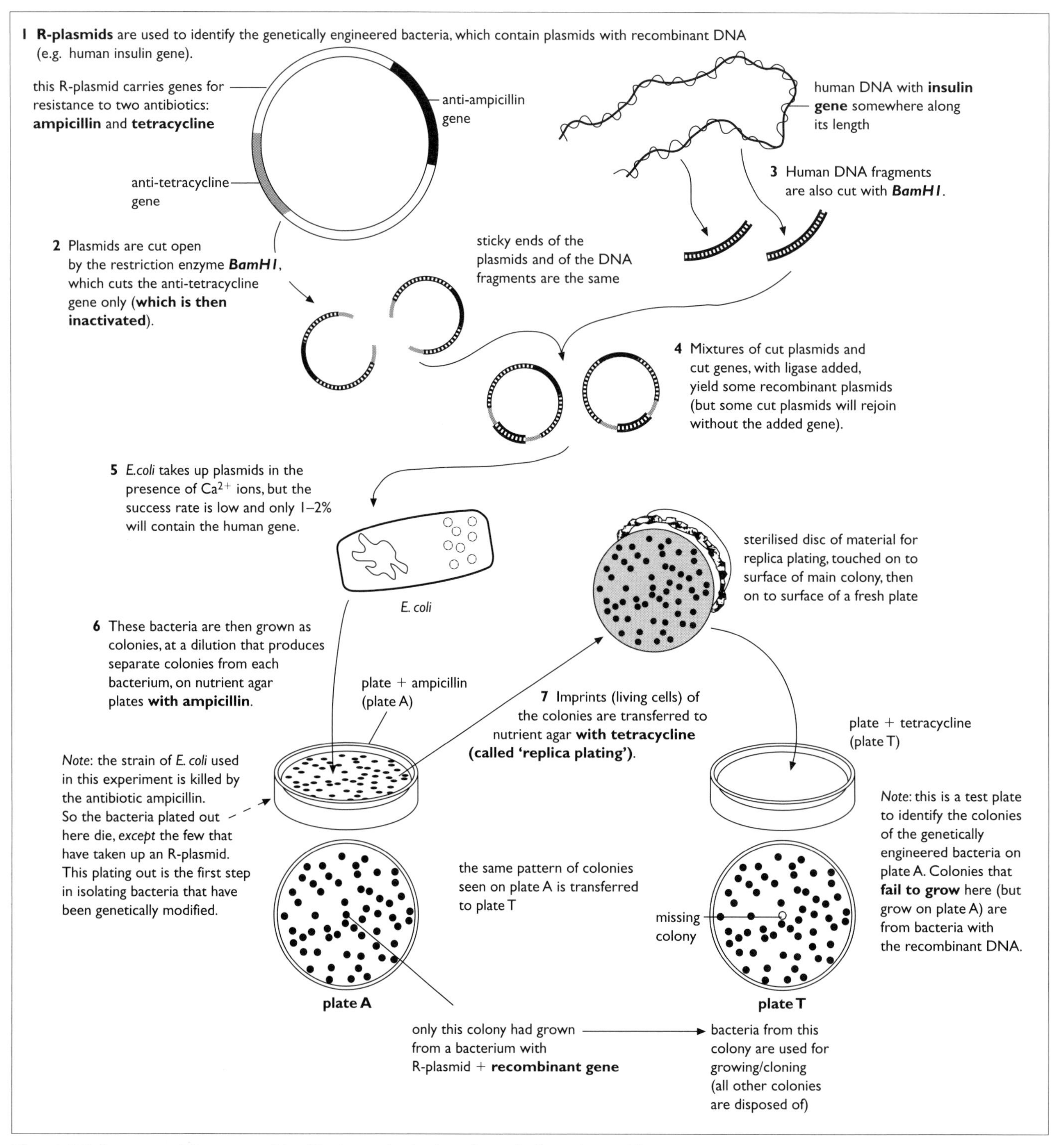

Figure 5.5 Summary of the steps to identification and selection of genetically engineered bacteria.

The regulation of engineered genes

Often, **genes must first be 'switched on'** before they are expressed. Many genes have to be deliberately activated in this way. (Other genes are automatically 'expressed' throughout the life of the cell, that is, continuously transcribed into mRNA.) A 'switch mechanism' found in bacteria is the 'operon' mechanism (for example, the **'lactose operon'**, Figure 5.6). This enzyme complex can be engineered into a bacterium, alongside other introduced genes. Then, the mere presence of lactose in the medium will activate the engineered genes.

3 What advantages are conferred on an organism by genes that require 'switching on' before being expressed?

Applications of the genetic engineering 'tool-kit' in biotechnology

- **Human insulin manufacture** allows people with insulin-dependent diabetes to be treated with human insulin. This avoids the possibility of them developing reactions to 'foreign' protein (often arising when unmodified cattle or pig insulin is used). Insulin (which exists as two polypeptide chains [A + B], linked by –S–S– bridges) is formed by genetically engineered *E. coli* bacteria. Forming the appropriate human gene for transfer involved the enzyme **reverse transcriptase** (see Figure 5.7).
- **Human growth hormone** has been genetically engineered into bacteria (again, *E. coli* has been the most popular), so that the human hormone can be harvested in bulk from the culture solution in the fermenter vessel, purified and used to treat children with specific growth defects.

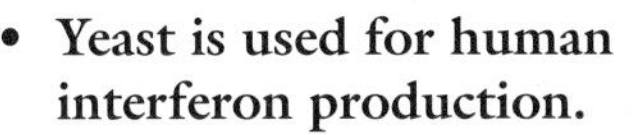

- **Yeast is used for human interferon production.** Unlike bacteria commonly used in recombinant DNA technology, yeast is a eukaryote (it has a nucleus bound by a nuclear membrane, and DNA in chromosomes). But, like the bacteria, yeast also has plasmids, and it may accept engineered plasmids from other sources too, when the cell wall is made permeable to them with lithium salts. Consequently, yeast is also used in genetic engineering, including human interferon production.

Figure 5.6 'Operon' gene regulation.

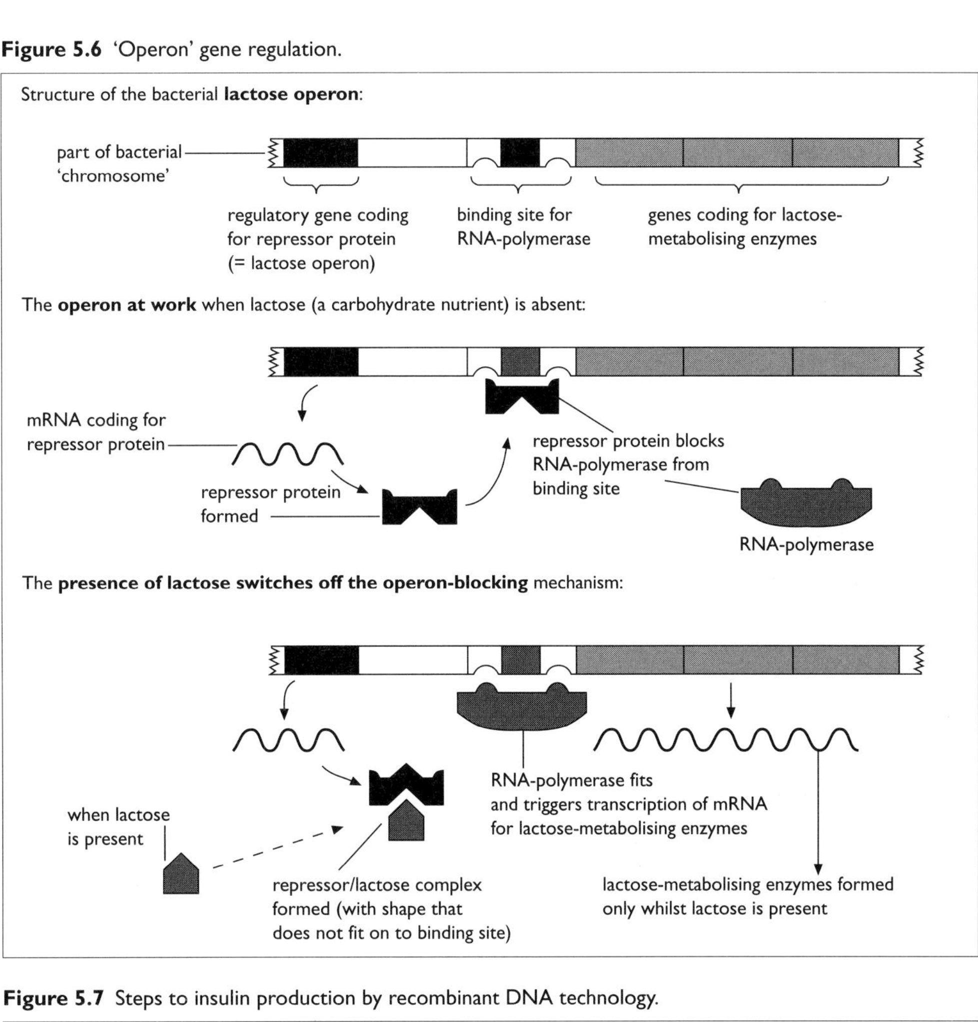

Figure 5.7 Steps to insulin production by recombinant DNA technology.

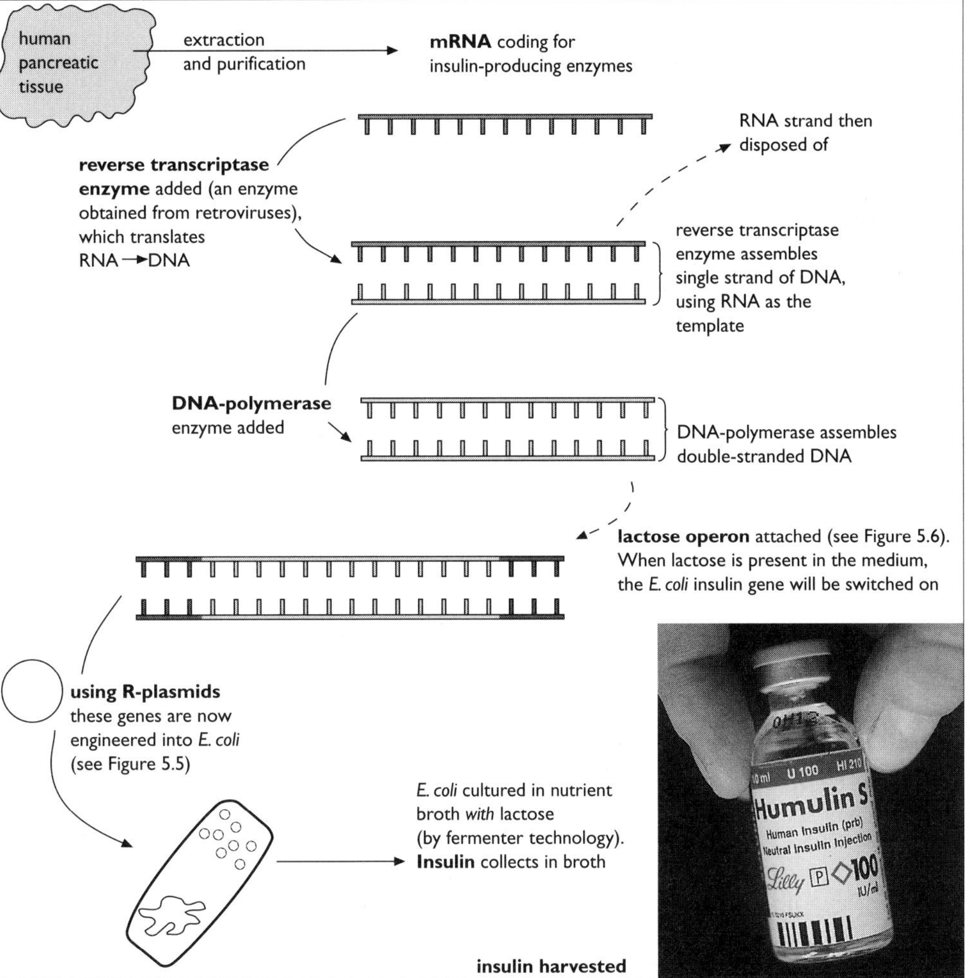

Genetic engineering in eukaryotes

Manipulating genes in eukaryotes presents many more challenges than in prokaryotes because:

- plasmids, the most useful vehicle for moving genes, do not normally occur in eukaryotes (except in yeasts, page 51) and, if introduced, may not be replicated there;
- eukaryotes are diploid organisms, so two alleles for every gene must be engineered into the nucleus, whereas prokaryotes have a single, circular 'chromosome';
- transcription of eukaryotic DNA to mRNA involves removal of introns by specific enzymes (Figure 4.16, page 46), whereas in prokaryotes no processing of mRNA is necessary;
- plant cell walls are a barrier to gene vectors, whereas the bacterial wall may be traversed by plasmids;
- the machinery for triggering gene expression in bacteria is known (Figure 5.6, page 51); in eukaryotes the machinery is more complex and is only partially understood.

Transgenic flowering plants may be formed using the tumour-forming bacterium, *Agrobacterium*, or via isolated protoplasts (the contents of a plant cell after the cell wall has been removed).

Figure 5.8 Transgenic plants via the Ti plasmid of *Agrobacterium*.

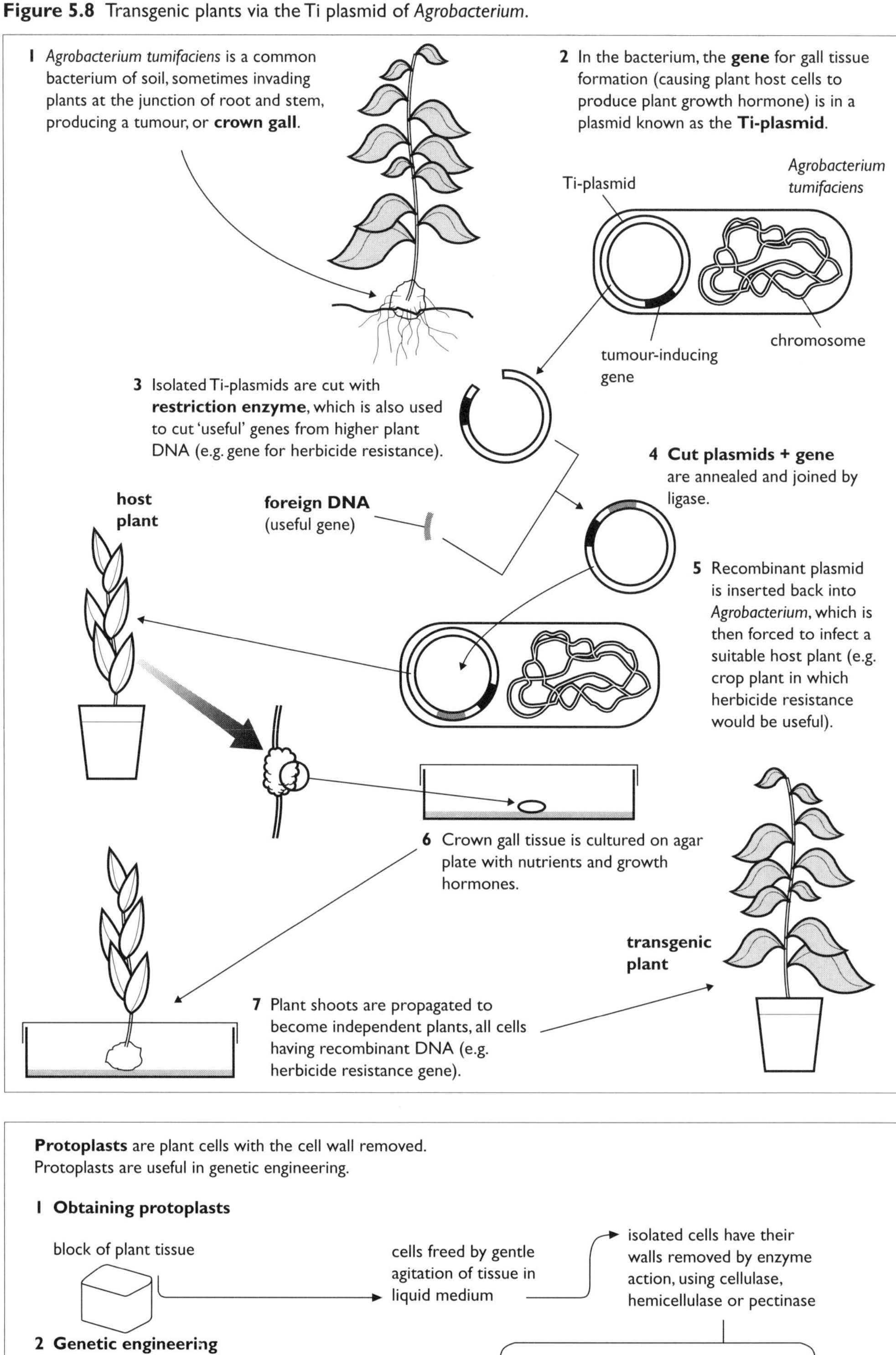

Protoplasts are plant cells with the cell wall removed. Protoplasts are useful in genetic engineering.

1 Obtaining protoplasts

block of plant tissue → cells freed by gentle agitation of tissue in liquid medium → isolated cells have their walls removed by enzyme action, using cellulase, hemicellulase or pectinase

2 Genetic engineering

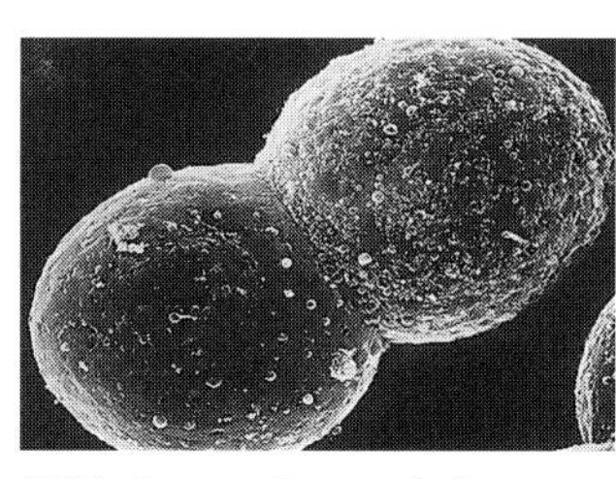

SEM of protoplasts at fusion

protoplasts from the same species or different species fused to form a polyploid (page 36)

plasmids from a bacterium are caused to invade the protoplast, e.g. from the bacterium *Bacillus thuringiensis* with its gene for a toxin that is lethal to the larvae of insects (i.e. it has a natural insecticide)

protoplasts' walls reform (naturally), cells divide and form callus tissue

cultured to form shoots

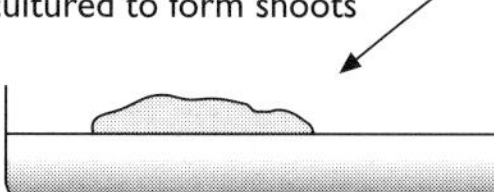

shoots grown into independent plants whose cells have been engineered to contain new genes

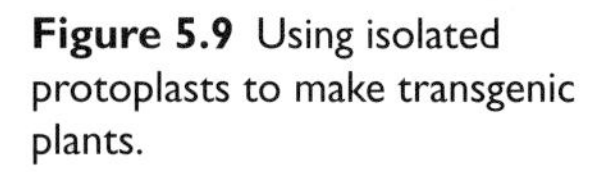

Figure 5.9 Using isolated protoplasts to make transgenic plants.

Recombinant DNA technology research in plants has produced resistance to insect attack in crop plants (for example, in cotton); the ability to grow in the presence of applied herbicide (for example, in sugar beet); and resistance to attack by viruses, bacteria or fungi (for example, in soya bean and tomato). Thale cress (*Arabidopsis thaliana*) has been engineered as a cheap, renewable source of the biodegradable plastic, polyhydrobutyrate (PHB); most plastics currently come from expensive petrochemicals and are slow to degrade.

Transgenic animals may be formed by direct uptake of DNA into the nucleus, or by replacement of treated cells.

The potential role of transgenic animals in spare parts surgery is illustrated on page 58.

4 What might be the advantage of eventually transferring genes for nitrogen-fixing nodules (in leguminous plants) to cereals?

Figure 5.10 Producing the giant mouse.

Figure 5.11 Inducing tumour resistance.

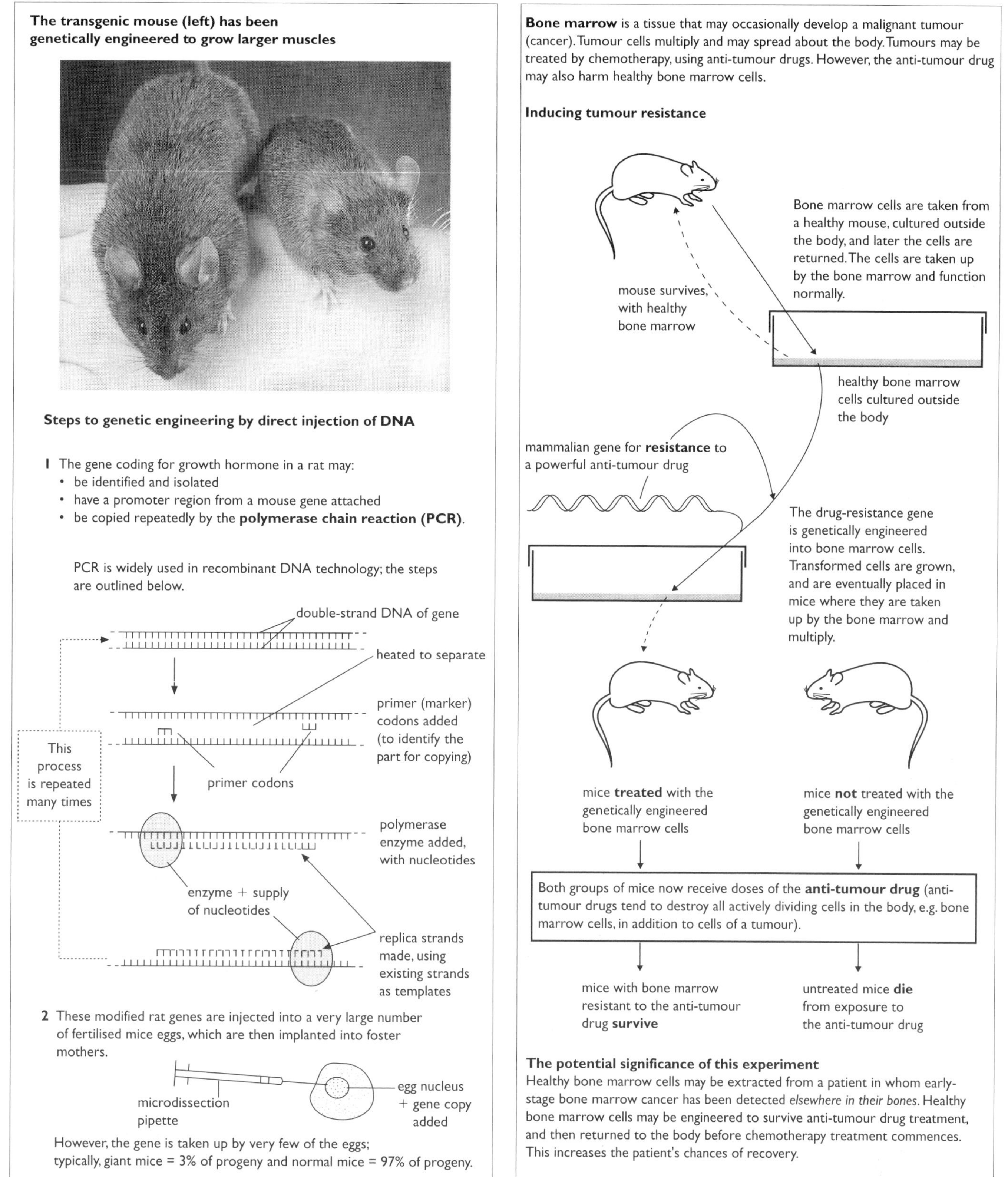

Genetic fingerprinting

The DNA coding for every individual is unique, and each of our cells carries an identical set of this unique DNA. These are the assumptions on which DNA fingerprinting is used in forensic science.

We believe our individuality is controlled by our genes (the combined 'exons' of the DNA strands of our chromosomes, Figure 4.16, page 46). The bulk of our DNA, however, does not code for proteins as far as we know (this includes the 'introns'). Surprisingly, it is parts of the non-coding regions as a whole that are exploited in 'fingerprinting', that is, in uniquely identifying individuals (Figure 5.12). This is because huge lengths of the non-coding DNA consist of unusual sequences of bases, repeated over and over again. We inherit a distinctive combination of these apparently non-functional 'repeat regions', half from our mother and half from our father.

5 Explain why the composition of the DNA of identical twins challenges an underlying assumption of DNA fingerprinting, but that of non-identical twins does not.

Figure 5.12 Steps to genetic fingerprinting.

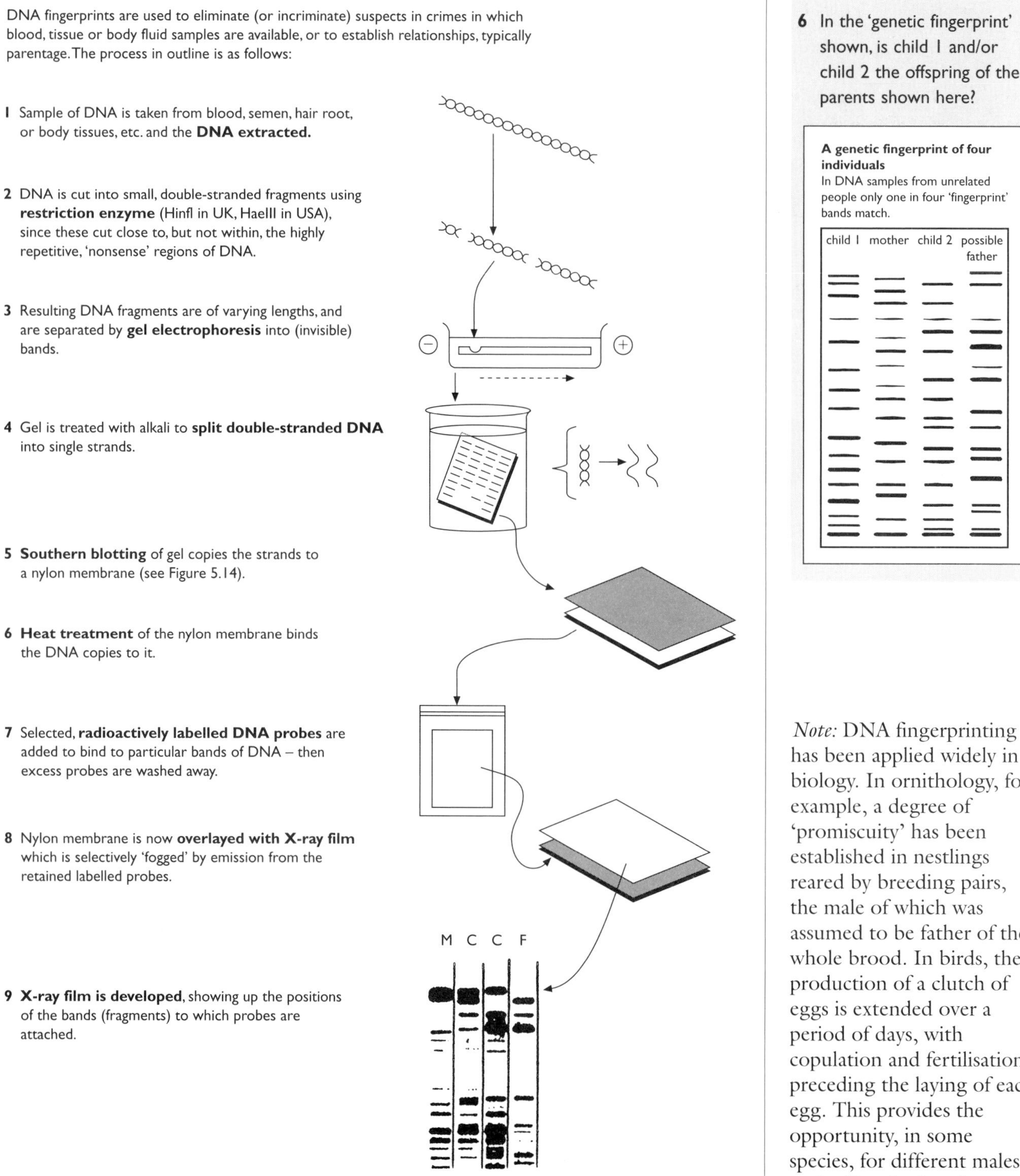

6 In the 'genetic fingerprint' shown, is child 1 and/or child 2 the offspring of the parents shown here?

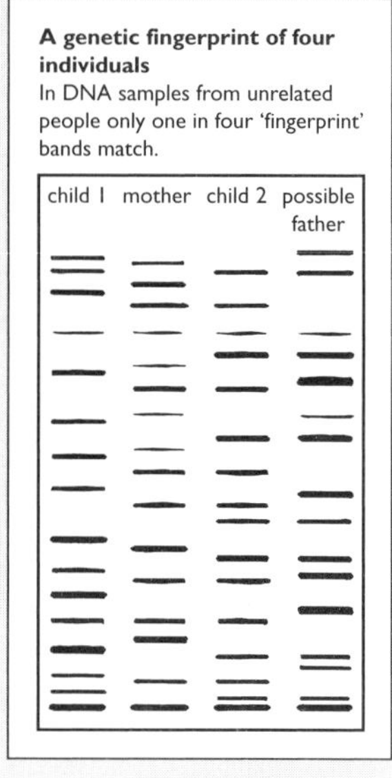

Note: DNA fingerprinting has been applied widely in biology. In ornithology, for example, a degree of 'promiscuity' has been established in nestlings reared by breeding pairs, the male of which was assumed to be father of the whole brood. In birds, the production of a clutch of eggs is extended over a period of days, with copulation and fertilisation preceding the laying of each egg. This provides the opportunity, in some species, for different males to fertilise the female.

Human Genome Project

A coordinated, international project with the aim of mapping the entire human genome on the 46 chromosomes began in 1990. The outcome, which is apparently now technically feasible, will involve the eventual recording of the sequence of base pairs that contains the instructions to make a human being. The work has been shared out between 250 laboratories around the world, to avoid unnecessary duplication of effort.

The investigation involves establishing the positions of genes relative to others on the same chromosome (page 22). Then the base sequence of the genes has to be determined. The DNA of chromosomes is sliced into pieces, the position of the fragments in the chromosome as a whole is worked out, and the base sequence of the fragments analysed. The task is a huge one.

Flowering plants
Birds
Mammals
Reptiles
Amphibians
Bony fish
Cartilaginous fish
Echinoderms
Crustaceans
Insects
Moulds
Algae
Fungi
Gram-positive bacteria
Gram-negative bacteria
Base pairs 10^6 10^7 10^8 10^9 10^{10} 10^{11}

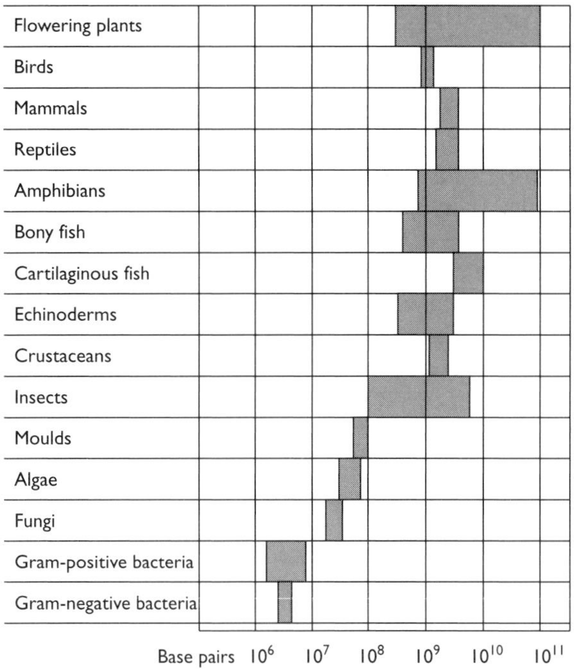

Figure 5.13 The genome size range of organisms. The genome sizes of major groupings of animals and plants are compared. Note that the size is logarithmic, so each division is x 10 larger than the preceding one.

Table 5.1 Points for and against the Human Genome Project.

For:	Against:
1 Many currently incurable diseases arise from defects in genes. Finding cures depends on identifying the relevant genes and understanding how they are regulated.	1 The project is expensive and time consuming, and progress in prevention of genetic diseases might be much quicker if efforts were exclusively focused on relatively few 'problem-causing' genes.
2 This work is one more example of a successful quest for knowledge about ourselves, our world and how life has come about. The evolution of humans from other hominids may become clearer.	2 Information of this type raises problems of ownership of information about an individual's genome, and how it is used by the state, businesses (such as insurance companies) and doctors.

Advances in the 'tool-kit' of techniques

Radioactive DNA probes and 'Southern blotting' are now exploited in several aspects of recombinant DNA technology in the identification of DNA fragments, including genetic fingerprinting (page 54) and the work of the Human Genome Project (above).

Figure 5.14 'Southern blotting' and labelled probes.

In **'Southern blotting'** (named after the scientist who devised the routine):
- extracted DNA is cut into fragments with restriction enzyme
- the fragments are separated on electrophoresis gel
- fragments are made single-stranded by treatment of the gel with alkali.

Then a copy of the distributed DNA fragments is produced on nylon membrane:

weight
layers of blotting paper
nylon membrane
gel
blotting paper 'wick'
glass block
buffer tray

nylon membrane is heated to bind the DNA fragments, which can then be detected by radioactive probes

Making **radioactively labelled DNA probes**:
- Single-stranded DNA has the ability to form a stable double strand with another single strand of DNA, provided the bases are complementary (i.e. pair). If one strand is 'labelled', the presence of the paired strands is easily detected.
- Short lengths of single-stranded DNA are made in the laboratory for this purpose, by enzymically combining and then adding **selected nucleotides**, one at a time, in a precise sequence.
- Consequently, the base sequence of probes is predetermined and known.
- All the nucleotides used contain radioactive phosphorus (^{32}P), so the subsequent positions of the probes (and the location of a complementary strand of DNA, e.g. on a nylon membrane) can be located by autoradiography.

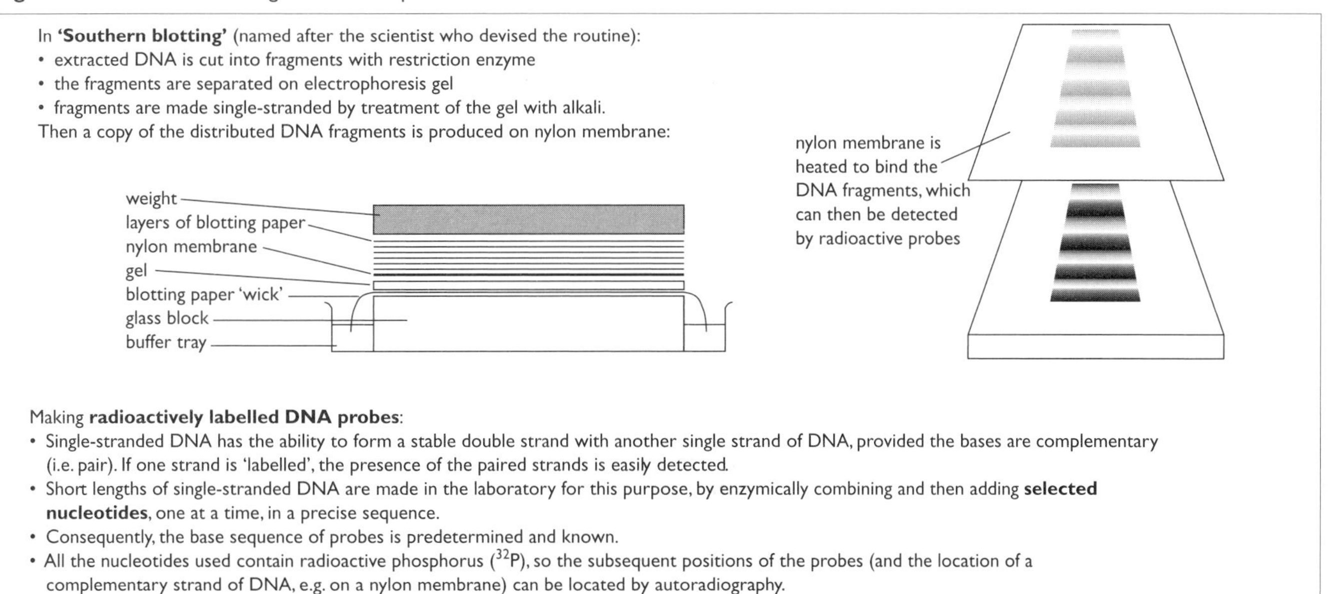

Genetic diseases and gene therapy

Genetic diseases cause suffering in about 1–2% of the population. Common genetic diseases include cystic fibrosis (page 33), sickle-cell disease (page 39), Duchenne muscular dystrophy (page 25), haemophilia (page 26) and Huntington's disease.

More than half of all genetic diseases are due to a mutation involving a single gene. The mutant gene is commonly recessive; for example, cystic fibrosis is due to a recessive gene on chromosome 7 (that is, autosomal). However, some are dominant; for example, Huntington's disease is due to a dominant allele on chromosome 4. Duchenne muscular dystrophy and haemophilia are due to recessive alleles on the X (sex) chromosome.

Gene therapy is the use of recombinant DNA technology to overcome genetic disease, where this is thought to be safe and ethically sound. For example, the body may be **supplied with the missing gene's product** (and then periodically resupplied), or the **missing gene may be introduced** into body cells (in such a way that it may become permanently functional). ***It is not considered safe or ethical to attempt to tamper with germ cells (in testes and ovaries).*** Gene therapy is a very recent, experimental science. Two approaches are illustrated in Figure 5.15 (below) and Figure 5.16 (on page 57).

7 What is the difference in terms of genetic disease of the possession of a single allele for cystic fibrosis compared with the possession of a single allele for Huntington's disease?

Figure 5.15 Cystic fibrosis; getting the healthy gene into cells in the lungs.

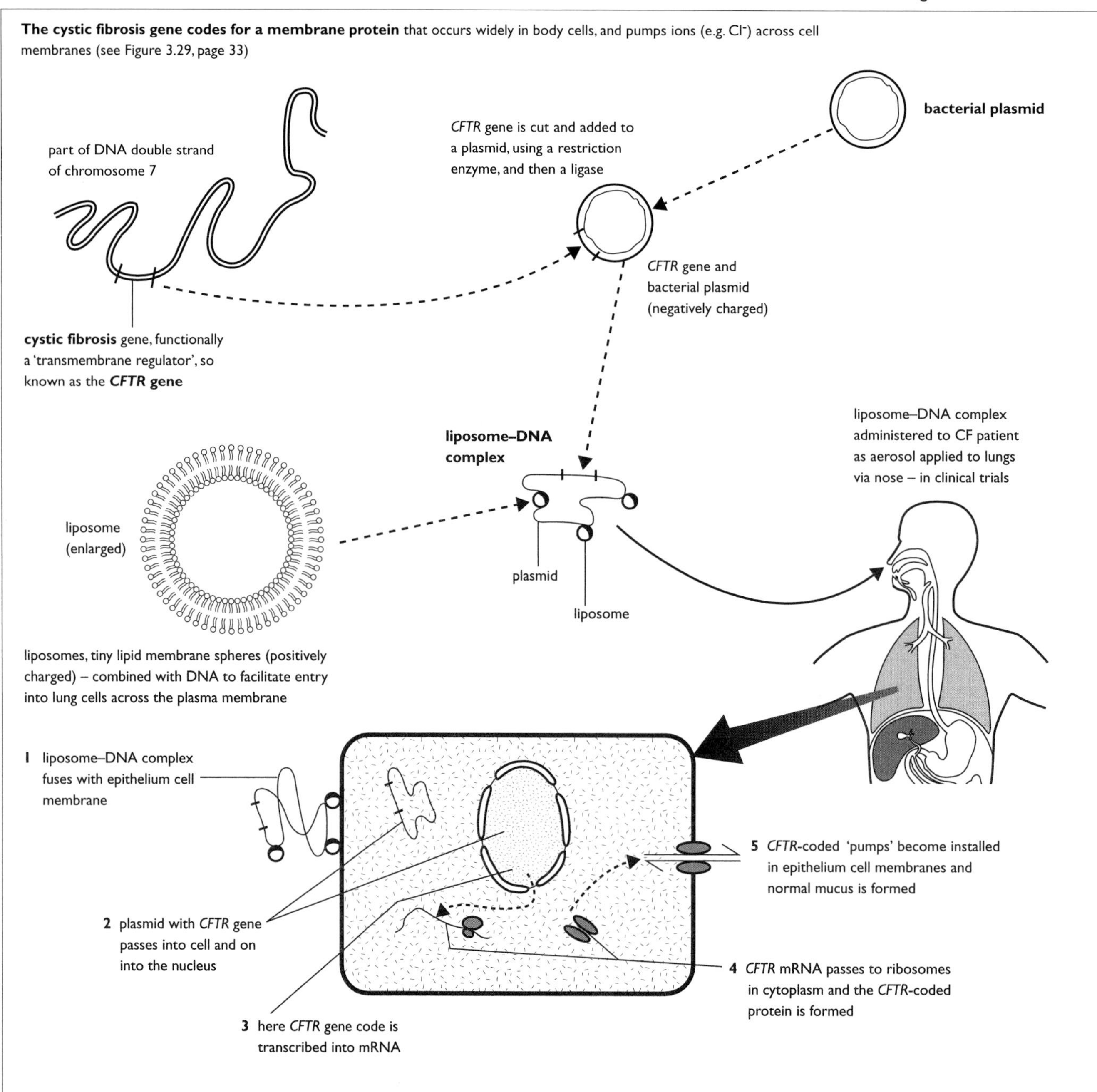

Genetic screening

Family pedigrees (page 10) show the probability of a potential parent as a carrier of or a sufferer from a genetic disease. Those at risk can be screened. DNA from a sample of blood or cheek cells may be taken and checked with specific gene probes for the presence of mutant alleles. Probes have only been made for certain diseases so far.

Genetic screening of a fetus *in utero* is possible, using either amniocentesis or chorionic villus sampling (Figure 5.17).

Figure 5.16 Familial hypercholesterolaemia (FH); correcting liver cell functions.

Lipids are transported around the body and across the cell membranes as lipoproteins, e.g. low-density lipoproteins (**LDLs**). In the genetic disease **familial hypercholesterolaemia** (**FH**), the membrane receptors for LDLs are defective, and LDL accumulates in the blood, leading to damaged arteries and coronary heart disease.

Gene therapy may involve engineering a healthy gene into a sample of liver cells so that genetically corrected cells may be re-established in the liver and restore correct functioning.

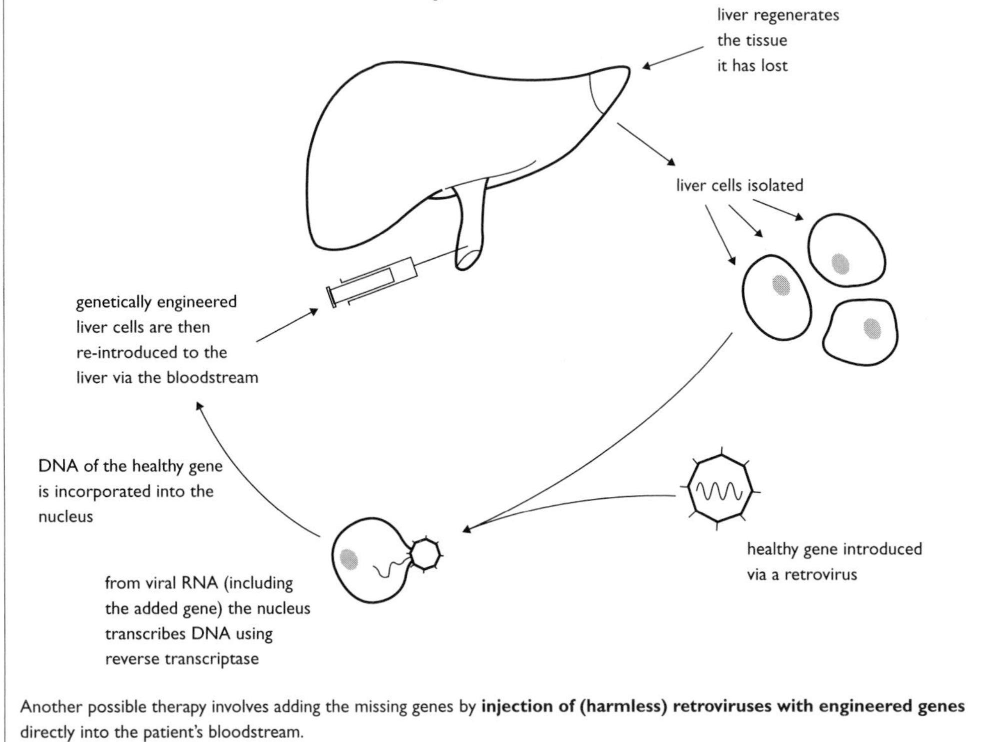

Another possible therapy involves adding the missing genes by **injection of (harmless) retroviruses with engineered genes** directly into the patient's bloodstream.

Figure 5.17 Screening of a fetus *in utero*.

Cells from the fetus can be obtained for examination of their chromosome complement and for screening for certain defective genes by:

1 Amniocentesis – withdrawal of a sample of the amniotic fluid in the period 16–30 weeks of gestation; the fluid contains cells from the surface of the embryo.

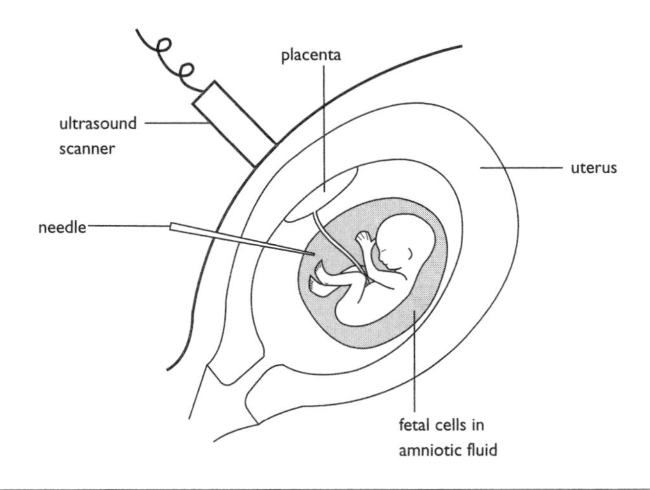

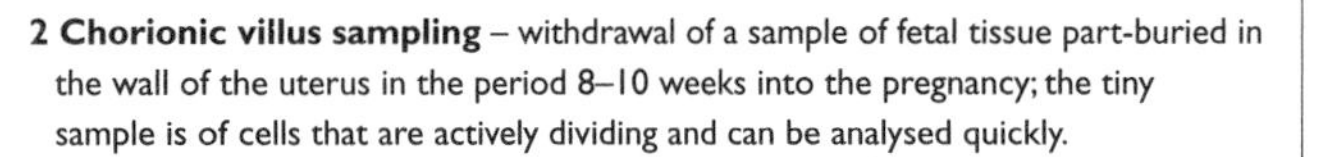

2 Chorionic villus sampling – withdrawal of a sample of fetal tissue part-buried in the wall of the uterus in the period 8–10 weeks into the pregnancy; the tiny sample is of cells that are actively dividing and can be analysed quickly.

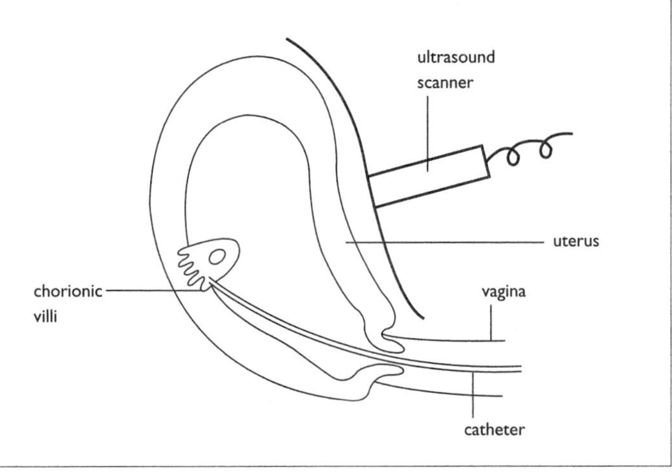

Genetic counselling

People with a history of genetic disease can consult a genetic counsellor for advice on the risk of having an affected child, before and after screening.

Table 5.2 Examples of issues a genetic counsellor might be asked to advise on.

- Should a couple have children if, for example, both are 'carriers' of a faulty gene, or should they apply to adopt a child?
- Should a pregnancy be planned in such cases, but terminated if the fetus proves to be affected?
- Is artificial insemination by donor (gamete donation), or embryo donation a practical alternative?
- Is *in vitro* fertilisation and the testing of embryos prior to implantation a possible option?

Transplant surgery and the quest for spare organs; will recombinant DNA technology have a part to play?

Transplanting human organs has become a routine and largely successful surgical technique, mainly because of our knowledge of the immune system and the availability of drugs to suppress rejection of 'foreign' tissues. The success of this technology has produced long waiting lists for transplants of kidneys, hearts and livers. The resulting organ shortage has led to research into the use of animals, specially bred to supply compatible organs (**xenotransplantation**).

Incompatible organs from a donor are identified in the recipient's body by the proteins or glycoproteins on cell surface membranes of the donated organ, which may then be rejected. A human regulator protein prevents rejection, when it is present on the cells of a compatible organ. This protein is coded for by a gene called *HDAF*, which has been isolated from human cells and cloned. Pigs transgenic for the *HDAF* gene have been produced and used for organ transplantation in clinical trials.

Figure 5.18 Genetic engineering of pigs for xenotransplantation.

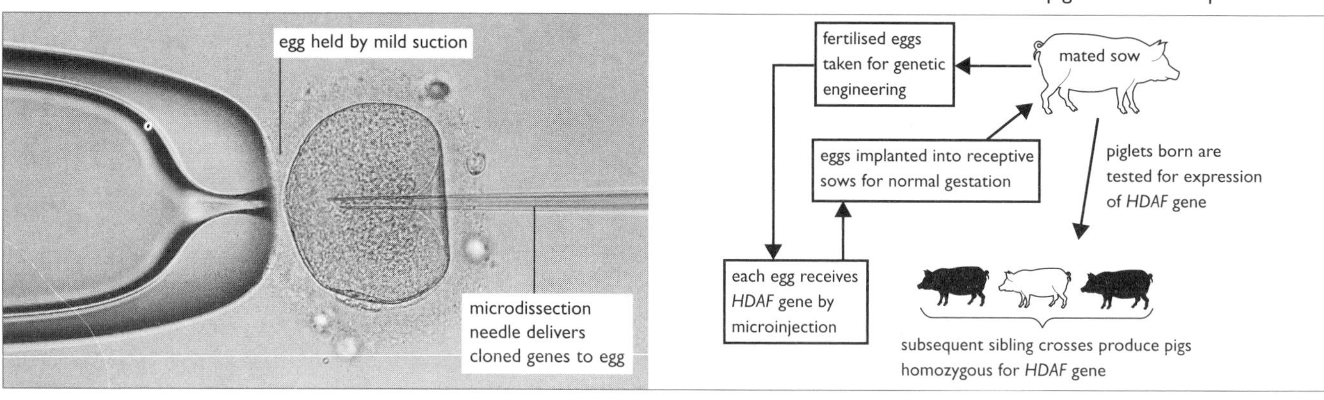

Research into the safety of pig transplants continues. If it proves difficult to breed pigs totally free of potentially harmful retroviruses (that is, viral disease) then pig xenotransplantation might not be safe. For some there is also an ethical issue involved here. Meanwhile, research has produced:

- a mammal (Dolly the sheep) that has been grown **from the genome of a mature** (udder) **cell**;
- a vertebrate (tadpole), with the genes for 'head' inactivated, that would otherwise have grown healthy, normal tissues and organs. The frog genes for 'head' and 'central nervous system' **perform the same function in humans**.

Can the laboratory skills underlying these developments be combined and applied to human cells? That is, could people requiring transplants have organs grown for them, to order, from their own cloned cells? Use of cloned human embryos would be unacceptable, but it might be acceptable to use a mature cell, made embryonic, and induced to grow a required organ (for example, liver, pancreas or kidney), plus heart and blood circulation (but no head or nervous system), in culture solution in a bottle (*in vitro*). There are enormous technical problems remaining here, even if the idea were to be ethically acceptable.

Dolly meets the world's press!

Figure 5.19 Dolly the sheep, cloned by Ian Wilmut and colleagues at the Roslin Institute, Edinburgh.

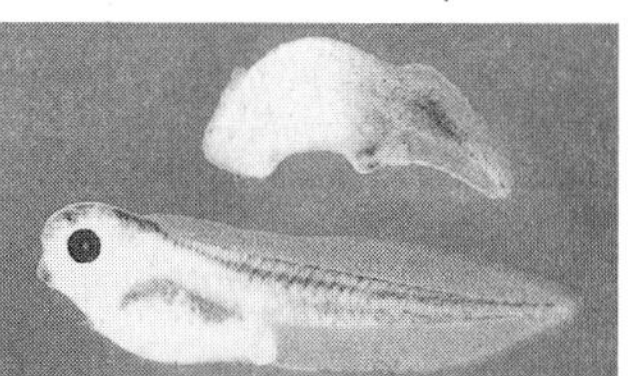

Figure 5.20 Tadpoles, normal and headless, from the laboratory of Professor Jonathan Slack at the University of Bath. The genes that produce a 'headless' tadpole could be used in a genetically engineered mammal cell.

Genetic engineering – hazards and ethical issues

Geneticists are really producing new organisms when genes are transferred between organisms. Consequently this work is potentially a source of hazards and it certainly generates concerns.

Table 5.3 Hazards and ethical issues in recombinant DNA technology.

- Will a gene, added to a genome, function in an unforeseen manner, perhaps even triggering cancer in the recipient, for example?
- Might an introduced gene for resistance to adverse conditions be transferred from a crop plant or farm animal into a weed species or to some predator?
- Is it possible that a harmless organism, for example, the human gut bacterium *E. coli*, with recombinant DNA technology might be transformed into a harmful pathogen that escapes the laboratory and moves into the population at large?
- Is there an important over-riding principle to be held to, that humans should not tamper with 'nature' in a deliberate way?
- Genetic engineering is likely to be mostly beneficial to the health and life expectancy of people of developed nations. If a large part of the funds made available for genetic engineering were diverted to solve more basic problems of housing, health and nutrition (for example, clean water supply) worldwide, would the money not benefit far more humans, immediately?

Genetic conservation

When a particular species becomes extinct, its genes are permanently lost, and the total pool of genes on which life operates is diminished. One consequence is that plant and animal breeders and genetic engineers are deprived of potential sources of useful genes. The loss of major habitats around the world, for example, destruction of forests or permanent water meadows, effectively decreases the genetic heritage. So, too, does the careless or excessive use of pesticides, so that much adjacent wildlife is obliterated as well as the 'pests' within the crop. Genetic conservation seeks to prevent such losses by regulating pesticide use effectively, acting to preserve vulnerable habitats and establishing 'gene banks' of various types, for example, seed banks and sperm banks.

Figure 5.21 Forest habitats as threatened environments.

Tropical rain forest
The destruction of these forests receives more international attention than the logging of boreal forests of Canada and Russia, and the disappearance of hedgerows in the UK.

A lakeland valley
Once covered by woodlands, but now cleared where human activities (housing, farming, transport) have developed.

Evolution

By evolution we mean the **development of life in geological time**. The word evolution is used widely, but in biology the term specifically means the processes (for example, **natural selection**, page 67) that have transformed life on Earth from its earliest beginnings to the diversity of forms we know about today, both living and extinct. Evolution is an organising principle of modern biology. It helps us to make sense of the ways in which living things are related to each other, and to understand the significance of their ways of life.

Evidence for evolution

The range of **evidence for evolution** also shows us what 'natural selection' has to explain.

a) **Evidence from fossils** (palaeontological evidence) is the main source of information about life forms that are now extinct. Fossilisation is an extremely rare, chance event; scavengers and bacterial action normally dismember and decompose dead plant and animal structures before they can be fossilised. Most fossils are overlooked or are accidentally destroyed before discovery. Nevertheless, numerous fossils have been found.

1 Most fossils are preserved in sedimentary rocks. Why is this so, and how are sedimentary rocks formed?

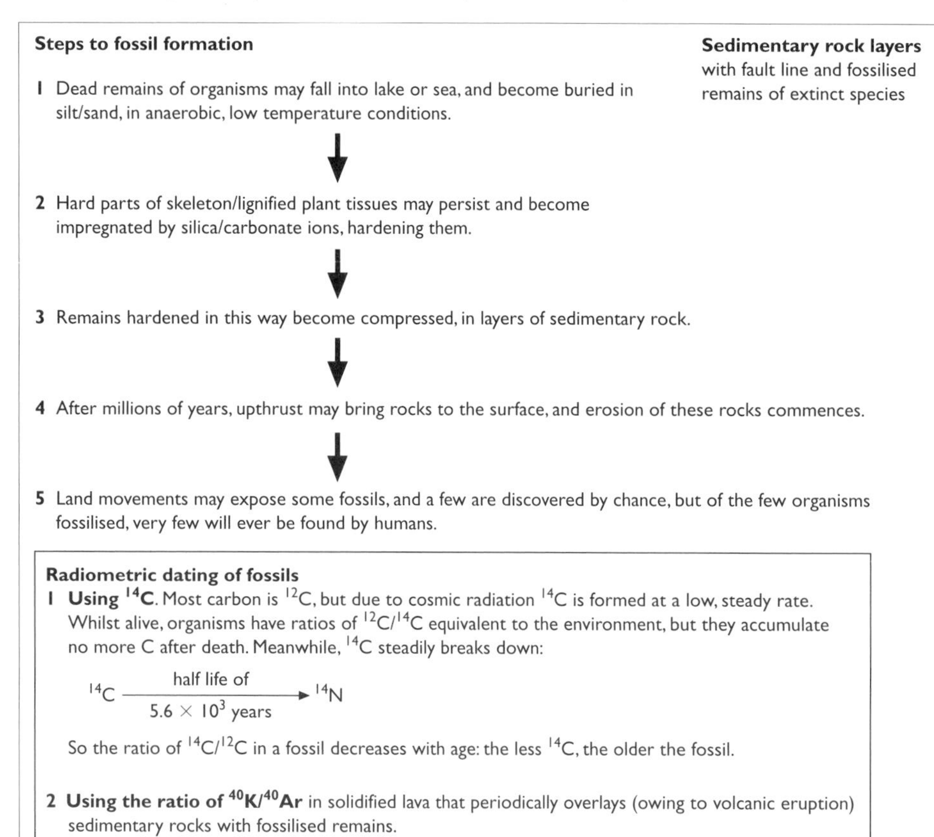

Figure 6.1 Fossilisation.

Table 6.1 Forms of fossilisation.

- **Petrification** – in which the organic matter of the dead organism is replaced by mineral ions (Figure 6.1)
- **Mould** – the organic matter decays, but the vacated space becomes a mould, occupied by mineral matter
- **Trace** – an impression of a form, for example, a leaf or a footprint (Figure 6.42), is made in layers that then harden.
- **Preservation** of the intact whole organism, for example, in amber (resin exuded from a conifer that is then solidified), in tar, in ice, or in anaerobic, acidic peat

Figure 6.2 Fossil trilobites.

Trilobites, hard-shelled animals, related to living crabs and shrimps, first appeared in significant numbers 500 mya and finally died out 250 mya. Apparently, they changed very little over many millions of years.

The **mini car** first appeared in 1962, and changed little in external design. But, as with fossils, the external outline tells us nothing about 'evolution' of the internal machinery. This has developed almost beyond recognition in the case of the car (and possibly did in Trilobites too). Most fossils give us an idea about external form, but little or nothing about how the organism functioned.

b) **The geographical distribution of living things** (biogeographical evidence) shows that flora and fauna of comparable parts of the Earth cannot be accounted for by climate or habitat alone. For example, similarities and differences in the organisms of parts of South America, Africa and Australia have an evolutionary explanation.

2 What geological evidence supports the plate tectonics explanation of the origins of Australia, southern Africa and South America?

Figure 6.3 South America, Africa and Australia and their changing fauna.

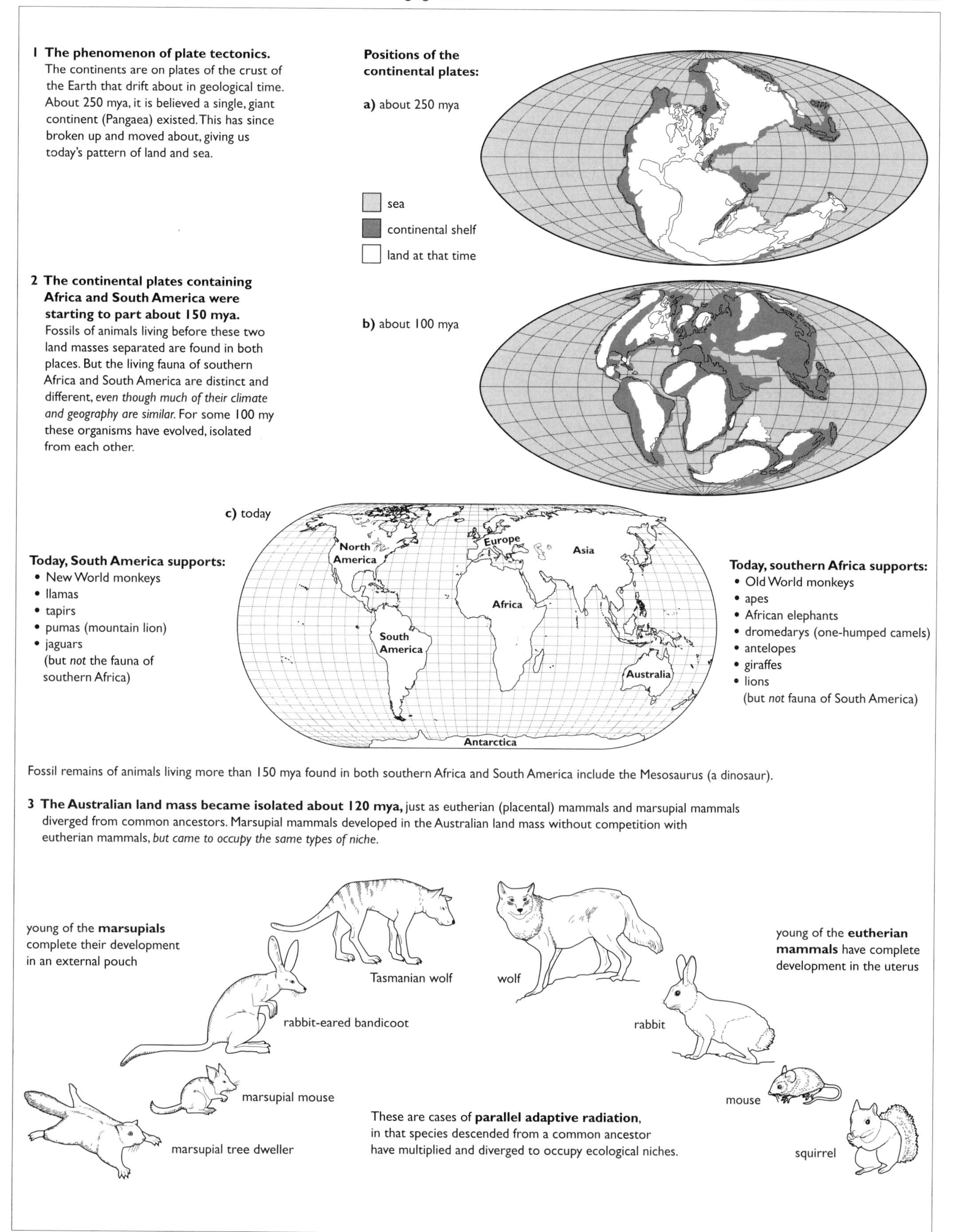

c) **Studies of the comparative anatomy** of many groups of related organisms show that, although adapted to different habitats or life styles, their underlying organisation is similar (that is, they have **homologous structures**). In such cases, a likely explanation is that they share a common ancestor, and show adaptive radiation from a basic plan.

3 Give a likely example of adaptive radiation in **a)** the bodies of insects, and **b)** the organs of flowering plants.

Table 6.2 Homologous and analogous structures.

Homologous structures	Analogous structures
(for example, arm of human and wing of bat):	(for example, wing of insect and wing of bird):
• similar in fundamental structure;	• differ in fundamental structure;
• similar in position and development (but not necessarily in function);	• resemble each other in function;
• similarity due to common ancestry.	• similarity due to a superficial resemblance.

Figure 6.4 Adaptive radiation in the forelimbs of vertebrates.

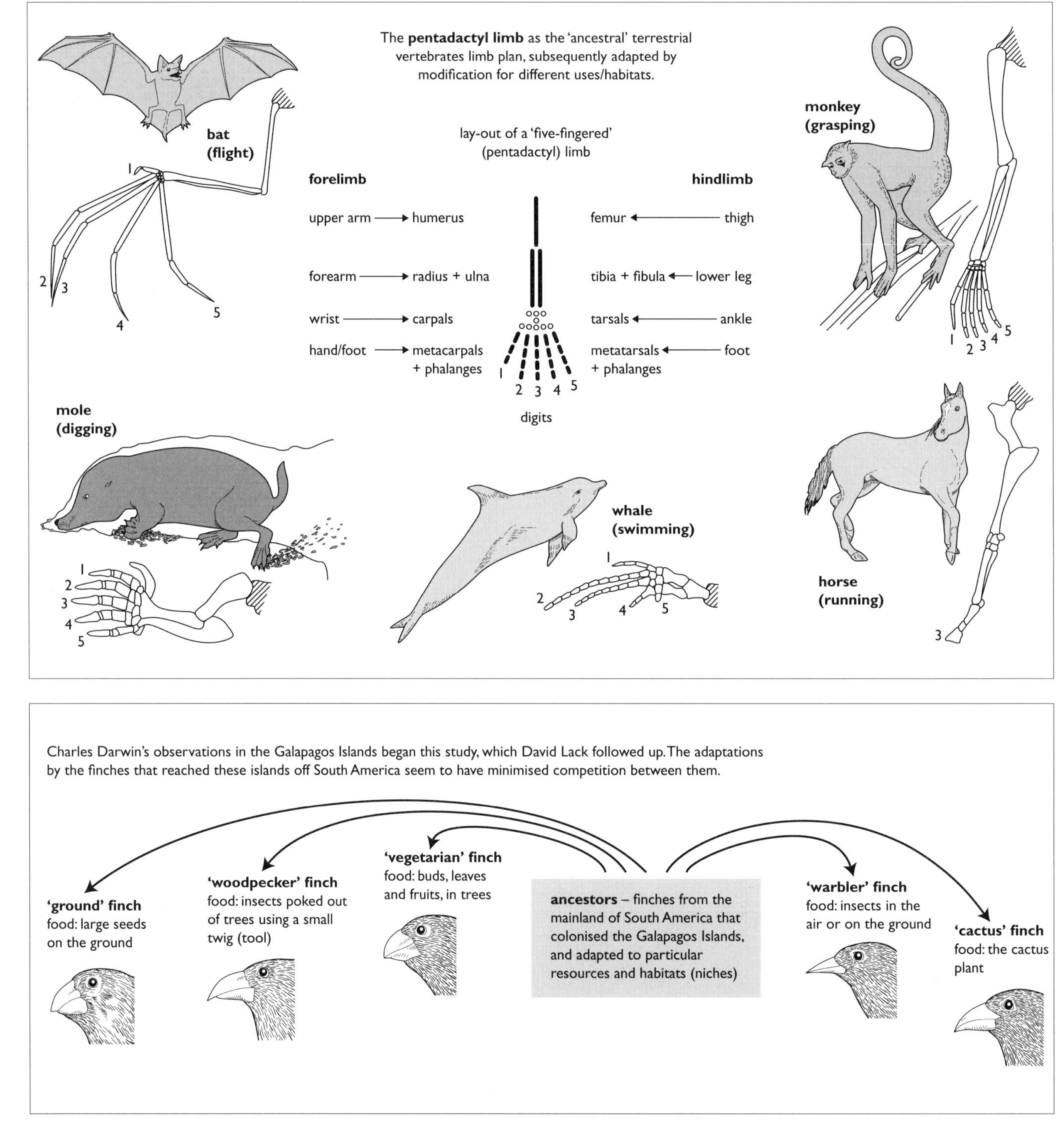

Figure 6.5 Adaptive radiation in Galapagos finches.

d) **Studies in comparative physiology and biochemistry** show that similar chemicals exist in related organisms. The biochemical differences between living things of today are limited. This makes it possible to measure the relatedness of different groups of organisms by the amount of the differences between specific molecules such as DNA, proteins and enzyme systems.

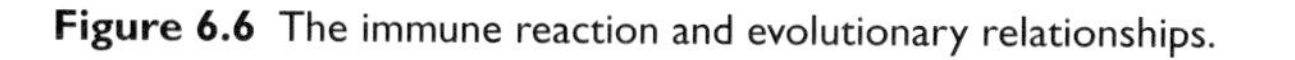

Figure 6.6 The immune reaction and evolutionary relationships.

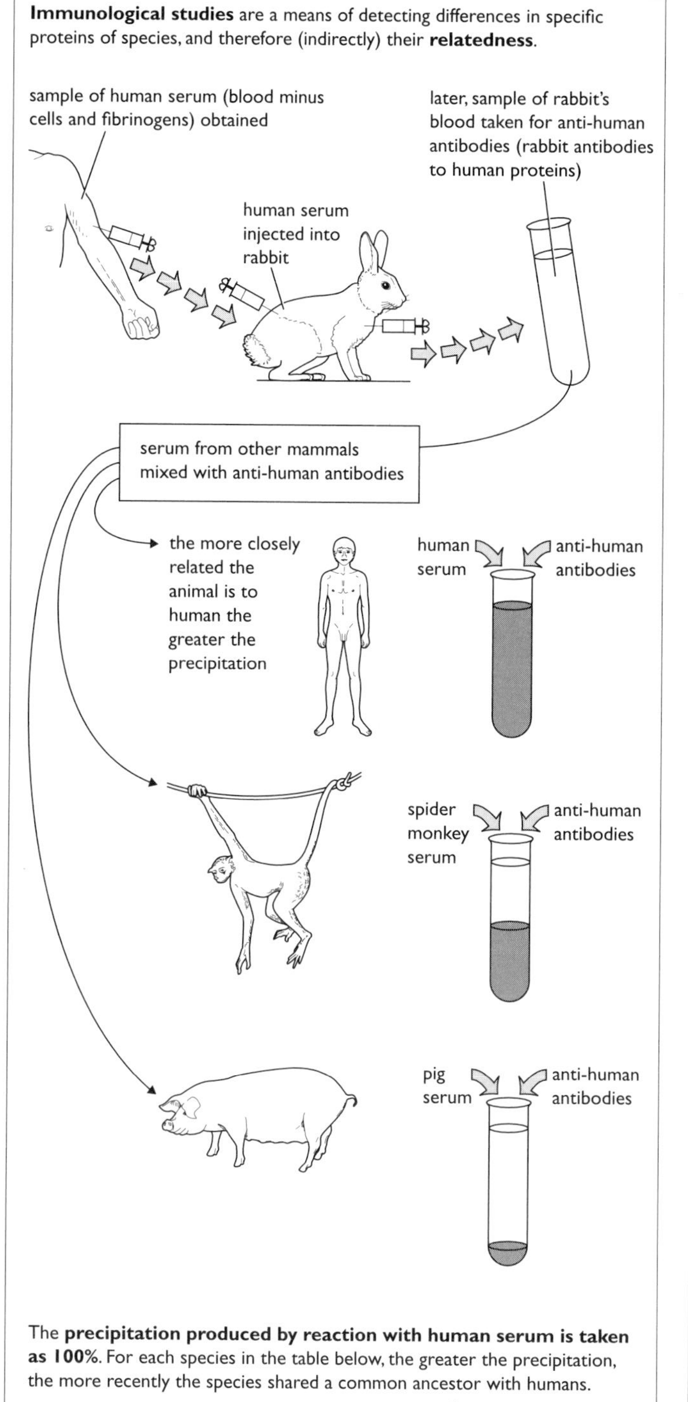

The **precipitation produced by reaction with human serum is taken as 100%**. For each species in the table below, the greater the precipitation, the more recently the species shared a common ancestor with humans.

Species		Precipitation (%)
chimpanzee, gorilla	– African apes	97
gibbon	– Asian ape	92
baboon	– Old World monkey	75
spider monkey	– New World monkey	58
lemur	– prosimian (page 79)	37
hedgehog	– insectivorous mammal	17
pig	– even-toed, hoofed mammal	8

4 Mitochondrial DNA, in contrast to chromosomal DNA, has no enzymes (for example, ligase) to repair damage to it. Far fewer mutations accumulate in chromosomal DNA. How might these observations be related?

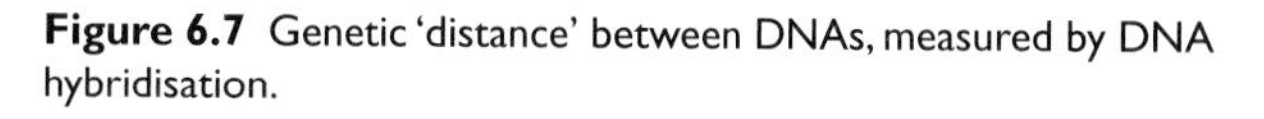

Figure 6.7 Genetic 'distance' between DNAs, measured by DNA hybridisation.

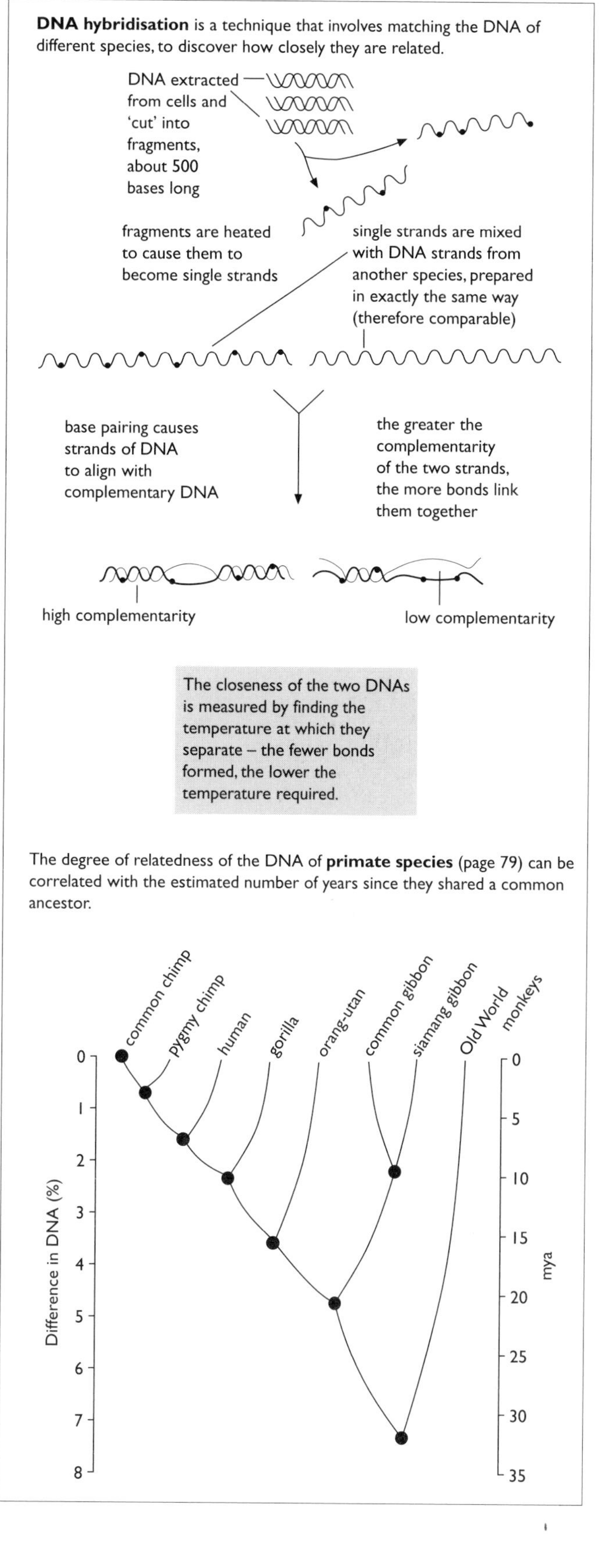

e) **Artificial selection** is the process by which all the plants and animals used by humans (for example, in horticulture, agriculture, transport, companionship and leisure) have been derived from wild organisms. Artificial selection involves identifying the largest, the best or the most useful of the progeny for the intended purpose, and using them as the next generation of parents. The continuous culling out of progeny deficient in the desired features, generation by generation, leads to deliberate genetic change. The genetic constitution of the population changes rapidly.

5 Darwin argued that the great wealth of varieties we have produced in domestication supports the concept of evolution. How is this so?

Figure 6.8 Charles Darwin's observation of pigeon breeding.

From his breeding of pigeons, Darwin noted that there were more than a dozen varieties that, had they been presented to an ornithologist as wild birds, would have been classified as separate species.

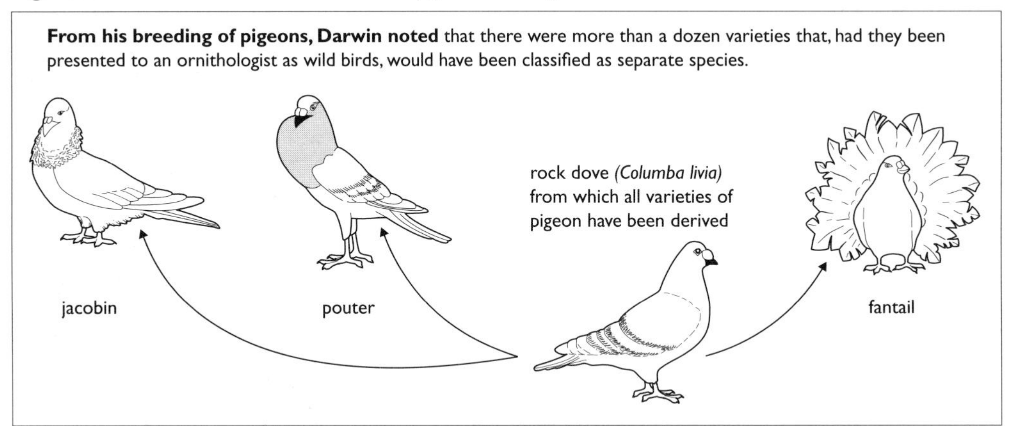

Figure 6.9 Dog breeding.

The dog was domesticated from the wolf about 13 000 years ago. It was the first animal to be domesticated.

Wolf *(Canis lupus)*

The differences in size and other features of American, European and Asian wolves are reflected in the breeds that have been developed.

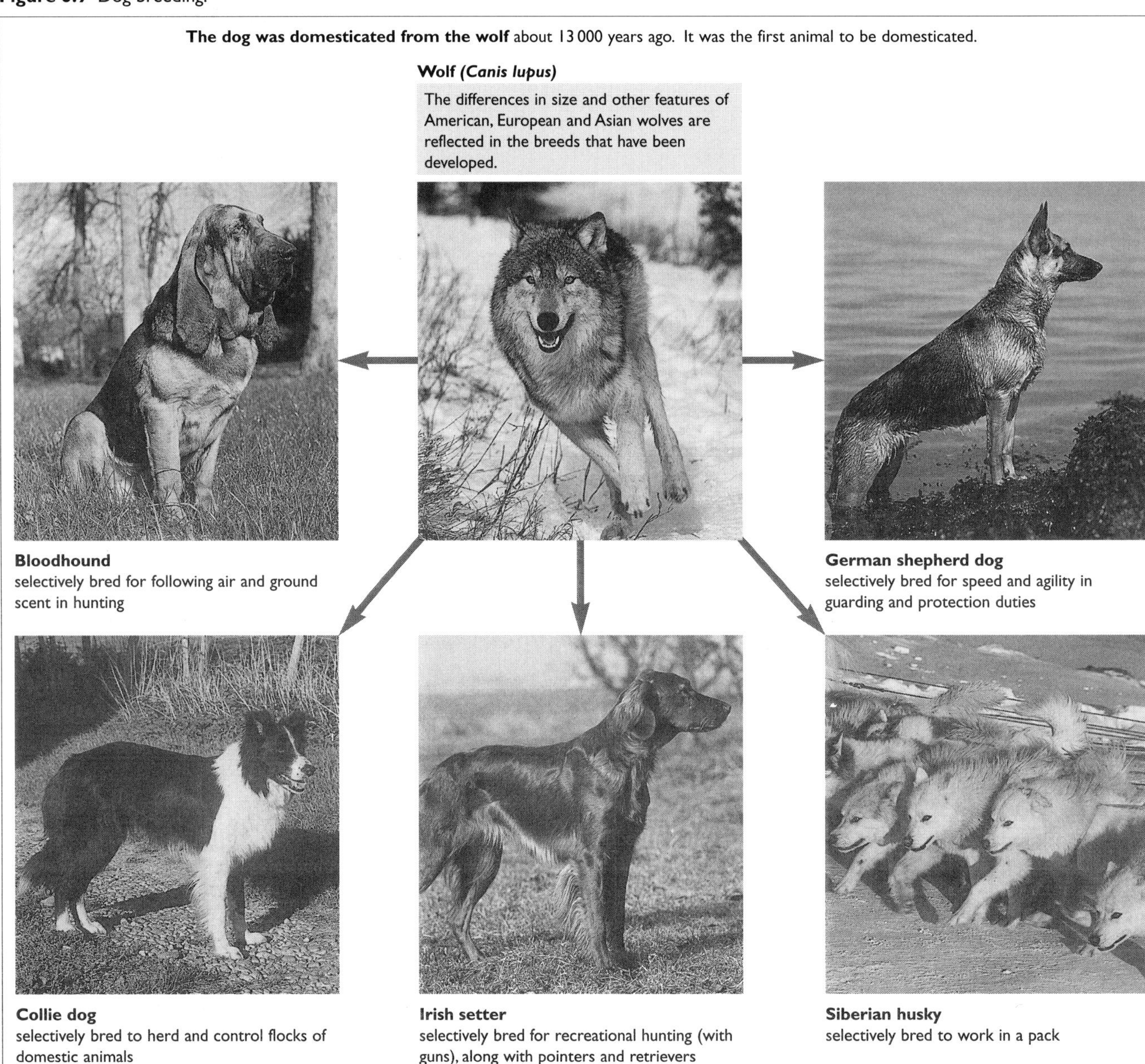

Bloodhound
selectively bred for following air and ground scent in hunting

German shepherd dog
selectively bred for speed and agility in guarding and protection duties

Collie dog
selectively bred to herd and control flocks of domestic animals

Irish setter
selectively bred for recreational hunting (with guns), along with pointers and retrievers

Siberian husky
selectively bred to work in a pack

Evolution needs time!

In Western culture, the biblical account of creation was generally accepted as authoritative until the eighteenth century, at least. Furthermore, the chronology detailed in the Bible suggested that life had appeared on Earth a mere few thousand years ago. In 1654, Archbishop James Ussher calculated that **creation occurred in 4004 BC, and this timescale (that is, the Earth was only 5–6000 years old) was widely accepted in Europe until well into the nineteenth century.**

Early geologists realised the Earth was very old. A Scottish polymath, James Hutton (1729–1797), observed erosion on the hillsides of his farm, and guessed that the sedimentary rocks of existing mountains had once been the bedrock of lakes and seas, and, **before that**, had been the rock of even older mountains. Hutton did not estimate the age of the Earth, but he asserted that it was more or less 'without beginning' when compared with the biblical account. This work was picked up by the geologist Charles Lyell (1797–1875) and effectively publicised. Lyell had great influence on Charles Darwin.

Today, geologists estimate the age of the Earth as being 4500 million years, and propose that life originated 3500 million years ago. Only on this sort of timescale is it possible to imagine organic evolution as a possibility.

Figure 6.10 A mountain peak of sedimentary rock.

Table 6.3 The geological timescale and some biological events. (The comments on climate refer to what is now the UK.)

Era	Period	Epoch	mya	Climate	Animal life	Plant life
Cainozoic	Quaternary	Holocene Pleistocene	0.01 2	Postglacial Ice ages	Historic time, dominance of humans Origin of humans	Flora of modern UK
	Tertiary	Pliocene Miocene Oligocene Eocene Palaeocene	65	Part of SE England submerged; climate warm to sub-tropical	Development of most mammal groups, and of pollinating insects	Development of angiosperms
Mesozoic	Cretaceous		135	Climate cool; sea covers much of England (chalk deposited); fresh water covers SE England	Worldwide extinction of many large reptiles; extinction of ammonites; beaked birds appear; mammals all small	Flowering plants appear
	Jurassic		200	Climate warm and humid	Large dinosaurs dominate; mammals all small	Floating phytoplankton abundant
	Triassic		250	Climate hot, with alternating wet and dry periods	Adaptive radiation of reptiles; first mammals appear	Development of conifers and related plants
Palaeozoic	Permian		290	Desert conditions	Insects diversify on land and in fresh water	First conifers
	Carboniferous		355	Equatorial climate; coal measures laid down	Reptiles and insects appear; development of amphibians	Widespread 'coal forests' and swamps, that is, tree-like ferns
	Devonian		405	Climate warm to moderate; sandstones laid down	Amphibians appear; development of bony fish	Development of fern-like plants
	Silurian		440	Climate warm to moderately warm	Invasion of land by arthropods	First vascular land plants
	Ordovician		500	Climate warm to moderately warm	First vertebrates (jawless fish)	Marine algae abundant
	Cambrian		580	Climate uncertain	Origin of many non-vertebrate phyla	Many algae
	Precambrian	75% of Earth's history	700 1500 3000 5000	? ? Origin of Earth?	Origin of first animals Origin of eukaryotes Oldest fossils (prokaryotes)	First photosynthesis

A mechanism for evolution

The idea of evolution did not originate with Charles Darwin. Biologists and geologists discussed this issue before Darwin, and various hypotheses were proposed.

George Cuvier (1769–1832), a determined creationist, attempted to account for the succession of fossils in sedimentary strata (those fossils in the oldest/lowest strata had least in common with living forms). His explanation (called **'catastrophism'**) suggested that the many extinctions and the new species that had appeared subsequently were due to periodic catastrophes (for example, floods, earthquakes), followed by the devastated areas being repopulated by species from elsewhere, or (some said) by new creations of species.

George-Louis Buffon (1707–1788) came to challenge the idea of species being 'immutable' (unchanging). He suggested that organisms changed when their structures fell into disuse and degenerated. He saw the lateral toes on a pig's foot as an example of a degenerate or **vestigial form**. Buffon also claimed the ape was a degenerate human.

Erasmus Darwin (1731–1802), having read Buffon's ideas, came to believe in evolution by variation and 'improvement of species', which occurred (he said) when characteristics acquired by parents were transferred to the offspring (that is, 'inheritance of acquired characteristics', page 69). However, 'evolution' became **a dangerous idea** in his lifetime, associated with political revolution (for example, the French Revolution, 1789). Erasmus's books went out of print – but his grandson, Charles, read them.

Charles Darwin (1809–1882) was a careful observer and a fine naturalist who made many original contributions to biology. After abandoning two choices of career (first studying to be a doctor, at Edinburgh; later for the Church, at Cambridge), he became the resident (unpaid) naturalist on an Admiralty-commissioned expedition to the southern hemisphere on HMS *Beagle*. On this five-year expedition, and during his numerous later investigations and reading, over many years, he developed the idea of organic evolution by natural selection. But he remained very anxious about how his ideas of evolution would be received, and he was very slow to publish them.

Figure 6.11 Vestigial forms; the snake's limb girdle and limb bones as degenerate forms of structures found in other reptiles.

snake

vertebral column

pelvic girdle

vestigial hindlimb bones

lizard

vertebral column

pelvic girdle

bones of the foot

fibula

tibia

femur

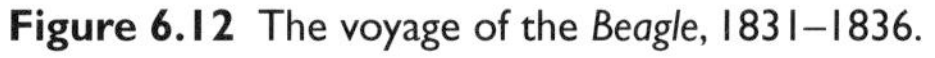

Figure 6.12 The voyage of the *Beagle*, 1831–1836.

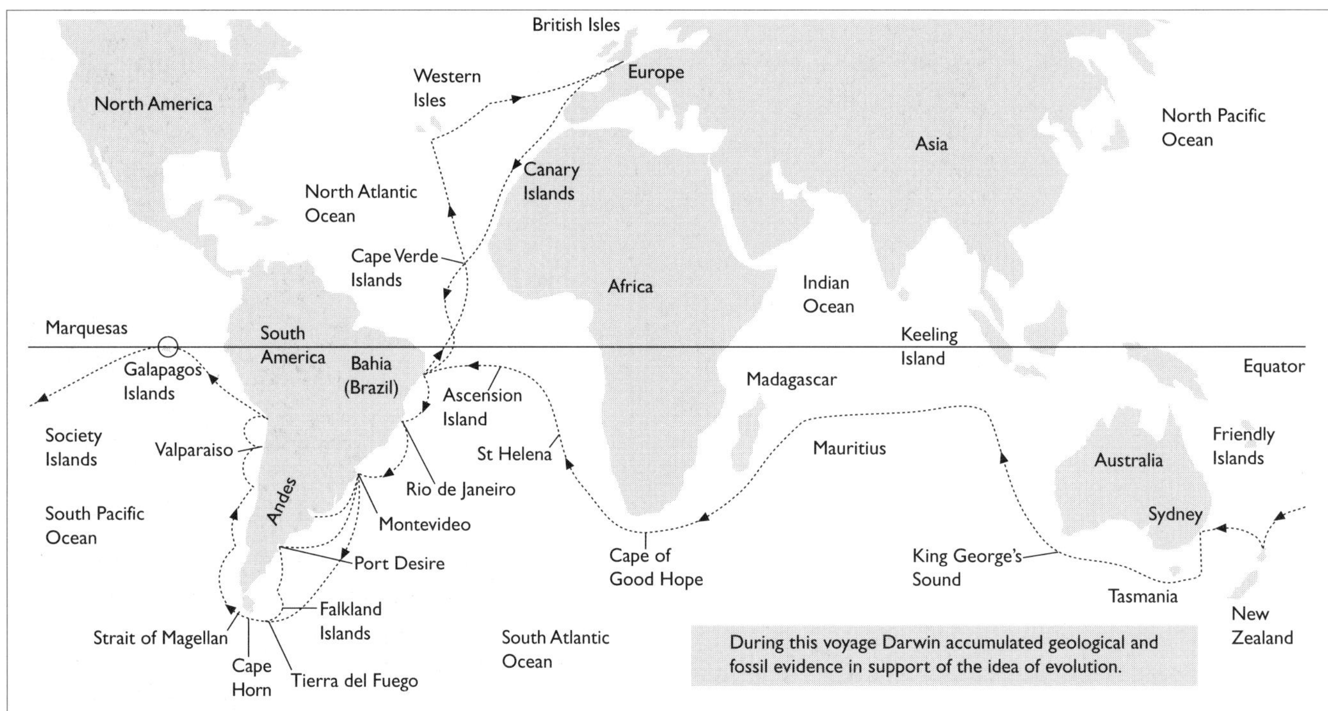

Two years after his return from the *Beagle* expedition, Darwin married his cousin, Emma Wedgwood. They soon moved to Down House, where most of his studies and experiments were conducted. Here he wrestled in private with his Theory of Natural Selection, before the same ideas were presented to him by Alfred Russel Wallace, in a letter. Only then (1859) was Darwin's *'On the Origin of Species by Natural Selection'* completed and published. Darwin continued to avoid public controversy, leaving this to his outspoken supporter and friend, Thomas Huxley.

In the area of evolution, Darwin's achievements were to:

- state the evidence for evolution convincingly;
- show that the objections to the idea of evolution were answerable;
- propose a mechanism for evolution that could be tested, and that excluded supernatural forces.

Figure 6.13 Down House, Downe, near Bromley, Kent.

Table 6.4 The arguments of the *'Origin of Species'* can be summarised in four statements (**S**) and three deductions (**D**):

S1	Organisms produce a far greater number of progeny then ever give rise to mature individuals.
S2	The number of individuals in species remain more or less constant.
D1	Therefore, there must be a high mortality rate.
S3	The individuals in a species are not all identical, but show variations in their characteristics.
D2	Therefore, some variants will succeed better than others in the competition for survival. So the parents for the next generation will be selected from among those members of the species better adapted to the conditions of the environment.
S4	Hereditary resemblance between parents and offspring is a fact.
D3	Therefore, subsequent generations will maintain and improve in the degree of adaptation of their parents, by gradual change.

A **tragic event** in the lives of Emma and Charles Darwin was the death of their eldest daughter, Annie. The death of a child was relatively common in Victorian Britain, compared with today. Nevertheless, the death of Annie, an especially delightful character, was a savage blow for both, with profound consequences for Charles's beliefs and outlook.

The story of Charles Darwin's life and of the development of his ideas in the context of his times is told in: Adrian Desmond and James Moore (1991) *Darwin*, Penguin Books, London.

Figure 6.14 Charles Darwin 1809–1882. A statue in the University Museum, Oxford.

Figure 6.15 Annie's grave in Malvern Priory churchyard.

Annie had been taken to Malvern for the 'water cure', all other treatments having failed. The inscription reads:

Anne Elizabeth Darwin
Born March 2 1841
Died April 23 1851
"A Dear and Good Child"

Neo-Darwinism

Charles Darwin (and nearly everyone else in the scientific community of his time) knew nothing of Mendel's work. Instead, biologists generally subscribed to the concept of 'blending inheritance' (page 2) (which would only reduce the genetic variation available for natural selection). Neo-Darwinism is an essential restatement of the concepts of evolution by natural selection in terms of Mendelian and post-Mendelian genetics, made possible by the rediscovery of Mendel's work (page 18), together with subsequent developments in genetics.

Table 6.5 The ideas of Neo-Darwinism.

Genetic variations arise via:

- mutations (chromosome mutations and gene mutations), page 36;
- random assortment of parental chromosomes in meiosis, page 14;
- recombination of segments of parental homologous chromosomes during crossing over, page 20 (and via the random fusion of male and female gametes in sexual reproduction – *understood in Darwin's time*).

Then, when genetic variation has arisen in organisms:

- it is expressed in their phenotypes;
- some phenotypes are better able to survive and reproduce in a particular environment;
- natural selection operates, causing changes in the proportions of particular genes in an isolated population;
- it may lead to new varieties and new species.

The subsequent development of the **analytical techniques of population genetics** (page 70) has allowed natural selection to be detected in populations.

Punctuated equilibria: an extension of Neo-Darwinism?

From the theory of evolution by natural selection we would expect species to disappear gradually, and to be replaced by new species at a similar slow rate. Instead, new species often appear relatively quickly (in geological time), but then tend to remain unchanged or little changed for millions of years, followed by periodic mass extinctions, all observed in the fossil record. Some say the fossil record looks like this because we have a partial (distorted) fossil record when compared with the numbers of organisms that have lived. Niles Eldridge and Stephen Gould have an alternative explanation, which they published in 1972. They maintain that the fossil record for some groups is not significantly incomplete, but rather, accords with their view of the origins of new species ('punctuated equilibria', Table 6.6). It is probable that there is evidence for **both** processes in the geological history of life.

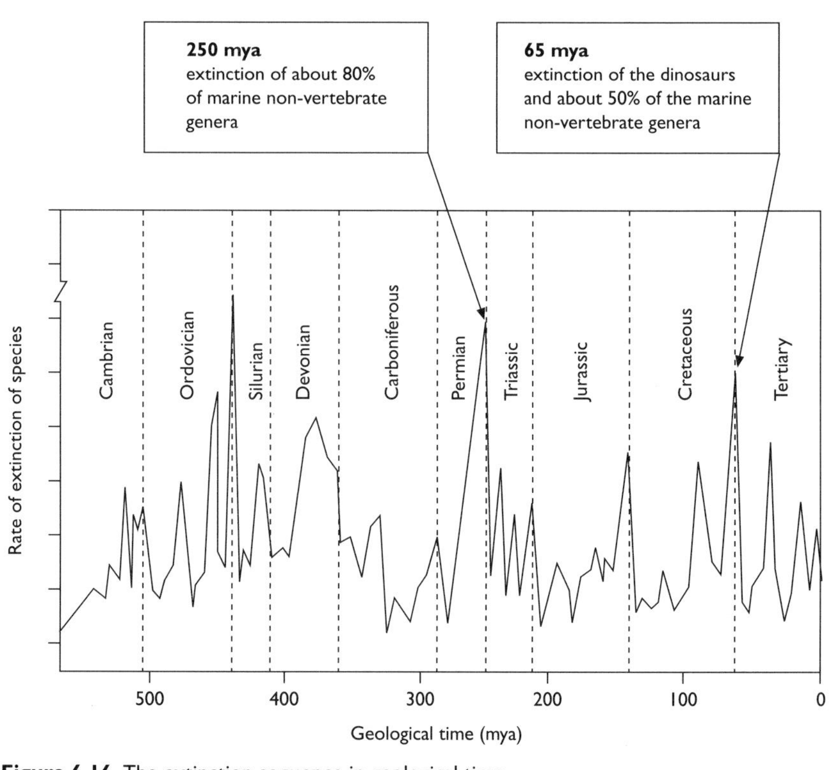

Figure 6.16 The extinction sequence in geological time.

Table 6.6 Eldridge and Gould's 'punctuated equilibria', an addition to evolutionary gradualism?

- When environments become unfavourable, populations attempt to migrate to more favourable situations. If the switch to adverse conditions is very sudden or very violent, then a mass extinction occurs.
- Populations at the fringe of the disturbance may be sheltered or protected from extreme conditions, and survive. They may become small, isolated reproductive communities, demonstrating the 'founder effect' (Figure 6.20, page 70) and adapting to the new conditions quickly.

6 What sorts of events might, in the past, have caused violent and speedy habitat change over a substantial part of the surface of the Earth?

Lamarck, and the place of evolution in biology

Lamarck (1744–1829) made a major contribution to the development of biology and was the first to develop and publicise evolution as a central, unifying idea. For this he brought down on himself the disapproval of the 'catastrophists', whose ideas about evolution were (relatively briefly) influential. He died, blind and destitute, and was buried in Paris in an unmarked grave. Subsequently he has continued to be 'lightly esteemed', continuously blamed for the idea of the **'inheritance of acquired characters'**. This later idea was part of his general theory, but it was also commonly held by many people at the time. Lamarck also invented the dichotomous key, established a detailed study of non-vertebrate animals, and (with Cuvier) created the science of palaeontology.

7 List three ways in which Lamarck's theory of evolution differs fundamentally from that of Darwin's.

Can characteristics acquired during life be transmitted to offspring?

Biologists today do ***not*** accept that new characteristics, acquired during an organism's lifetime, can be transmitted to its offspring through sexual reproduction. In an organism's body, the gametes are produced by gonads (the germ plasm) that, apart from the supply of nutrients, are independent of the body cells (the soma). Changes to the body are not 'recorded' in the gonads. Animals and plants ***cannot*** inherit acquired characteristics through sexual reproduction. This idea is expressed by the phrase **'continuity of the germ plasm'**.

However, plants can transmit mutations in body cells via vegetative propagation. Animals with a significant degree of parental care of their offspring (for example, birds and mammals) can transmit a 'culture', through their rearing and training regimes. 'Culture transmission' is highly developed in humans.

Figure 6.17 Lamarck's theory of evolution, and the evidence he believed supported it.

Figure 6.18 The ways offspring may inherit from their parent(s).

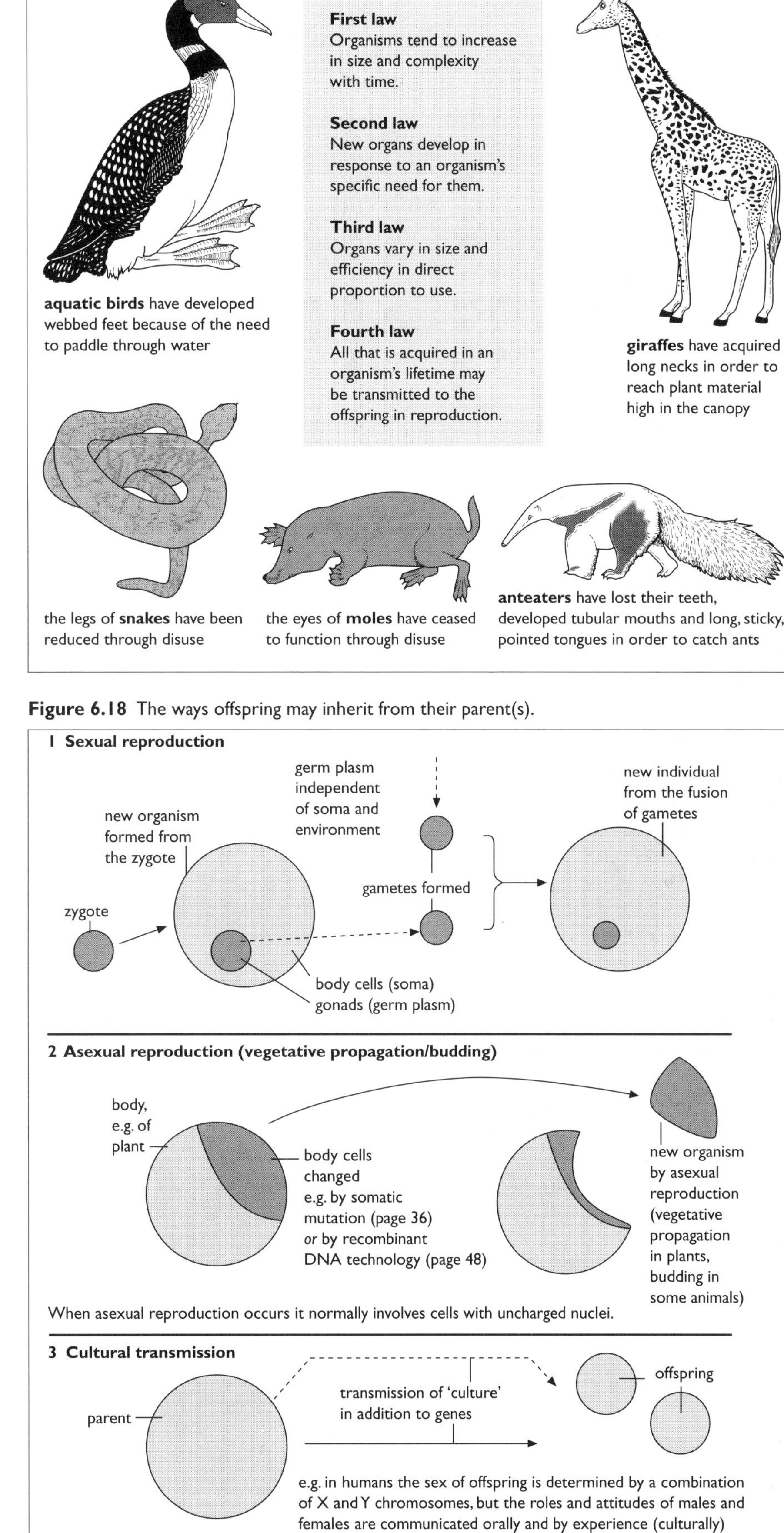

Populations and gene pools

A **population** is a group of individuals of a species, living close enough to be able to interbreed. So a population of garden snails might occupy a small part of a garden, say around a compost heap. A population of thrushes might occupy some gardens and surrounding fields. In other words, the area occupied by a population depends on the size of the organism and on how mobile it is, for example, as well as on environmental factors (such as, food supply, predation, etc.).

The boundaries of a population may be hard to define. Some populations are fully **'open'**, with individuals moving in or out, from nearby populations. Alternatively, some populations are more or less **'closed'**; that is, isolated communities, almost completely cut off from neighbours of the same species.

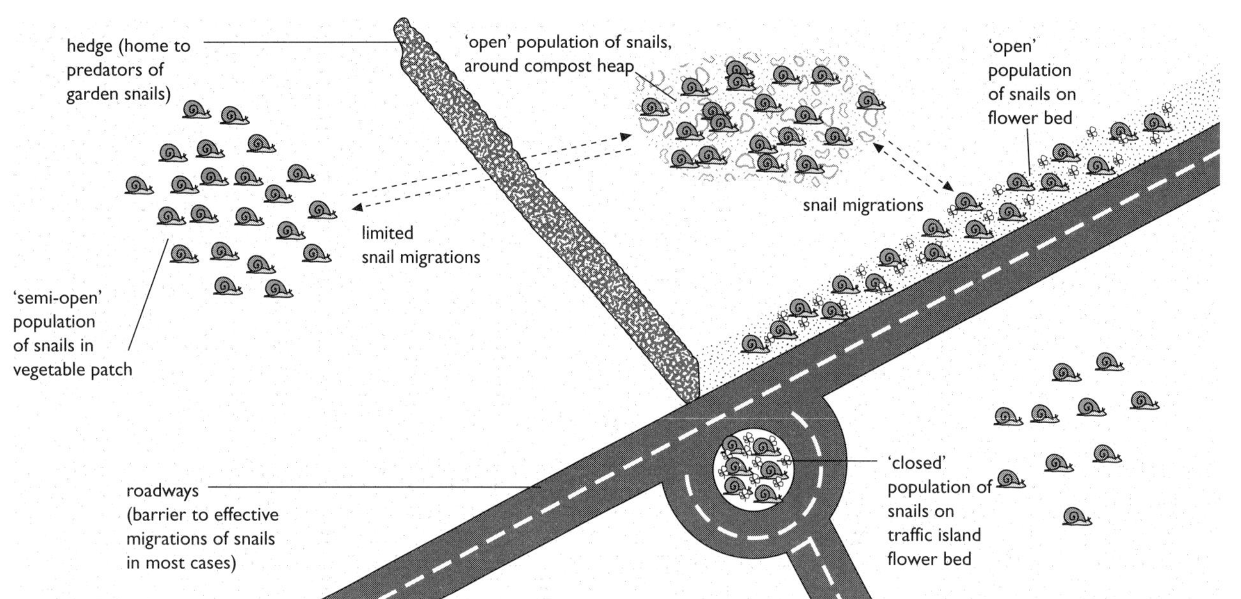

Figure 6.19 The concept of population.

Population genetics is the study of genes in populations (breeding groups). In any population, the total of the genes located in the reproductive cells of the individuals makes up a **gene pool**. A sample of the genes of the gene pool will contribute to form the genomes (gene sets of individuals) of the next generation, and so on, from generation to generation.

Studying gene pools shows that, in some populations, the composition of **the gene pool changes**, owing to a range of factors that alter the proportions of some alleles. These 'disturbing factors', as they are called, are identified in Figure 6.20.

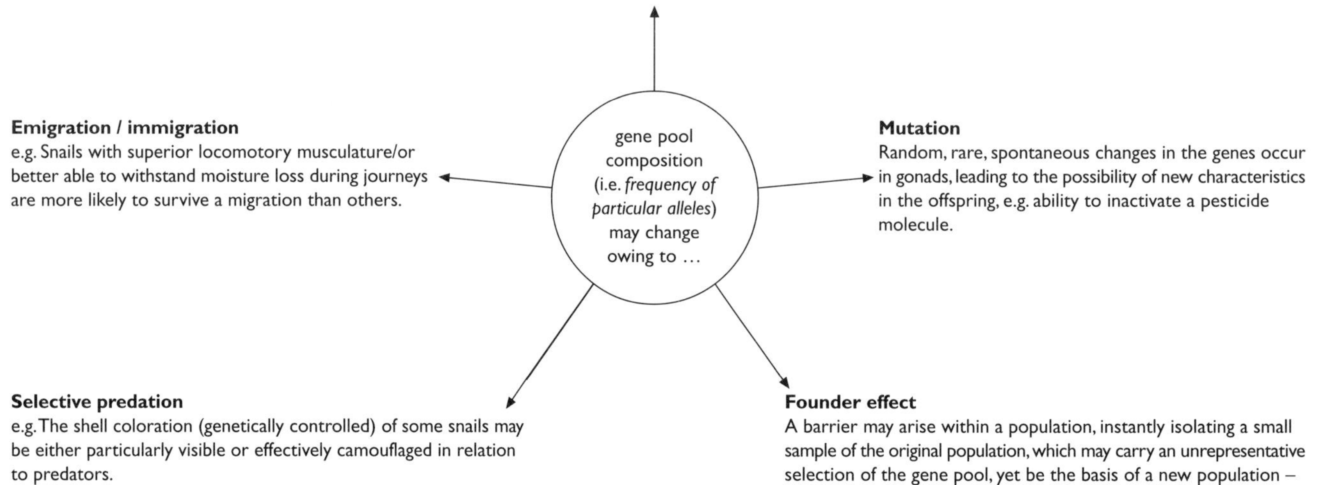

Figure 6.20 The compositions of gene pools can change due to certain 'disturbing factors'.

In other situations, the composition of **the gene pool does not change**. In fact, in the absence of disturbing factors, no change occurs from generation to generation. The reason for this is shown in Figure 6.21.

Figure 6.21 Why the gene pool is unchanged, in the absence of disturbing factors.

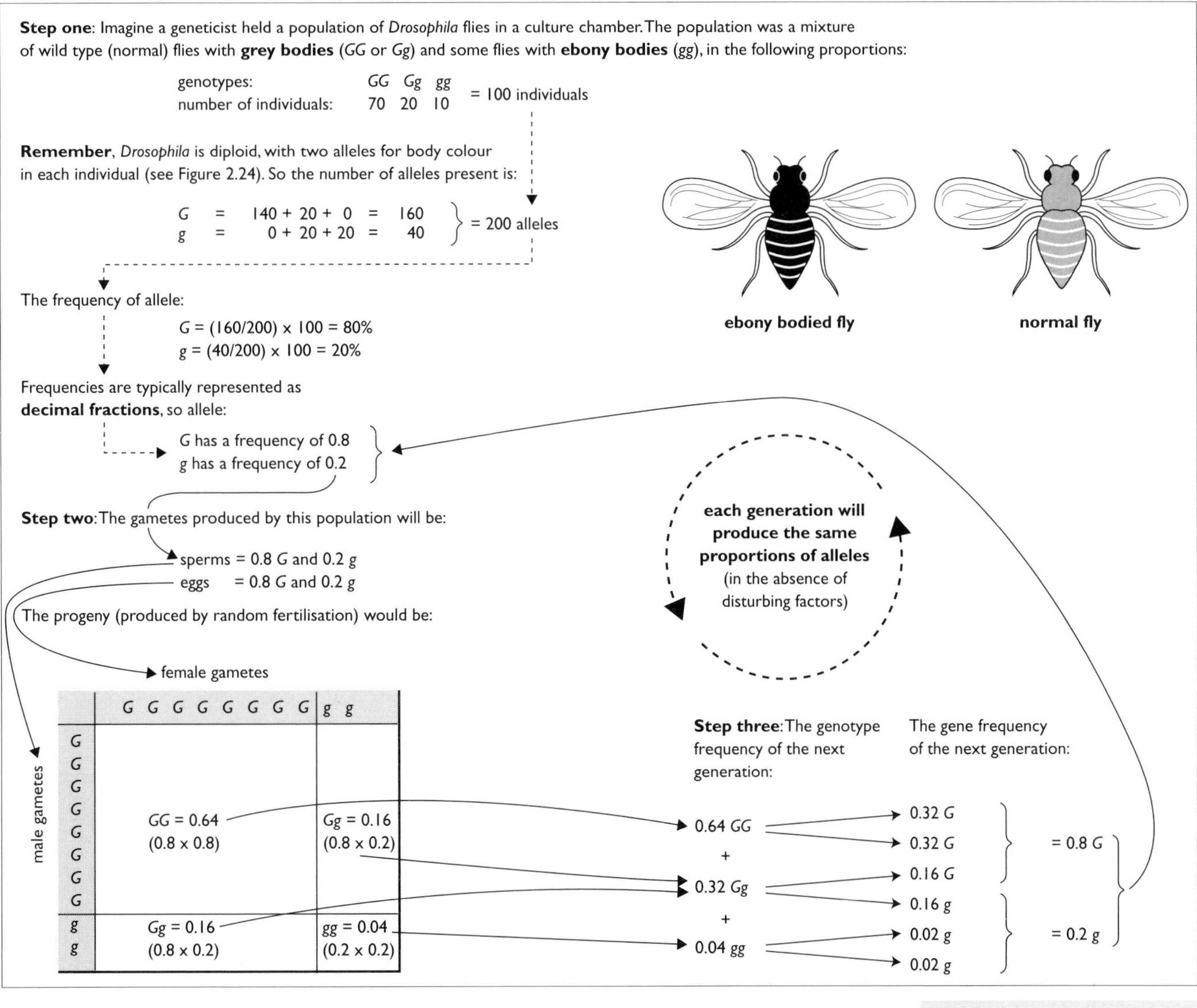

The **Hardy–Weinberg principle** states that, in the absence of disturbing factors, genes and genotype frequencies normally remain constant in a large, randomly mating population. A mathematician, GH Hardy, discovered this principle, in answer to a geneticist's question 'If brown eyes are dominant to blue eyes, why is it that the population does not steadily become brown-eyed?'. He published his answer in 1908, at the same time as the discovery was published by a German doctor, W Weinberg, and so the principle was named after both of them.

8 We now know that the example chosen by the geneticist, of brown and blue eyes, was not a sound one to work on for strictly Mendelian reasons. Why is this so?

Figure 6.22 The Hardy–Weinberg formula.

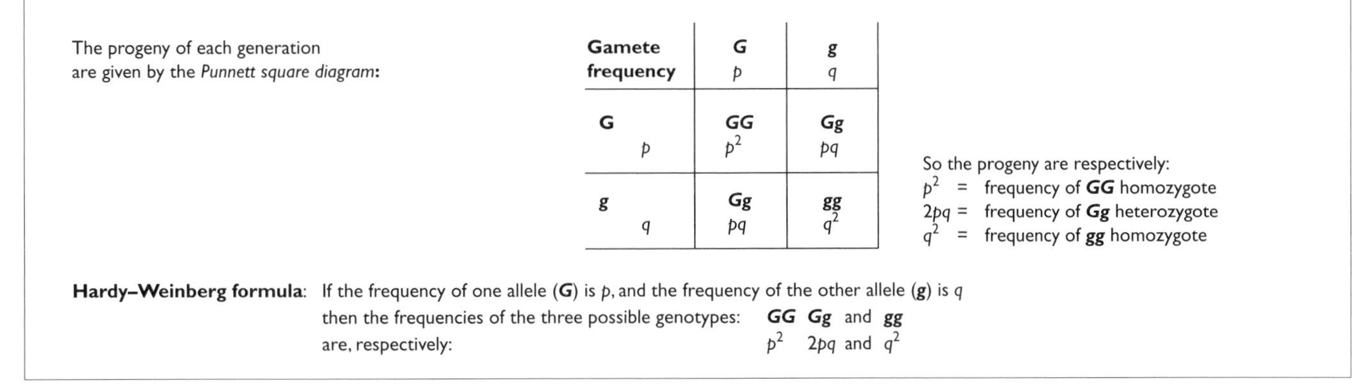

Steps to speciation

We have seen that species exist almost exclusively as local populations, even though the boundaries to these populations are rather open and mostly ill-defined. Individuals of local populations tend to resemble each other more closely than they resemble members of other populations. Local populations are very important in that they are potentially a starting point for speciation.

Speciation is the name given to the process by which one species may evolve into another. A first step to speciation may be when a local population (particularly a *small*, local population) becomes completely cut off in some way. Even then, many generations may elapse before the composition of the gene pool has changed sufficiently to allow us to call the new individuals a different species. Such changes in local gene pools may be detected at an early stage by application of the Hardy–Weinberg formula (page 71).

9 Why are members of a local population likely to have detectable resemblances?

a) Speciation by isolation

When two populations are isolated, certain 'disturbing processes' like natural selection, mutation and random genetic drift may occur independently in both populations, causing them to diverge in their features and characteristics.

Geographic isolation between populations occurs when natural (or human-imposed) barriers arise and sharply restrict movement of individuals (and their spores and gametes, in the case of plants) between the divided populations. Geographical isolation is also known as allopatric ('different countries') isolation.

Figure 6.23 Examples of geographic isolation.

1 Isolation by a new, natural physical barrier
A natural habitat became divided when a river broke its banks and took a new route:

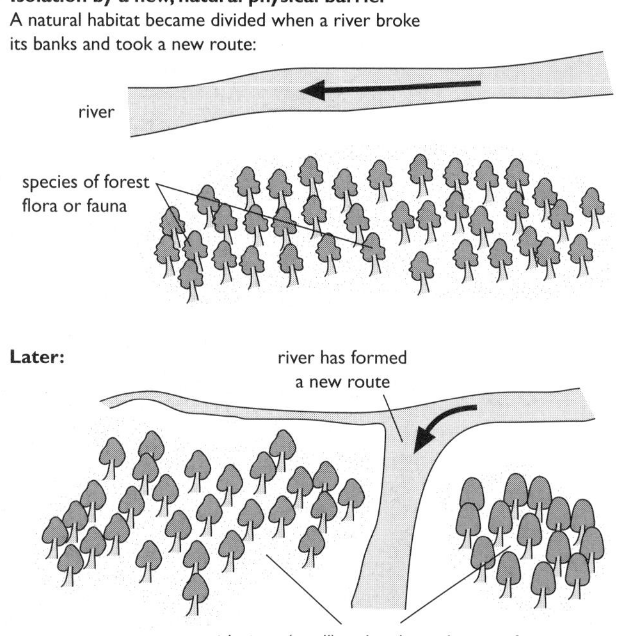

2 Isolation by a human-imposed barrier
The bypass at Newbury cuts through established habitats, separating local populations:

3 Isolation when motile or mobile species are dispersed to isolated habitats
e.g. Finches of the Galapagos Islands (see Figure 6.5, page 62).

Reproductive isolation occurs when barriers strong enough to prevent interbreeding between members of a population living in the same geographic area arise. Cases of reproductive isolation are probably less effective than geographic isolation in bringing about complete isolation. Reproductive isolation is also known as sympatric ('same country') isolation.

Figure 6.24 Types of reproductive isolation.

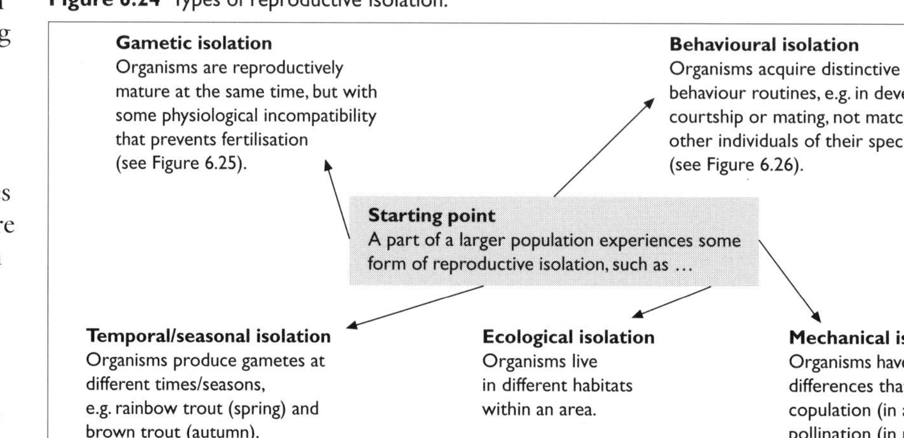

Figure 6.25 Incompatibility mechanism in flowering plants.

LS of stigma of flower, showing pollen grains and pollen tubes
Some pollen fails to 'germinate', other tubes grow but quickly fail, whilst others are sufficiently compatible with the stigma tissue to grow down and reach the ovule.

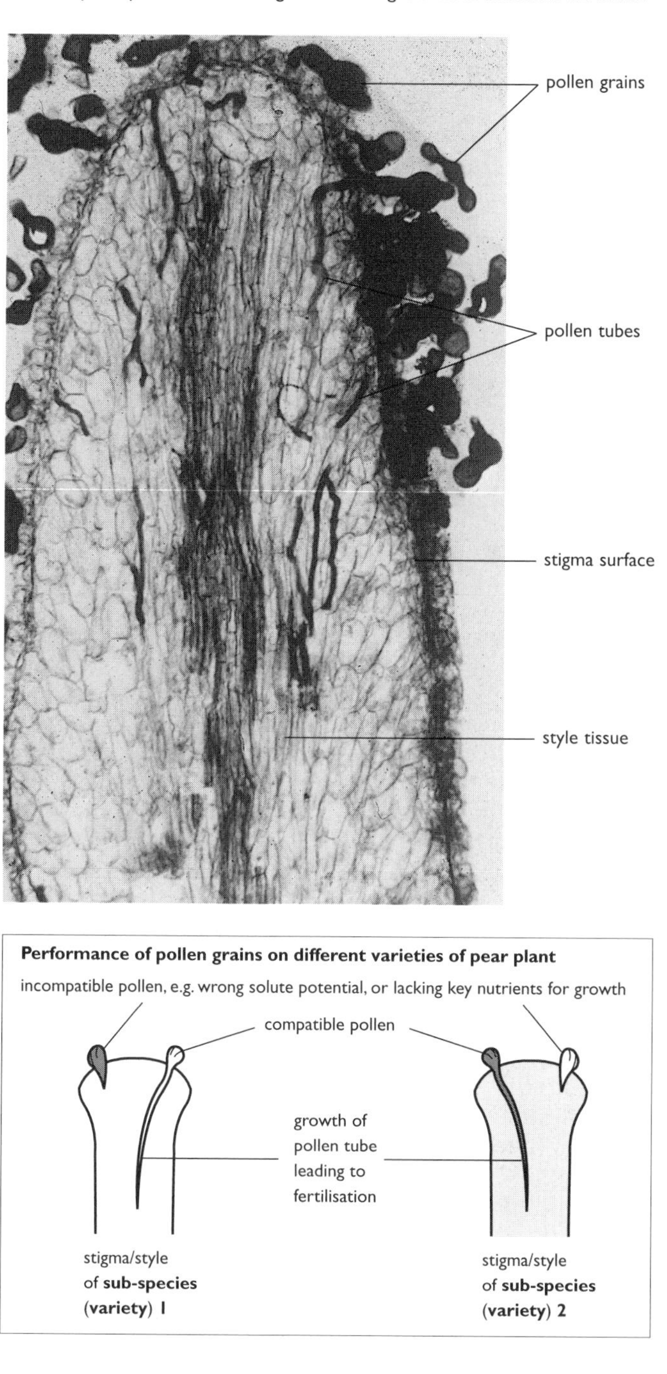

Figure 6.26 Behavioural mechanism of reproductive isolation.

When geese (and swans) hatch the chicks 'imprint' on the adult birds that are in the immediate vicinity and are caring for them. So, for example, ducks that are reared entirely by humans, imprint on humans. (You can read about the experiment in imprinting with greylag geese, carried out by Konrad Lorenz, in CJ Clegg with DG Mackean (1994) *Advanced Biology: Principles and Applications*, John Murray, London.)

Here, a gosling has imprinted on a swan parent (or a cygnet on a goose parent), and has been reared by the 'foster' parent. The initial imprinting has persisted to the adult breeding phase, and so a swan and goose have mated. The photo shows one of the progeny.

Normally, **behavioural mechanisms** prevent breeding between geese and swans, so 'gwans' are very rare. Clearly, swans and geese have evolved apart sufficiently for their progeny to be infertile, but not sufficiently to completely prevent the formation of a hybrid.

A very rare 'Gwan', obtained from goose x swan parents. It has the body of a large black swan, but feet (and 'honk') of a goose. This is an infertile hybrid.

b) Speciation by polyploidy

In plants polyploidy is a rare occurrence, but one which more or less instantly creates a new species (provided the polyploid survives the early period when its numbers are incredibly low). Examples of plant species that have arisen in this way include cord grass (*Spartina anglica*) (page 36) and bread wheat (*Triticum sativum*) (page 37).

In animals, this mechanism is virtually unknown, possibly because the sex chromosome mechanism breaks down if a polyploid forms.

c) Natural selection and speciation

Natural selection operates on individuals, or rather on their phenotypes, produced by a particular combination of alleles. Thus, individuals with particular genotypes are, at certain times and under particular circumstances, more likely to survive and reproduce than other individuals of the species. Their combination of genes is then perpetuated at the expense of other genotypes (a case of **differential mortality**). So natural selection operates to change the composition of gene pools. But the effect this has varies, for example, depending on whether environmental conditions are stable, gradually changing or fluctuating. In effect, natural selection is as likely to maintain constancy of a species as to cause evolution of new species.

Stabilising selection is associated with stable environmental conditions, and it does not lead to evolution. Rather, it maintains favourable characteristics that enable individuals to be successful.

10 What is the modal value and the median of the birth weight data in Figure 6.27?

Figure 6.27 Birth weight and infant mortality, a case of stabilising selection.

The birth weight of humans is influenced by **environmental factors** (e.g. maternal nutrition, smoking habits etc.) and by **inheritance** (about 50%). When more babies than average die at very low and very high birth weights, this obviously affects the gene pool because it tends to eliminate genes for low and high birth weights.

The main graph shows **the birth weights of infants born in a London hospital 1935–1946** (histogram), and the **death rate in relation to birth weight** (broken line).

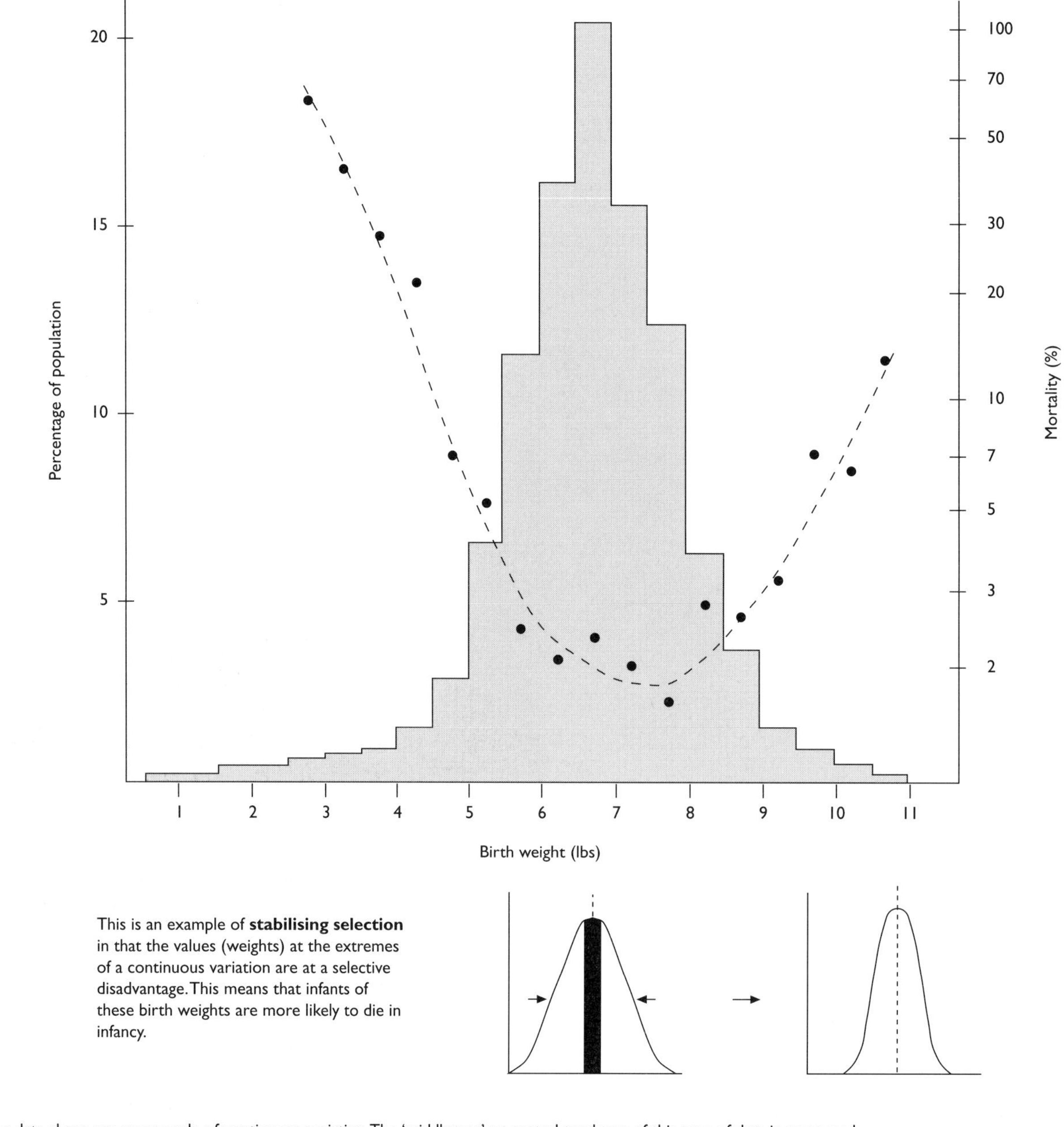

The data above are an example of continuous variation. The 'middleness' or central tendency of this type of data is expressed in three ways:

1 **mode** (modal value) – the most frequent value in a set of values;
2 **median** – the middle value of a set of values where these are arranged in ascending order;
3 **mean** (average) – the sum of the individual values, divided by the number of values.

Directional selection is associated with gradually changing conditions, producing change or evolution in a population. In this case the majority of an existing form of an organism is no longer best suited to the environment, and an extreme form has a selective advantage.

An example is the evolution of heavy-metal tolerance in grass species like *Agrostis tenuis* and *Festuca ovina*. Ions such as copper, zinc and lead are common in the spoil heaps of mines. The heaps are only slowly colonised, as a few individual surrounding plants with the capacity to inactivate poisonous ions (for example, by binding them to insoluble cell wall molecules) benefit from a new habitat where competition from other individuals is minimal.

Disruptive selection is associated with a fluctuating environment that favours two extremes of a variable characteristic. This rare form of selection is also associated with evolutionary change.

Festuca ovina plants with genes for resistance to heavy-metal ion poisoning are naturally selected for in the polluted soils of mining spoil heaps.

It is only individuals of the species with these genes that survive. So, the composition of the gene pool is altered.

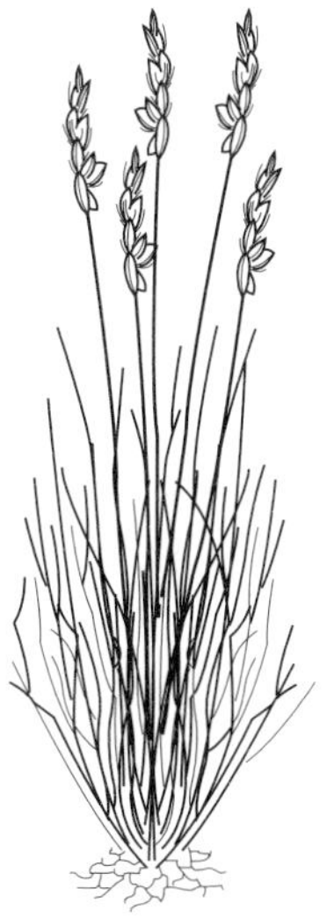

Directional selection shifts the population mean for the 'chosen' character towards the extreme.

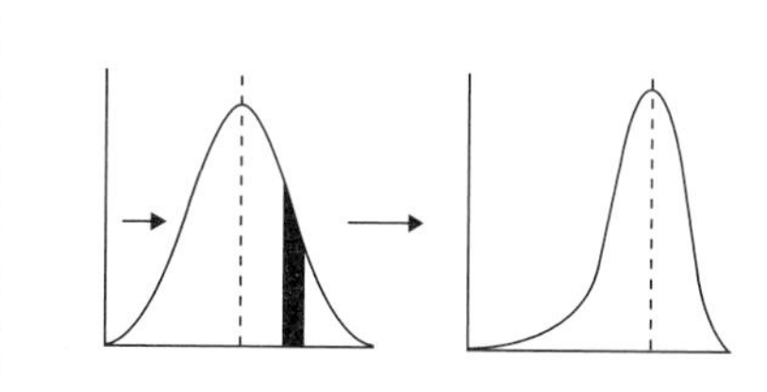

Figure 6.28 Directional selection.

- As a result of the Industrial Revolution in Britain, in areas of heavy industry and in the surrounding countryside, the pollutant chimney gases (e.g. SO_2) and the particulate matter (e.g. soot) had killed off epiphytes (lichens, algae and moss growing on the surface of trees, etc.) and had blackened exposed surfaces.
- Black and dark-coloured species of moth (known as **melanic forms**) tended to increase in these areas, but their numbers were low in unpolluted countryside, where **pale forms** of moths were far more common.
- Organisms that exist in two forms are examples of **polymorphism**.
- In areas where pollution has stopped, surfaces have been cleaned up and epiphytes have returned, pale forms of the moths have tended to be found again.

The moth *Biston betularia* is an example of this phenomenon, known as **industrial melanism**.

In different habitats, one or other form is effectively camouflaged, and is the dominant species. So, this is a case of **disruptive selection**. However, in the areas of the Industrial Revolution, during the hey-day of heavy industries, the fate of *Biston betularia* was a case of **directional selection** (i.e. exclusive selection of the melanic form).

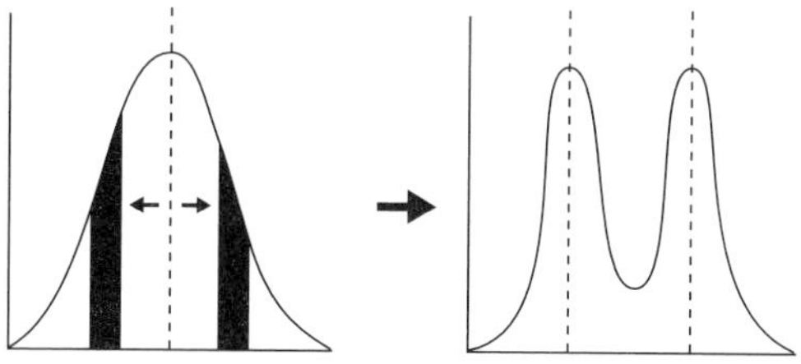

Disruptive selection favours two extremes of the 'chosen' characters at the expense of intermediate forms.

Biston betularia

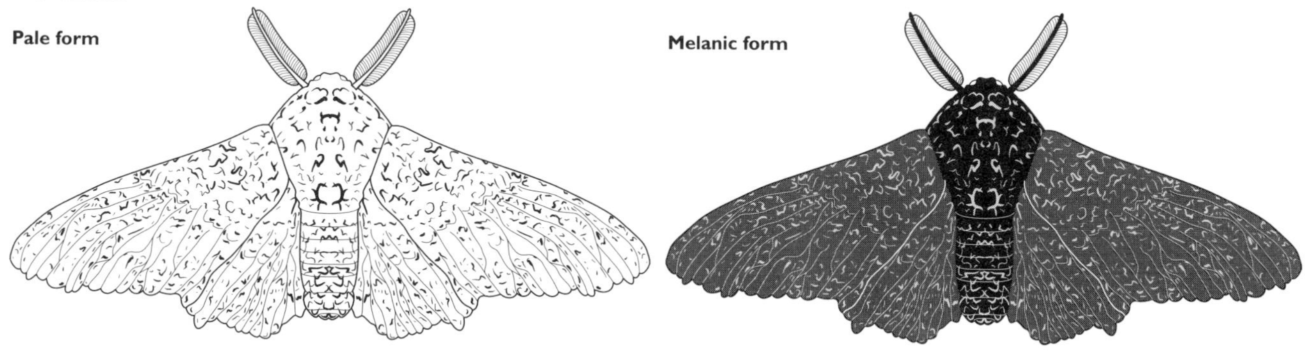

Pale form

Melanic form

Results of frequency studies in polluted and unpolluted habitats:

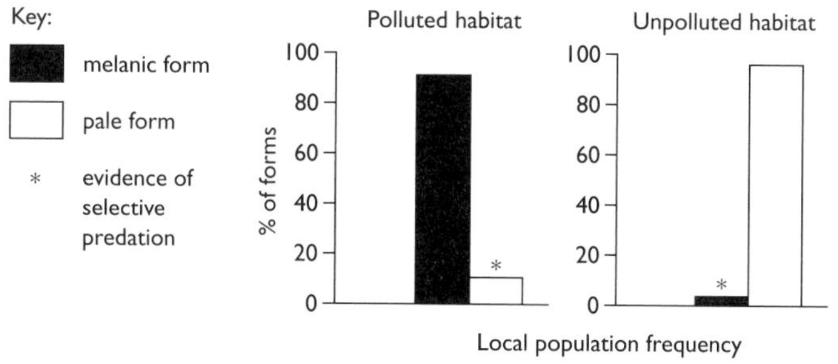

Mark–release–capture experiments using laboratory-reared moths of both forms, in polluted and unpolluted habitats:

Key:
- melanic form (black bar)
- pale form (white bar)
- * evidence of selective predation

Polluted habitat / Unpolluted habitat

% of forms (0–100)

Local population frequency

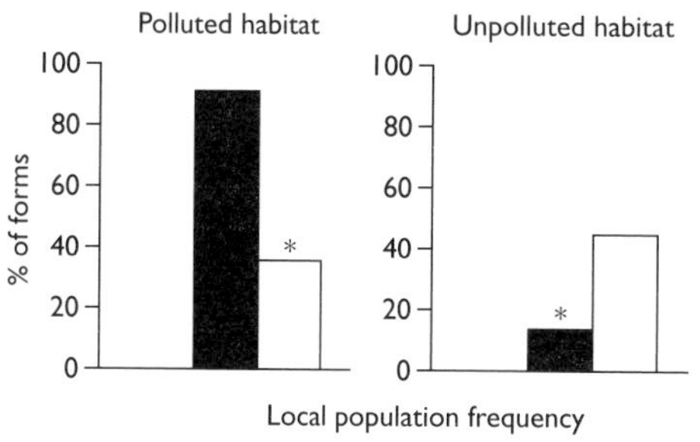

Figure 6.29 The peppered moth and industrial melanism – a case of disruptive selection.

Sexual selection is the name we give to the struggle between individuals of one sex (normally the males) for access to individuals of the opposite sex. Victory in this struggle depends on the use of special features such as antlers (for example, in male deer), distinctive plumage (for example, in the peacock and the pheasant) or adapted mouthparts (for example, mandibles in the stag beetle). The advantage of winning the struggle is the right to mate. The struggle is mostly ritualised (not life-threatening), but the loser's genes are much less likely to be perpetuated. Winning the right to mate, Darwin assumed, was a significant advantage, as the possession of special features may also make the owner much more vulnerable to predators. Today we assume that differences in size, shape or colour between males and females of the same species, occupying the same niche (known as **sexual dimorphism**), are due to sexual selection.

11 What does the term 'niche' mean?

Figure 6.30 Sexual dimorphism Darwin attributed to sexual selection.

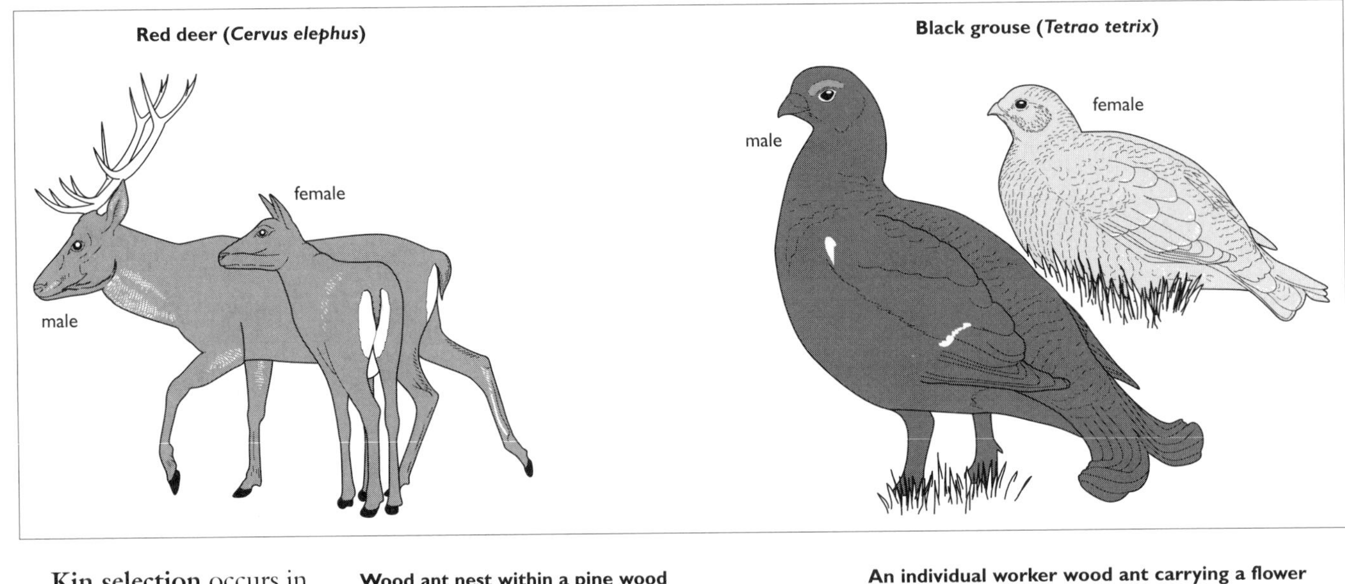

Kin selection occurs in social insects such as ants and bees. Many species of these organisms exist in huge communities consisting of sterile females (workers), genetically closely related to the fertile members (queens and males) on whose behalf they appear to work (page 35). Worker ants will sacrifice themselves, when necessary, aiding the survival of the community (altruism).

Acts of altruism may be explained as 'kin selection'. Organisms that share the same genes help to perpetuate these genes when they risk self-destruction if close relatives benefit. Darwin had argued that natural selection acted only on individuals, **not** for 'the good of the species'. But he made an exception in explaining altruism.

Wood ant nest within a pine wood

An individual worker wood ant carrying a flower

The number of wood ants running past a point on a foraging track in 3 minutes, during an April day.
The solid line is the soil temperature.

This sort of study of an ant community is highly practical. In the study, close observations may reveal individual acts of altruism arising in the daily life of worker ants faced with unexpected, external danger.

Number of ants: 0, 100, 200, 300, 400, 500
Soil temperature (°C): 0, 5, 10, 15, 20, 25
Time of day: 0500, 1300, 2200

Figure 6.31 The life of wood ants (*Formica rubra*).

Detecting evolution early, a new 'role' for mitochondrial DNA

An obstacle to establishing evolution theory has been the impossibility of observing evolution directly. The best short-term evidence comes from detecting changes in gene pools, using the Hardy–Weinberg formula (page 71). However, speciation at this level usually takes a very long time to become apparent.

DNA in eukaryotic cells occurs in chromosomes in the nucleus (99%) **and** in the mitochondria. Mitochondrial DNA (**mtDNA**) is a circular molecule, very short in comparison with nuclear DNA. Cells contain any number of mitochondria, typically between 100 and 1000.

Mutations occur at a very slow, steady rate in all DNA, but chromosomal DNA has with it enzymes that may repair the changes in some cases. These enzymes are **absent** from mtDNA. Thus mtDNA changes five to ten times faster than chromosomal DNA. Consequently, the length of time since organisms belonging to different but related species have diverged can be estimated by extracting and comparing samples of their mtDNA.

Furthermore, at fertilisation, the sperm contributes a nucleus only, so all the mitochondria of the zygote come from the egg cell. Since there is **no mixing of mtDNA genes at fertilisation**, the evidence about relationships from studying differences between samples of mtDNA is easier to interpret.

Figure 6.32 The use of mitochondrial DNA (mtDNA) in measuring evolutionary divergence.

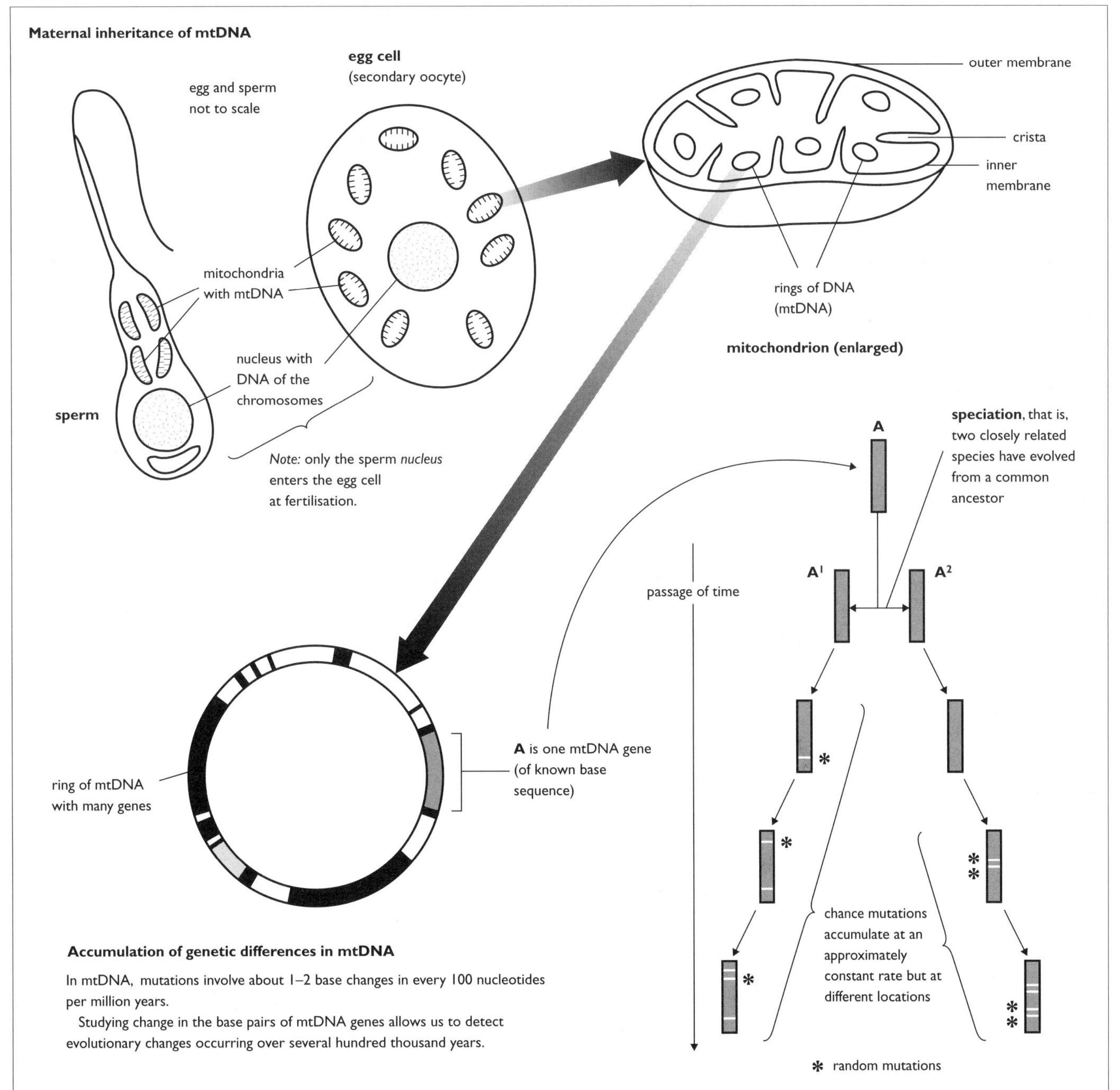

Issues in macro-evolution – a summary

Speciation (pages 72–76) is the key process in organic evolution by natural selection, but if evolution is a fact of life, then Neo-Darwinism should also account for the major steps in evolution (often called macro-evolution). These steps include the evolution of vertebrates from non-vertebrates, and of flowering plants from non-flowering vascular plants. A further implication is that life itself has evolved from the non-living, inorganic resources of the Earth. The issues of macro-evolution are given below.

In many of these cases **we know little or nothing about how these changes came about**, and current ideas are mostly speculative. It is possible that some of these issues will remain largely a mystery. However, the evolution of humans is so recent in geological terms that we can examine the evidence and speculate with some confidence on the possible steps and changes.

Figure 6.33 Issues in macro-evolution – an introduction.

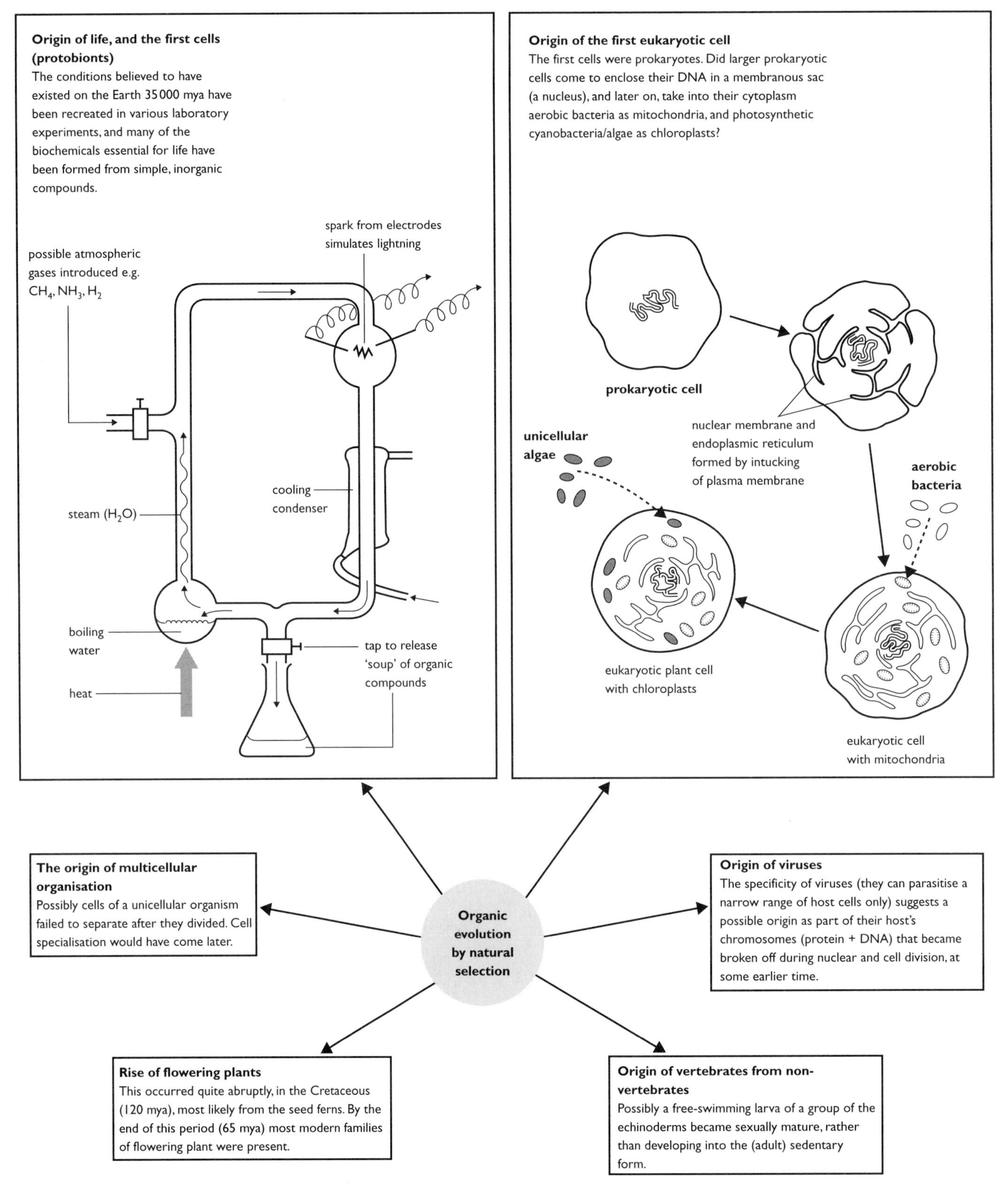

Human evolution

To begin, it is helpful to identify the features of humans that show us to be members of the mammalian order known as primates, in the context of the 35 million years (my) that have elapsed since the first apes appeared.

Table 6.7 The special features of mammals and primates.

Mammals	Primates
1 Young are nourished by **milk**, which is secreted by modified skin glands, known as the **mammary glands**.	**1** Retain the ancestral **pentadactyl limb** with five digits in hands and feet (grasping), plus free mobility of limbs, with unfused radius and ulna. (*Note:* many retain the **tail** as an organ of balance [but not in the apes], or as a grasping limb [in some New World monkeys].)
2 Skin is covered by **hair**, which is both an extension of the sensory system, and (most importantly in other mammals, but not in humans) functions as a **heat-insulating layer**.	**2** Progressive freedom in **mobility of the digits**, especially the thumbs and big toes, and the replacement of sharp claws by flattened nails, and with **sensitive touch pads** on tips of digits.
3 The skin has two types of glands, the **sweat glands** (secreting sweat when cooling of the blood circulating below the skin is necessary), and the **sebaceous glands** (secreting a greasy substance on to the hairs).	**3** Development of **erect posture** in many groups, with extensive head rotation. Forelimbs developed for specialised role in locomotion – **brachiation** – in apes.
4 The **cranial cavity** (brain box) **is large**. Below, the **secondary palate** shuts off the nasal passage from the mouth, allowing food to be retained and chewed before swallowing.	**4** Development of **nervous system** to give precise rapid control of musculature. The brain is large and complex, especially those parts involved with vision, tactile inputs, muscle coordination and control, memory and learning.
5 The brain has large **cerebral hemispheres**, and a large **cerebellum**, and the senses of sight and hearing are acute.	**5** Enlargement of the **eyes**, increasing the amount of light (and detail) received, with development of a retina increasing sensitivity to low levels of illumination and different frequencies (that is, colour).
6 There are three **auditory ossicles** (bones of the middle ear chamber), and there is an **external ear**.	**6** Eyes look forwards with **overlapping visual fields**, giving binocular (stereoscopic) vision. The eyes are contained within bony sockets, the orbits.
7 The thoracic and abdominal cavities are completely separated by a muscular **diaphragm**, and the ribs and diaphragm assist in **respiratory movements**.	**7** **Reduction in the apparatus** and function **of smell**, with flattened snout. Reduction in the number of teeth, and the retention of a simple cusp pattern in the molars.
8 Mammals are highly **active** craniates, with a **high metabolic rate**, 'intelligence' and a marked commitment to **parental care**.	**8** Lengthening **prenatal and postnatal life periods**, with increasing body size. Low reproductive rates.

The earliest primates

Small mammal species were around in the age of the dinosaurs (Jurassic, 200 mya), but new fossil evidence suggests that mammals arose much earlier (possibly in the Permian, 290 mya). Primates are most likely to have evolved from small, nocturnal, tree-living insectivorous mammals, related to today's tree-shrews (in the Cretaceous, 135 mya). The first primates would have shared similarities with today's prosimians ('before the monkeys') like the aye-aye, lemur and loris.

Philippine tree-shrew (*Urrogate everetti*)

Aye-aye (*Daubentonia madagascariensis*)

Figure 6.34 The tree-shrew and aye-aye, suggesting primate origins.

Figure 6.35 The human story over 35 million years, as a time-line.

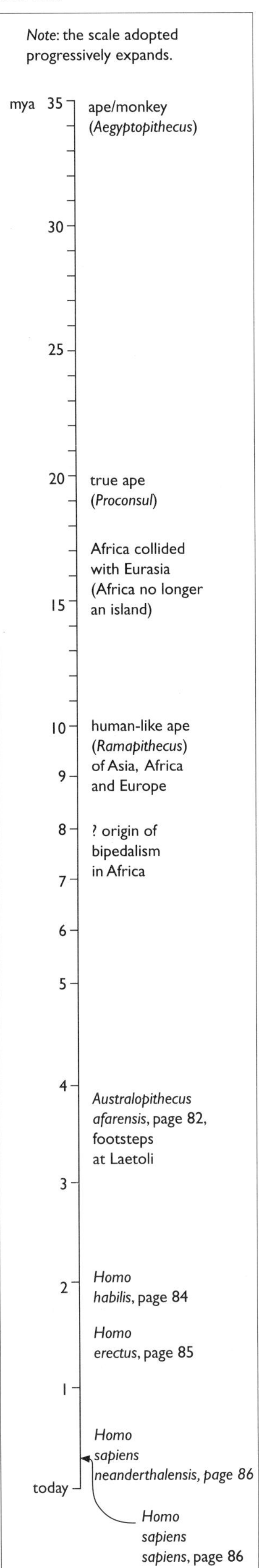

The first apes, and the development of anthropoid features

The fossil record shows us that mammals of many different orders (that is, not the primates alone) were 'radiating' and diversifying from about 40 mya (in the Eocene and Oligocene epochs of the Tertiary period). However, the first primate fossils that we can identify confidently as **anthropoids** (ape/monkey types) appear from about 35 mya. Humans are clearly one form of the anthropoid range of organisation, as we shall see, so we can say the human story has taken about 35 million years to tell!

Figure 6.36 The earliest apes.

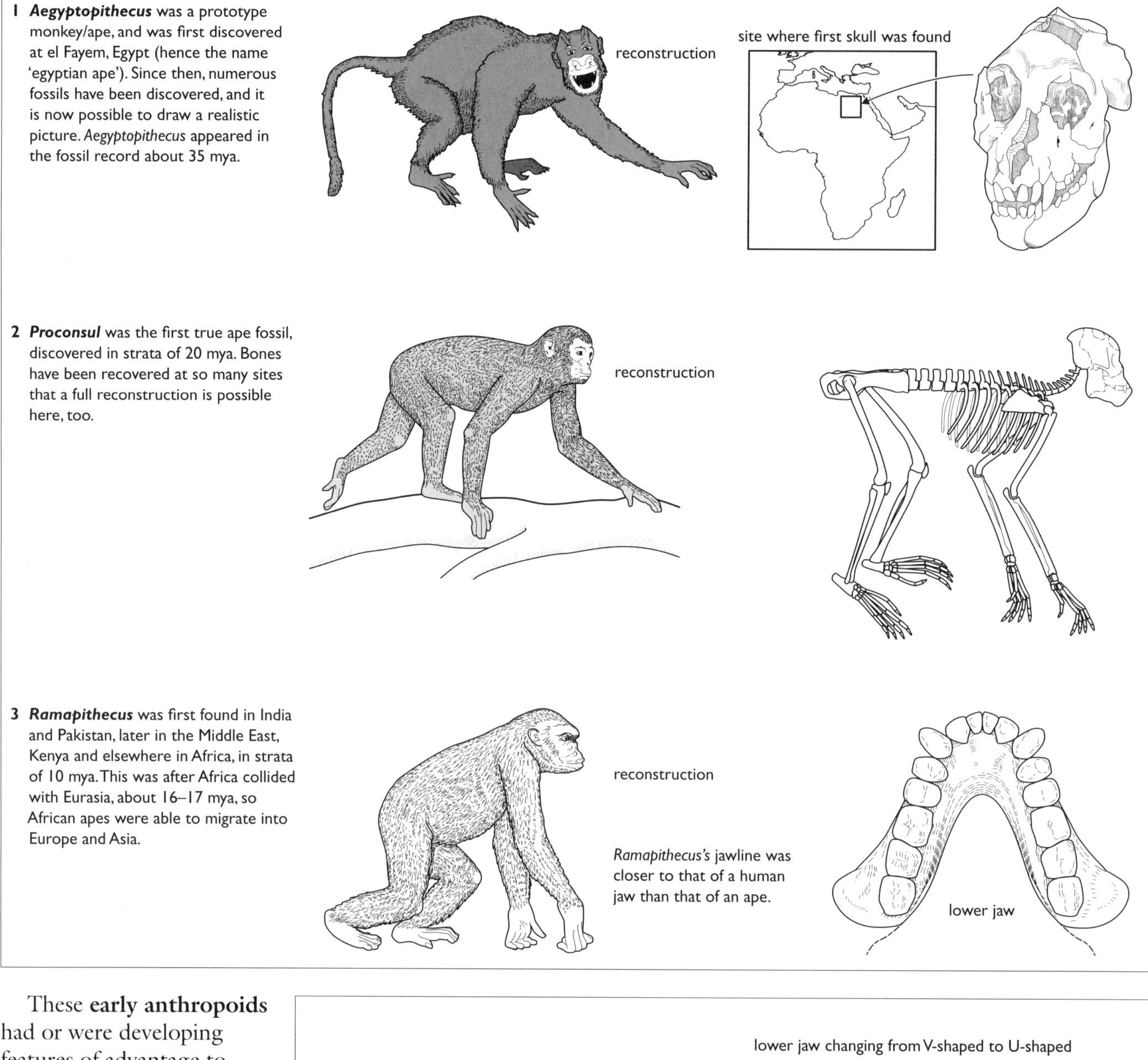

These **early anthropoids** had or were developing features of advantage to agile, rain forest dwellers, mostly daytime feeders on fruit and vegetation. Today, many of these features have persisted in the surviving apes (chimpanzees, gibbons, gorillas, humans and orang-utans).

12 What differences might you expect to find between the teeth of an insectivorous tree-shrew and an early, vegetarian ape?

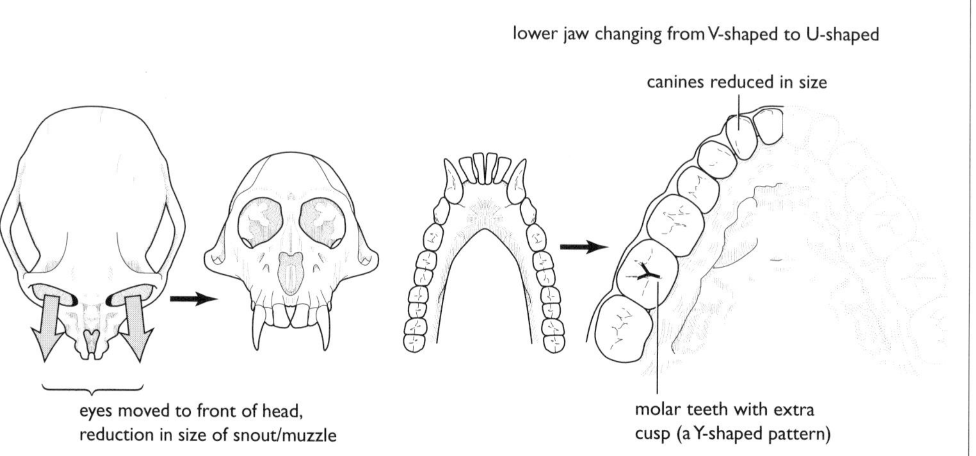

Figure 6.37 Anthropoid features of the skull and jaws.

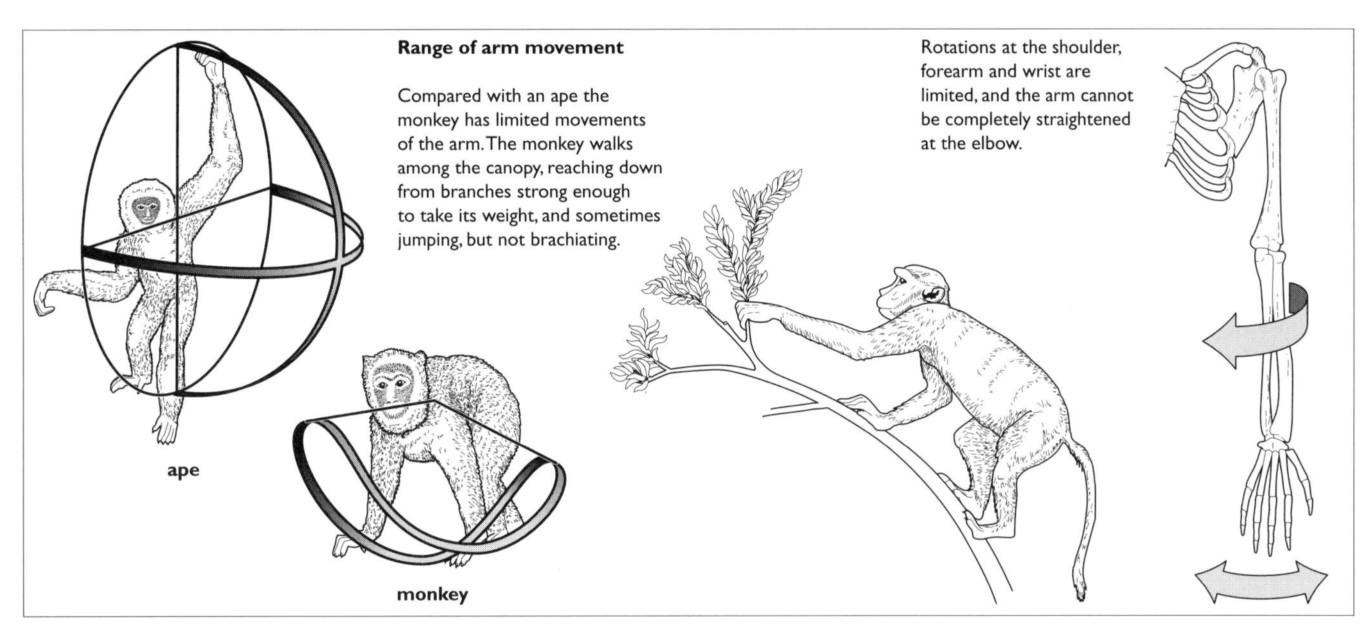

Figure 6.38 Monkey features.

Monkeys and apes diverged

Today, monkeys are indigenous to Africa and parts of Asia and Europe (the Old World monkeys) and to South America (the New World monkeys). These two groups shared common ancestors and diverged, about 35 to 40 mya, at about the time divergence from ape stock occurred. The ways in which monkeys are distinguished from apes include the ways they move in the canopy and feed.

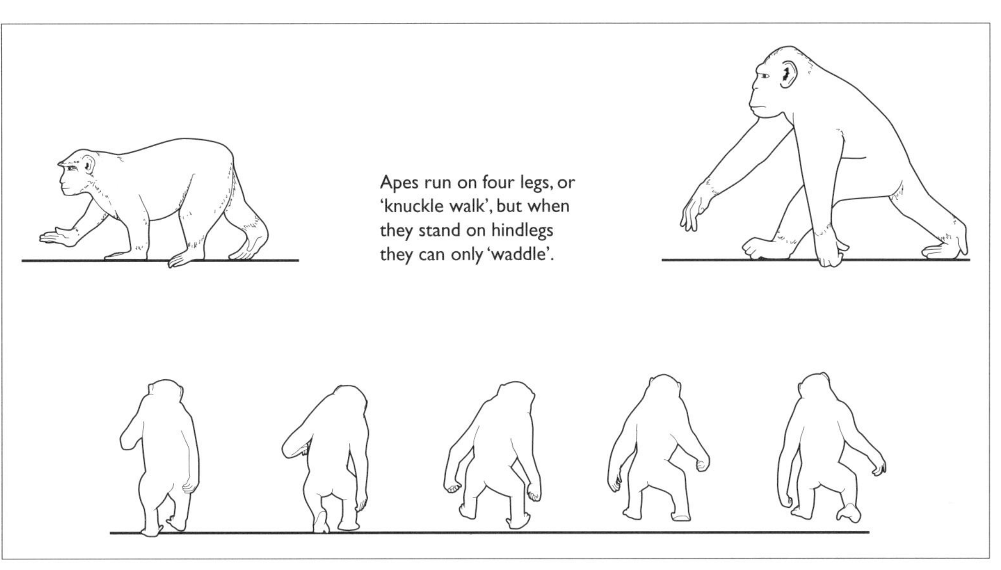

Figure 6.39 Walking is still a problem for apes.

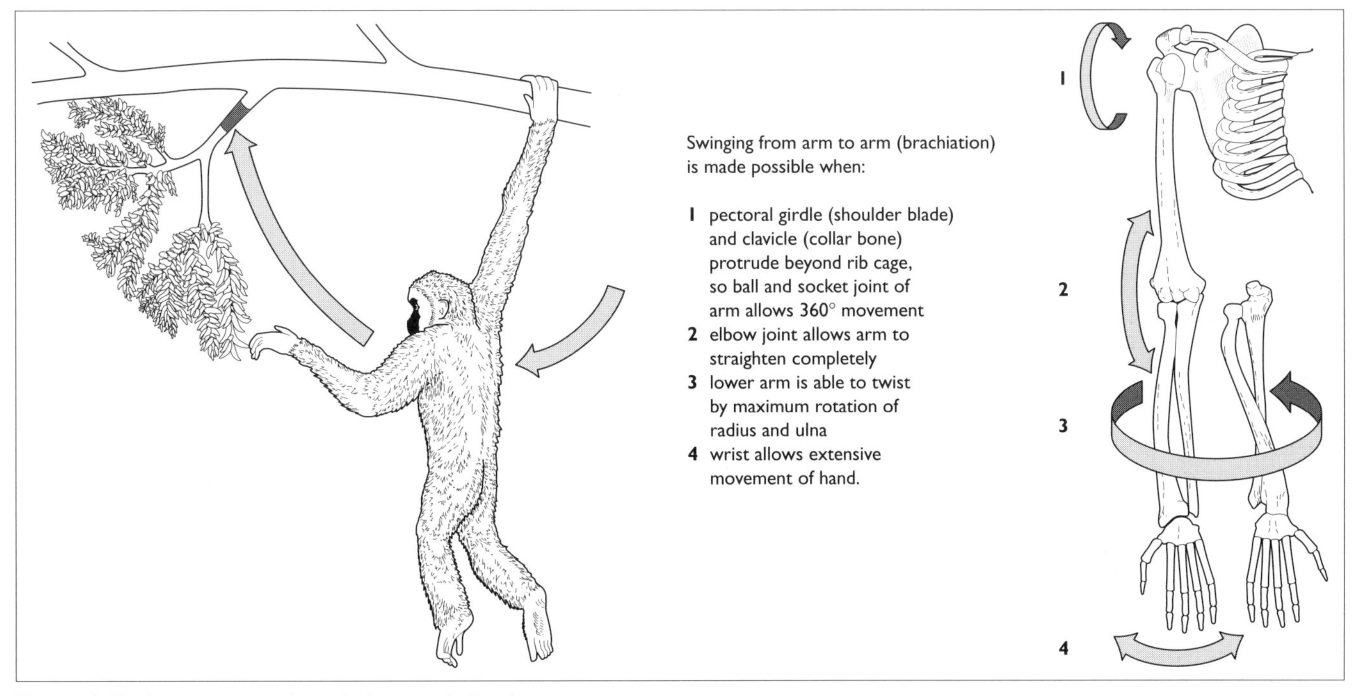

Figure 6.40 Ape movement through the trees by brachiation.

The 'southern apes', the first hominids

Australopithecines (the name means 'southern apes') lived in Africa from 5 to 1.5 mya. Parts of skulls of this genus have been uncovered in various locations (including at Taung, in 1924), prior to the discovery of 'Lucy' at Hadar in Ethiopia in 1974. Lucy is identified as *Australopithecus afarensis*. She was **ape-like** in that she had the same limited brain capacity as ape species of the period, but **hominid-like** in that she was a powerful, upright walker (the pelvis was of characteristically human form) and had no long 'muzzle'. We now recognise that upright walking (known as 'bipedalism') was an early stage in the evolution of the hominids. The Lucy fossil was laid down 3 mya.

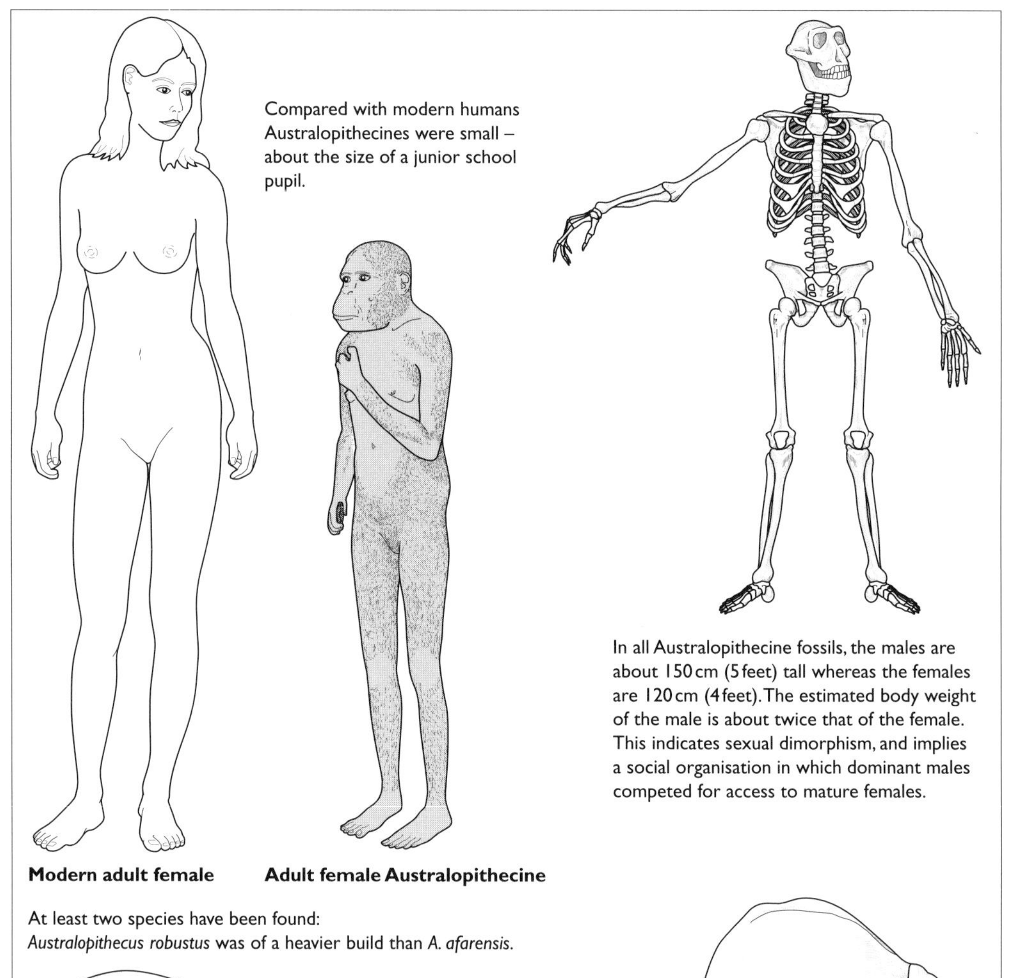

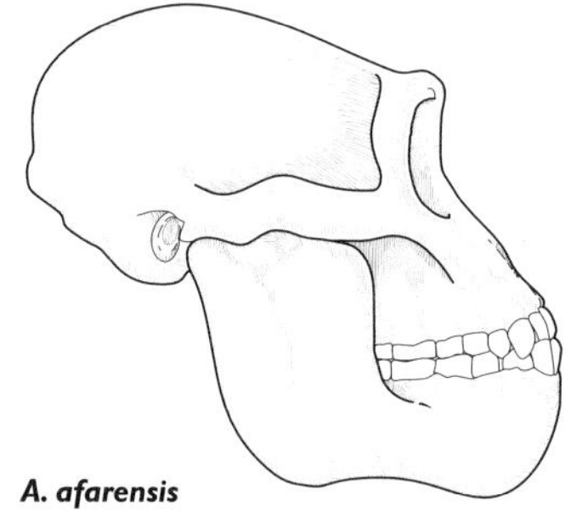

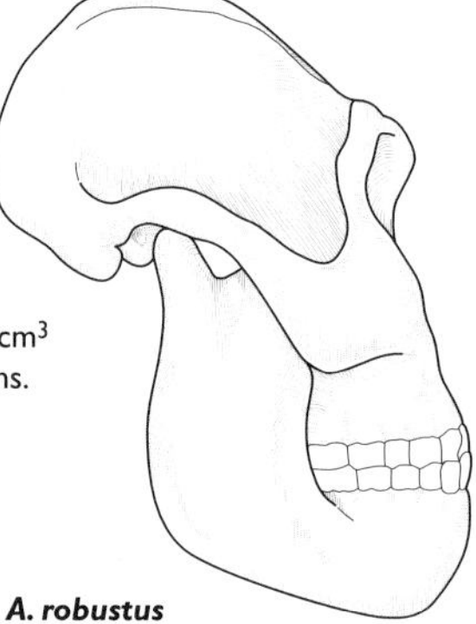

Figure 6.41 Reconstructions of Australopithecine species.

We are confident about bipedalism at this time because of **the discovery of the footprints at Laetoli**, imprinted in volcanic ash, 3.6 mya. The soft ash was presumably immediately moistened by rain (no additional prints added), baked into hard rock and then buried by soil blown in. The footsteps were rediscovered in 1976. Two adults had walked in line, in a northerly direction, with a youngster who later ran off to one side. Being volcanic ash, this 'trace' fossil can be dated precisely by the potassium/argon ratio method.

Figure 6.42 The Laetoli footprints.

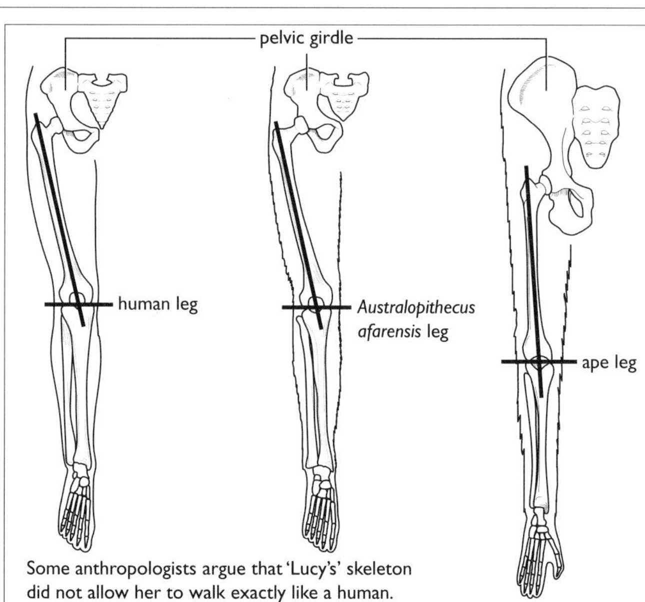

Figure 6.43 The angle of the femur at the knee allows a human to walk upright, with feet under the centre of gravity. The angle in an ape causes it to 'waddle' in attempting bipedal motion.

One advantage of bipedalism is as a mechanism to stay cool at the high midday temperatures of equatorial latitudes. Australopithecines lived in 'mosaic' environments, part tropical rain forest, part woodland and tree-savannah, part scrub. Wherever they lived, no doubt they preferred to shelter at times of highest temperature. However, they may have often needed to travel to new venues, visit water holes, or scavenge and collect food at times when faster and stronger predatory animals were most likely to be resting. If so, being bipedal gave them an advantage.

13 What is the advantage of keeping the head region cooler, even if the body temperature has to rise slightly?

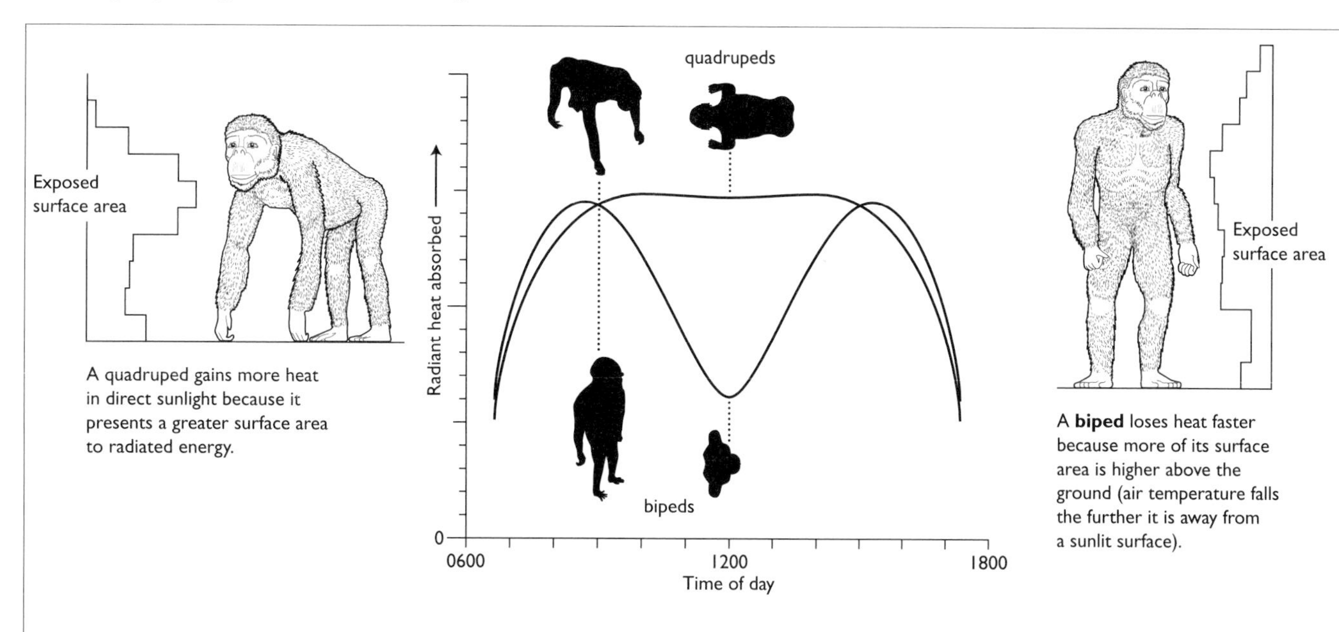

- Quadrupeds (e.g. the antelope) on the exposed savannah reflect sunlight by their short cropped fur, but are exposed to severe sunlight radiation all day, unless shade can be found.
- Typically, they allow their body temperature to rise in the midday heat, but cool the blood in the lining of the nostrils by the evaporation of water and the breathing current of air.
- Cooler blood from the muzzle is used to lower the temperature of blood entering the brain.

Note: an ape does not have this muzzle extension to enable this heat-exchange mechanism.

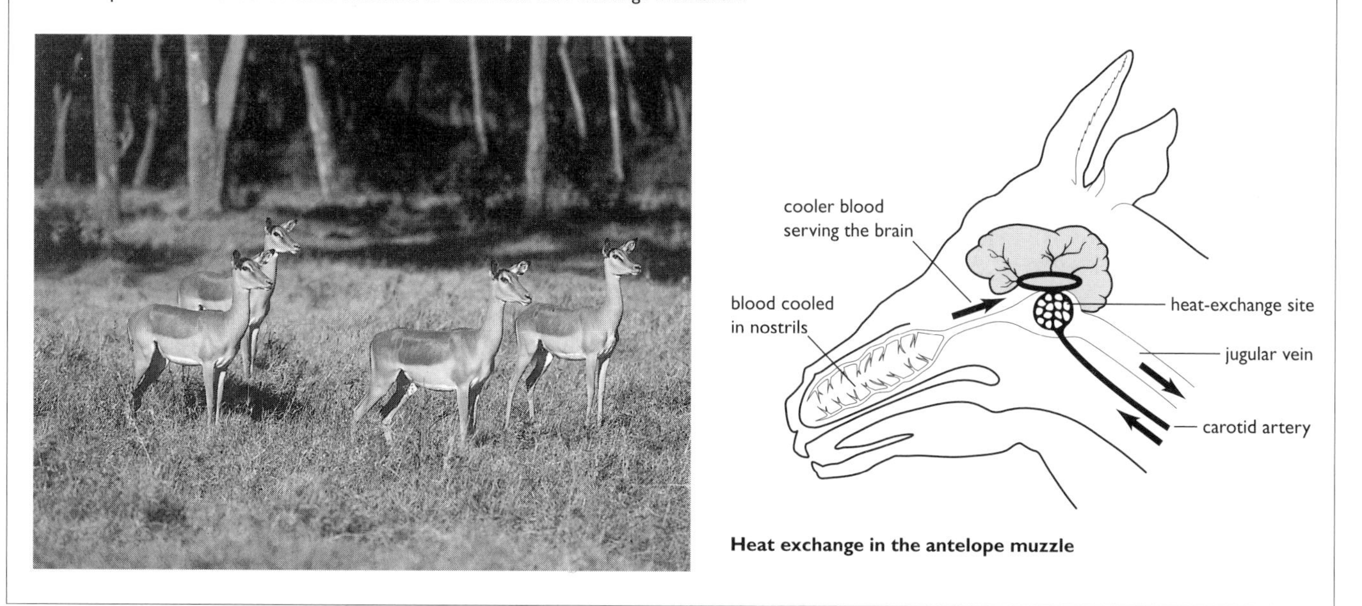

Figure 6.44 Methods of staying cool in the equatorial sun.

Probably **the critical advantage of bipedalism is that hands are freed for obtaining and carrying food**. Apes breed slowly, producing few offspring at a time. A male ape that mastered bipedalism could improve his mate's reproductive capacity by feeding her, thus freeing her to concentrate on the production and rearing of young. The genes of apes with a tendency for bipedalism will have had a better chance of replication in future generations. This would have been particularly effective in male–female pairs, rather than in troops of primates where males invested time and energy maintaining dominance over the females. On this account, hominids would have tended to be monogamous apes with lessened sexual dimorphism.

Early humans – enlarged brains and busy hands

a) ***Homo habilis***

The fossil record of *Homo habilis* shows that this hominid occurred in Africa in the period from 2 to about 1.5 mya. 'Habilines', as they are known, are clearly distinguished from Australopithecines by lighter cranial bones and by an **enhanced brain capacity** (typically about 750–800 cm^3). Also, they are the first hominids to be associated with tools, for they used large pebbles, chipped in at least two directions, as sharpened implements to crush, break and cut. Thus, their additional brain capacity resulted in advanced manual dexterity, and was applied to the making and using of simple tools (selected strong stones) to chip pebbles, for a purpose. Using **tools to make tools** (that is, the development of a tool industry) is what distinguishes hominid tool makers from all other tool users in the living world.

14 Give an example of the use of simple tools in the living world.

Figure 6.45 *Homo habilis* fossils, and a reconstruction of an early 'habiline'.

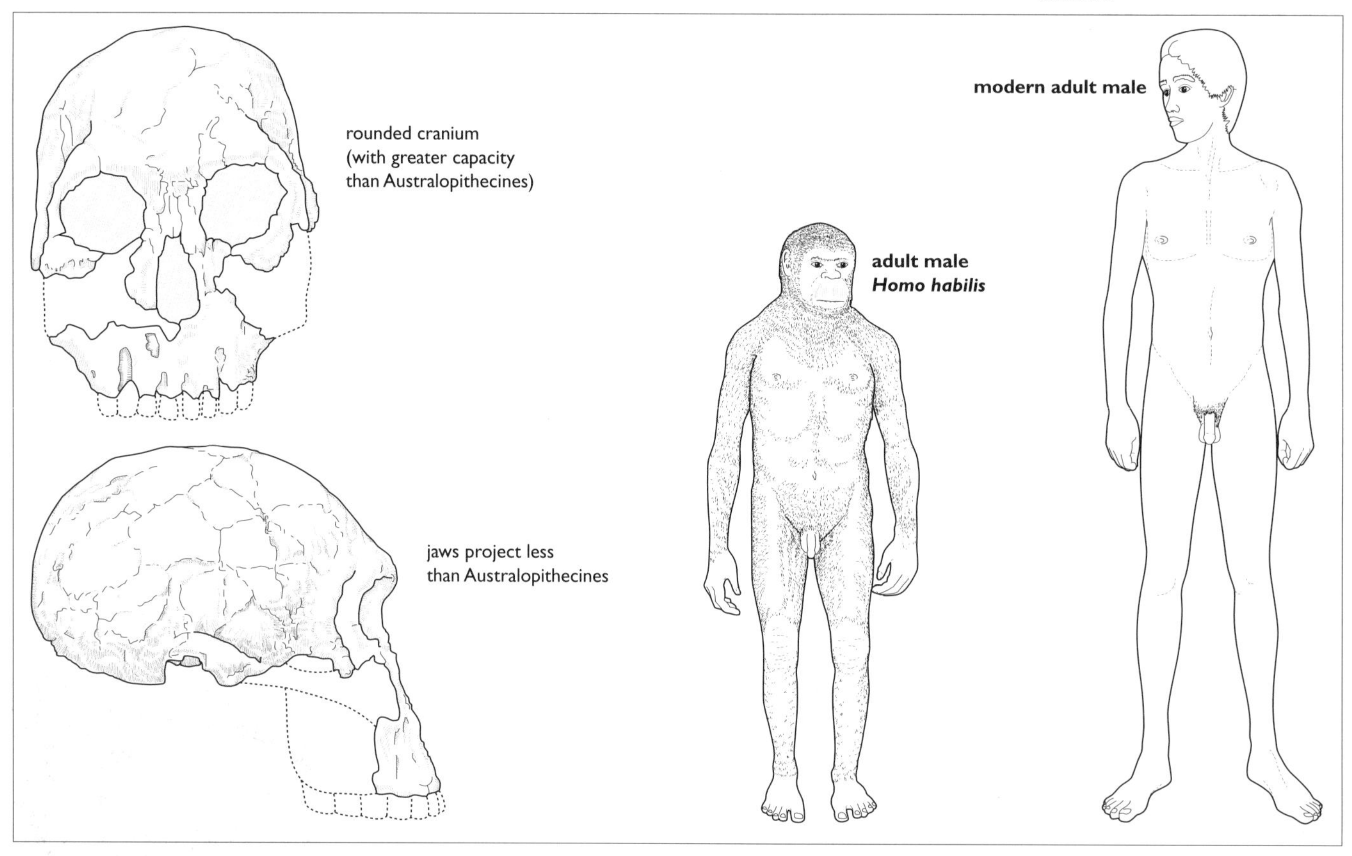

Figure 6.46 The power and precision grips, and tool making.

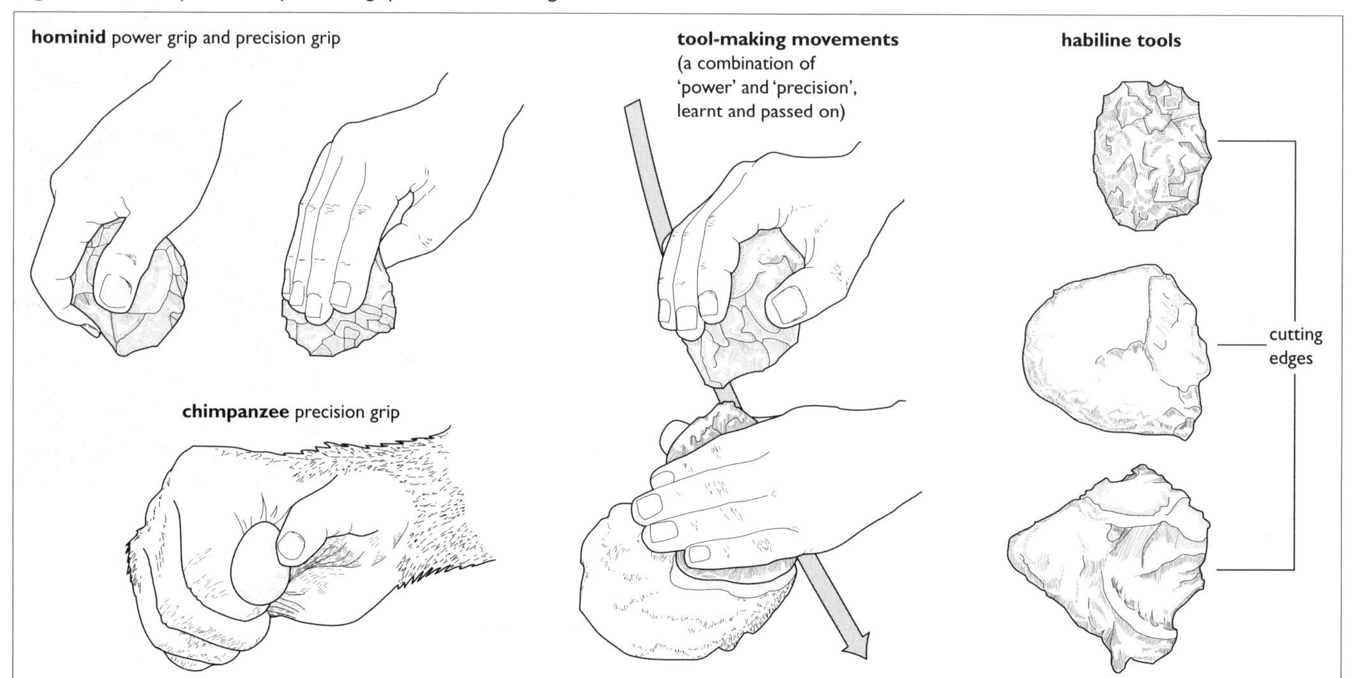

b) *Homo erectus*

Fossil remains of *Homo erectus* have been discovered in strata dating from 1.6 mya, up to as recently as 200 000 ya. This was the **first hominid to have extended its range beyond Africa**, and there are records of its habitation in east and north Asia, and over much of Europe. *H. erectus* is also distinguished by its body size (adults were typically 150–180 cm high) and by the size of its brain (900–1100 cm^3). Skull endocasts show that the areas of the brain associated with **speech and language were significantly developed**, so we can assume that cultural evolution was also underway. This was also the **first hominid to use fire** consistently, aiding the colonisation of areas far north of equatorial Africa, and it is also associated with the eating of meat. By modern human standards, *H. erectus* had a marked brow-ridge and protruding jaws, but the pronounced sexual dimorphism of earlier hominids was reduced, for adult males were now only about 20–30% larger than females.

Figure 6.47 *Homo erectus* fossils.

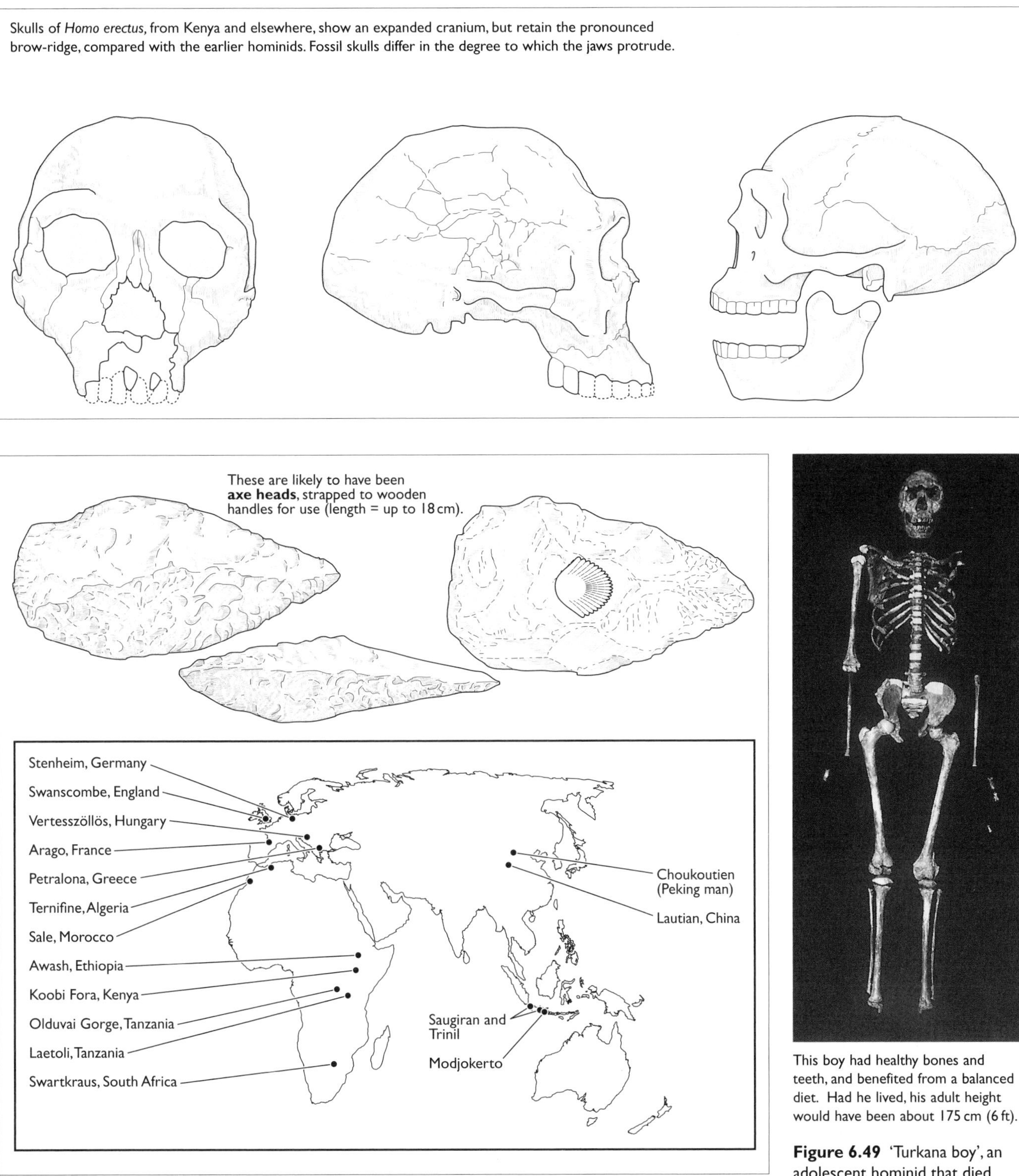

Figure 6.48 Stone tools and habitation sites where *H. erectus* occurred.

Figure 6.49 'Turkana boy', an adolescent hominid that died 1.6 mya.

The origin of humans

Archaic humans, *Homo sapiens neanderthalensis*, were heavier and more muscular than modern humans (but never the 'cave-men' of popular mythology). The fossil evidence shows that Neanderthals were established 125 000 ya, but died out quite abruptly, about 40 000 ya. Anthropologists continue to disagree about the origin of modern humans. They use evidence from fossil remains and from artefacts like stone tools that can be associated with particular hominids, which are frequently being discovered and/or re-interpreted, together with new, biochemical evidence, for example, from mitochondrial DNA studies (page 77). Two theories take turns at general acceptance:

i) **a multiregional model**, in which *Homo sapiens* emerged wherever populations of *H. erectus* had become established, in Africa, Europe and Asia. This makes *H. sapiens neanderthalensis* one example of archaic hominid forms, intermediate between *H. erectus* and modern humans. According to this model, there was on-going genetic exchange between populations;

ii) **an 'out of Africa' model**, in which people like us, known as *Homo sapiens sapiens*, appear to have a recent, common origin in Africa, approximately 80 000–115 000 ya. As members of this modern population migrated out of Africa they completely replaced premodern/archaic human populations, rather than interbreeding with them. This hypothesis carries the greater general support, probably because the new forms of evidence appear to support it.

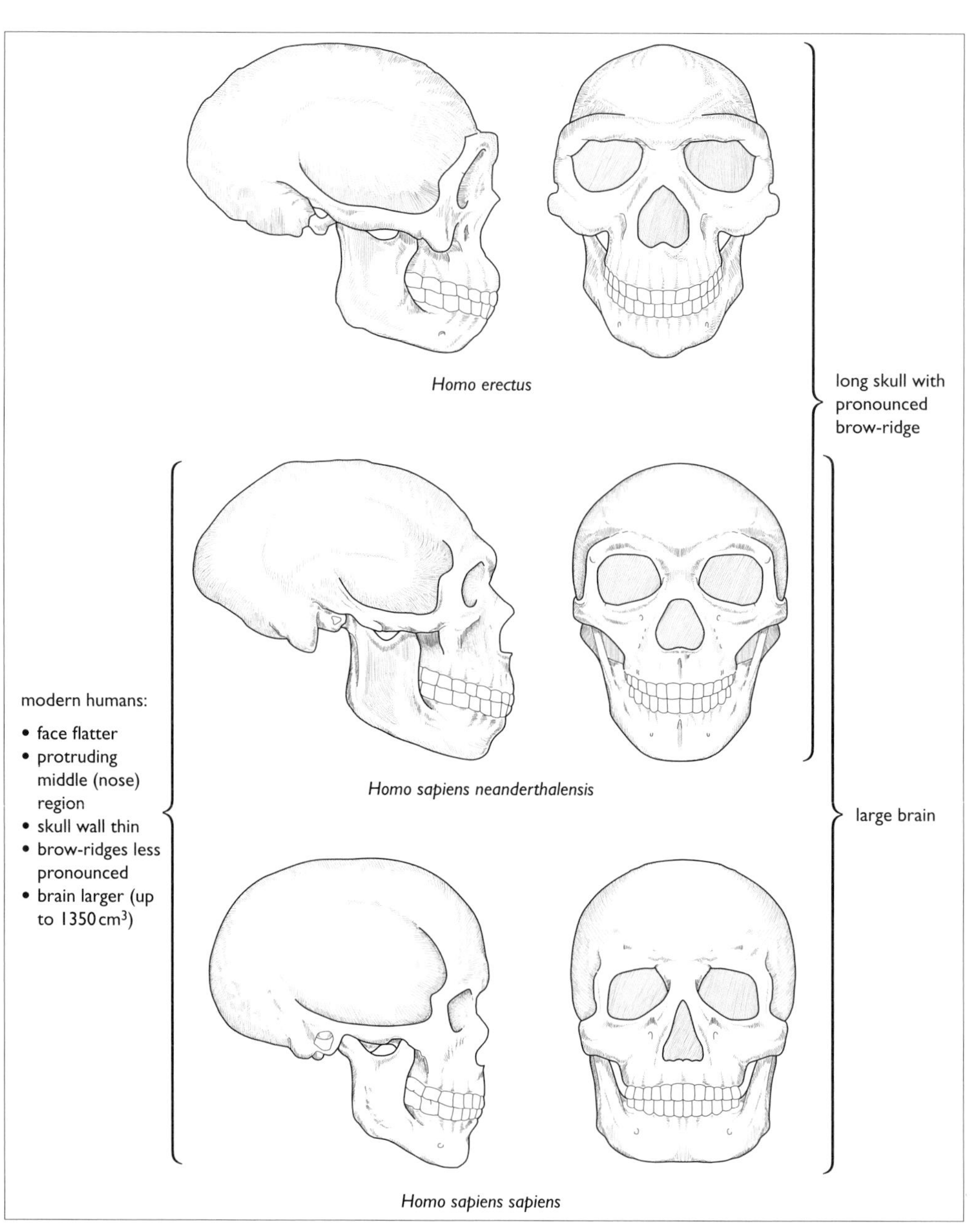

Figure 6.50 The characteristics of modern humans.

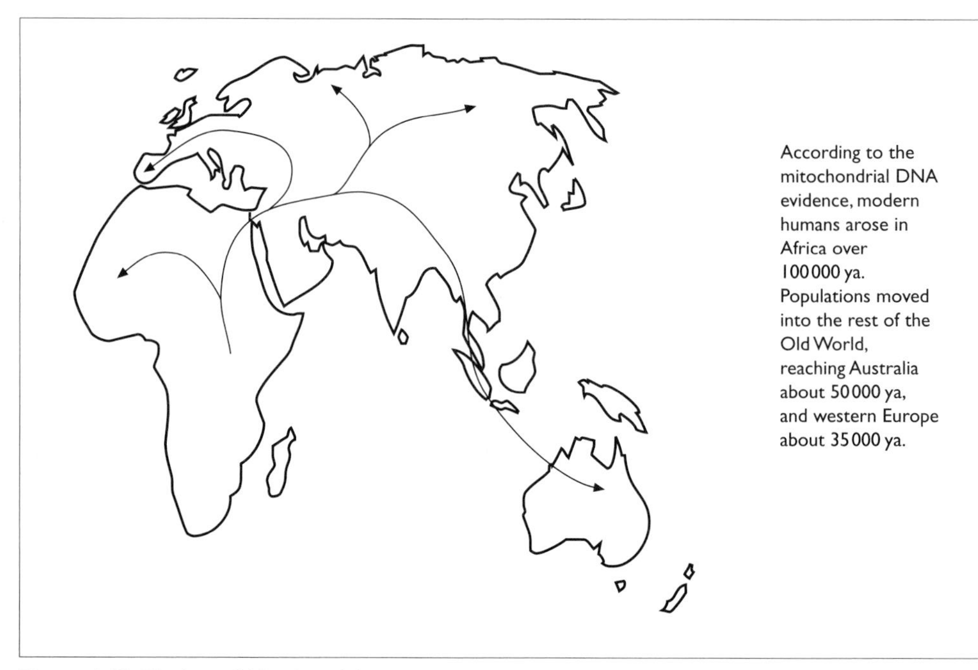

Figure 6.51 The 'out of Africa' model.

The **development of language** is one of the most important human 'characteristics', yet the evolution of this skill leaves scarcely any archaeological evidence for us to discover. Casts of the inside of the cranium (called endocasts) may give a slight impression of the areas of the brain that had developed and were enlarged (the chief neural machinery for speech in most modern humans is found in the left hemisphere). Also critical is the position of the vocal folds in the neck. On both counts it seems that only archaic *Homo sapiens* (and ourselves) achieved the structures necessary for elaborate vocal communication.

The **developments in (tool) technology** (another human characteristic), from about 35 000 ya, were also spectacular. At this time, bone and antler were added to the list of raw materials used, and advances in the skills of fashioning stone flakes and blades into finely worked scrapers, chisels, drills, arrowheads and barbs were great. Tool-kits from this period comprised hundreds of items, including tools for engraving and sculpture. Functional implements like spears might be decorated with life-like animal carvings.

The **vocal folds** in the human larynx (voice box), together with the complexity of musculature and innervation serving them, allow us to make a range of sounds used in speech. The tension on the ligaments within the folds and the width of the slit between them can be varied. When the folds are taut and the slit narrow, the passing air causes the folds to vibrate.

In humans the air passage has to be temporarily closed during swallowing. Apes can simultaneously swallow and breathe, but they cannot make the range of sounds necessary for speech.

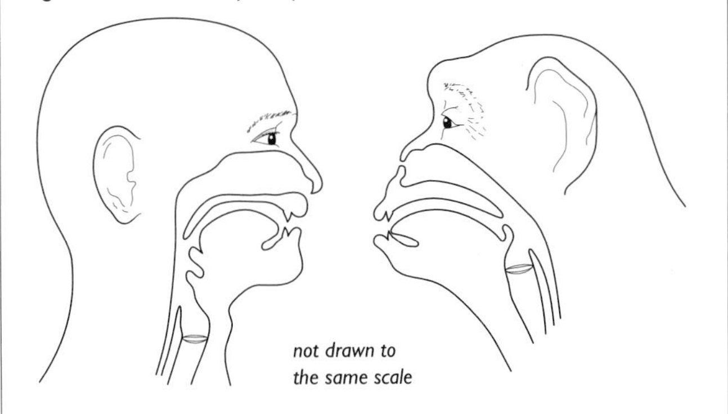

Figure 6.52 The critical position of the vocal apparatus.

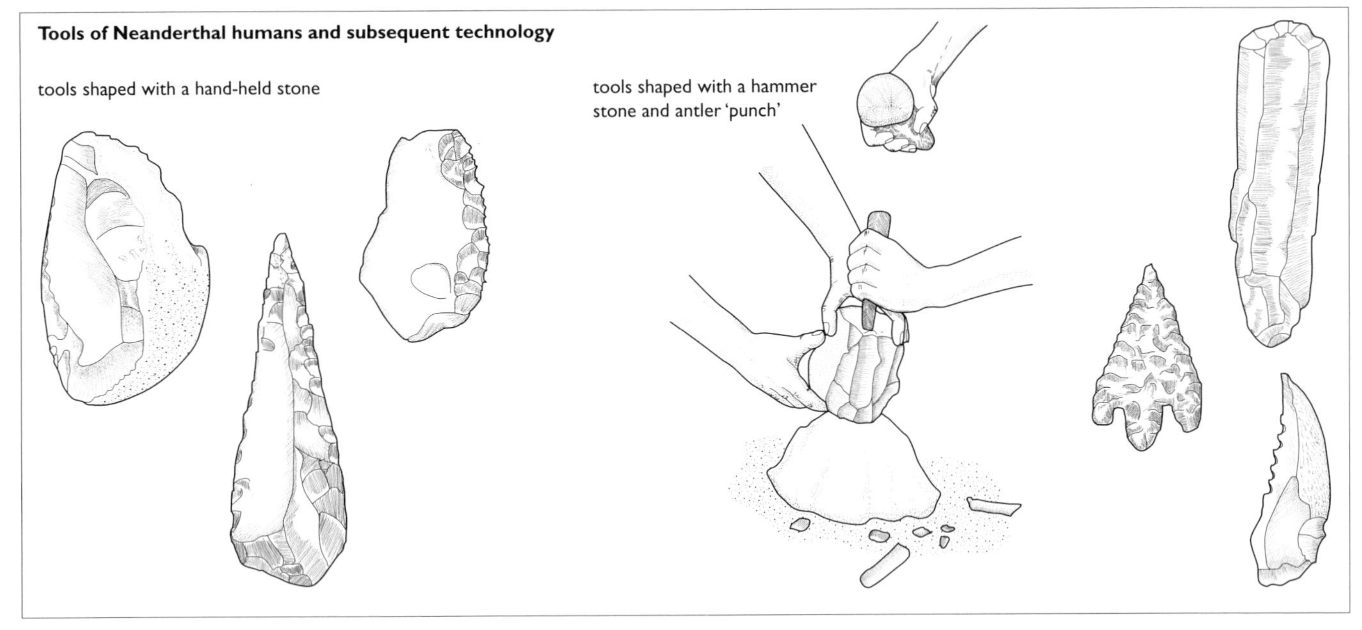

Figure 6.53 Stone tool technology changes between 60 000 and 30 000 ya.

***Homo sapiens sapiens*, as observers and artists,** achieved incredible feats at the earliest phase of their development. We have a remarkable record of the artistic skills of our first human ancestors in the cave paintings from this period that have been discovered. The drawings, produced by human communities, 25 000 to 10 000 ya, show contemporary animals in scientific detail. The pictures demonstrate perspective representation. At one time, art historians regarded perspective as a technique invented in Renaissance Florence.

Human population growth was not an issue initially. Indeed, until the Neolithic revolution (page 2), human communities were widely dispersed, yet probably surviving only 'by the skin of their teeth'. Humans were then hunter–gatherers, but, compared with many of the competing wild animals, were not especially strong or fast. Only with the development of agriculture and other advances in technology (for example, brewing and cheese making) did humans move into circumstances in which they could start to dominate their environment and become secure.

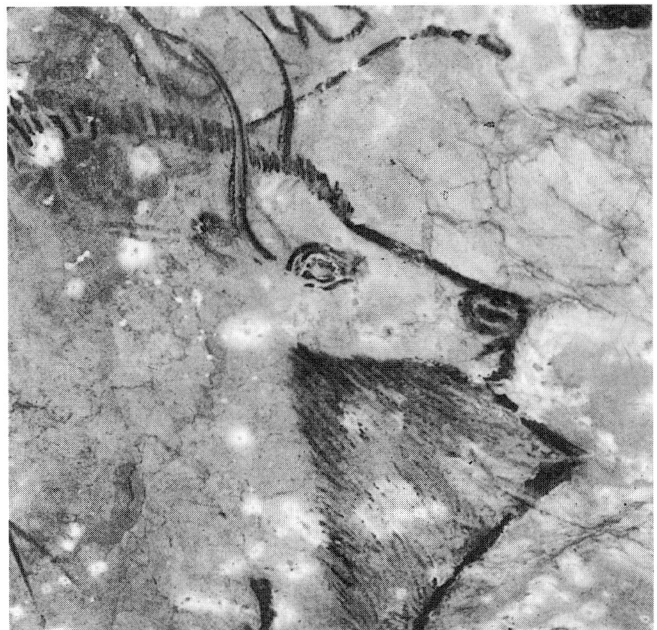

Figure 6.54 Head of bison, Niaux cave, France.

Answers

1 The first geneticists

1 See *What can go 'wrong'*, page 15.

2 Mendelian genetics

1 Homozygous is now used to mean 'breeding true'.

2 Pollination is the transfer of pollen from the stamens to the stigma. Fertilisation is the fusion of the nucleus of a male gamete with the egg nucleus in the embryo sac, to form a zygote.

3 The chromosome number is halved by meiosis, permitting fusion of gametes without the doubling of the chromosome number between parents and offspring.

4 100% of the progeny of homozygous tall peas, when crossed with homozygous dwarf peas, are tall.

5 **a)** The female grandchildren of Richard and Judith are Liz and Diana.
b) i) Alan's grandparents are David and Anne; ii) his uncle is James.
c) Richard, Judith, Anne, Charles, Sophie, Chris, Sarah and Gail (eight people in all) have parents unknown to us.
d) For example, Alan and Patricia; *or* Alan and Jessica.

6 **parental**

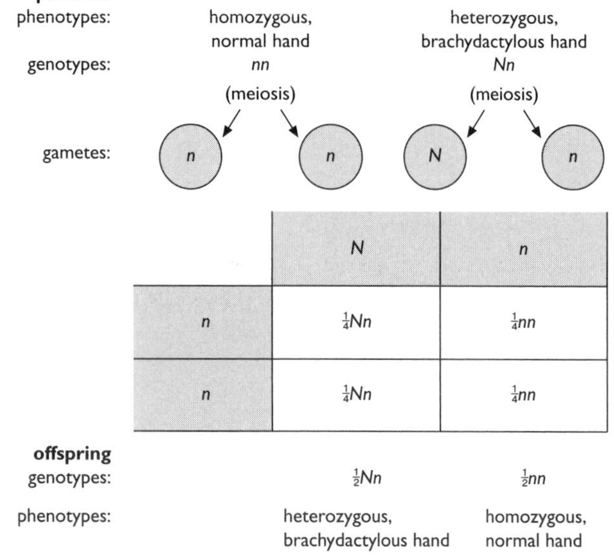

The probability of an offspring with brachydactylous hands is 0.5 (or 50%).

7 The genes for round/wrinkled and for yellow/green cotyledons are on separate chromosomes.

8 The roles of the centromere in the process of meiosis are: i) attachment to the spindle prior to separation of chromosomes and chromatids, and ii) to delay their division until meiosis II.

9 χ^2 was 0.552, so the deviation between the observed and expected result was an insignificant one.

10 A mutant is an organism that carries a mutation in its genetic make up (genome).

3 Genetics since Mendel

1 The number of chromosomes in diploid cells is always an even number because they are the product of fertilisation (at some stage), that is, the fusion of two haploid gametes.

2 **a)** The mechanical consequence of chiasmata is that they hold sister chromatids together (that is, to delay division) in meiosis I, after the attraction between homologues lapses.
b) The genetic significance of crossing over in meiosis is the recombination of segments of maternal and paternal chromosomes, producing greater variation.

3 The gametes *Gs* and *gS*, from parent *GgSs*, are the only ones that produce recombinant offspring.

4 The cross-over value for the *G/S* genes in the cross in Figure 3.7 is:

$$\frac{101 + 152}{101 + 152 + 536 + 481} \times 100 = 19.9$$

5 That slightly more boys than girls are born might be due to a higher tendency of female embryos to fail to implant in the uterus (or some variant of this kind of problem).

6

parental phenotypes:	red-eyed female			white-eyed male
genotypes:	X^RX^R		×	X^rY
offspring (F_1) genotypes:	X^RX^r			X^RY
(sibling cross)			×	
offspring (F_2) genotypes:	$\frac{1}{4}X^RX^R$ $\frac{1}{4}X^RX^r$	$\frac{1}{4}X^RY$		$\frac{1}{4}X^rY$
phenotypes:	red-eyed female	red-eyed male		white-eyed male
phenotypes ratio:	2	: 1	:	1

---

parental phenotypes:	white-eyed female			red-eyed male
genotypes:	X^rX^r	×		X^RY
offspring (F_1) genotypes:	X^RX^r			X^rY
(sibling cross)		×		
offspring (F_2) genotypes:	$\frac{1}{4}X^RX^r$	$\frac{1}{4}X^rX^r$	$\frac{1}{4}X^RY$	$\frac{1}{4}X^rY$
phenotypes:	red-eyed female	white-eyed female	red-eyed male	white-eyed male
phenotypes ratio:	1 :	1 :	1 :	1

7 The genetic constitution of a female who is red–green colour blind is represented by $X^{rg}X^{rg}$. It is impossible to have a 'carrier' male because he has a single X chromosome so the allele is always expressed.

8 The dangers to the body of clot formation in intact blood vessels are embolisms (obstructions in a small artery) and thromboses (blockages where the linings of arteries are already damaged). Either of these may obstruct the blood supply to the brain, causing a stroke. Either of these obstructing a coronary artery may cause pains in the chest (angina) and possibly a heart attack (myocardial infarction).

9 It is called the rhesus factor and is controlled by two alleles.

10 The possible progeny when rabbits of coat colour chinchilla ($c^{ch}c$) are crossed with himalayan (c^hc) are chinchilla ($c^{ch}c^h$, $c^{ch}c$), 50%; himalayan (c^hc), 25%; and albino (cc), 25%.

11 **a)** The variation in offspring you expect when many genes control one characteristic is continuous; **b)** when one gene controls one characteristic, there is discontinuous or discrete variation.

12

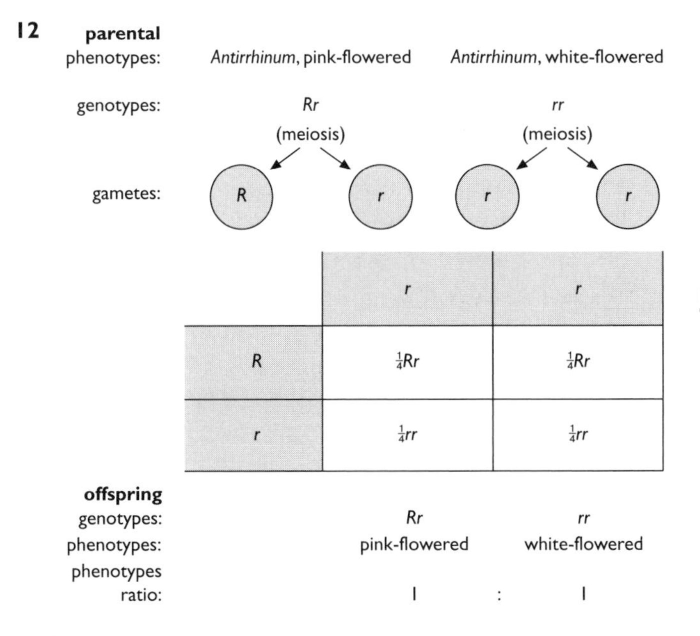

13 The phenotypes are:

a) *PpRr* × *ppRr* walnut × rose, giving all four comb types.

b) *PPrr* × *ppRR* pea × rose, giving walnut comb only.

14 The unbanded brown and pink snails are least conspicuous among the carpet of brown leaves present in woodlands, whereas the lighter coloured, banded snails are least conspicuous in habitats of rough grasses.

15 The extinction of the dinosaurs is probably associated with periods of prolonged 'Arctic winter', associated with violent impacts with the Earth's surface of matter from space. TSD would not deliver breeding pairs in these conditions.

16 The structural features likely to contribute to the continuing success of insects in general include the external skeleton (protective), the efficient sense organs, and the possession of both legs and wings for efficient movement, exploration and transport of materials.

17 These sets of chromosomes from different species, brought together in a new hybrid, are liable to fail to pair at bivalent formation stage in meiosis.

18 The other form of enzyme to occur in cells is made of RNA (for example, ribosomal RNA), and the other important role of proteins is structural.

4 Genetics and cell biology

1 Isotopes are different forms of the same element of slightly different masses, occupying the same place in the Periodic Table. Stable isotopes, for example, ^{12}O and ^{13}O, are non-radioactive. ^{14}C is an unstable (that is, radioactive) isotope of ^{12}C. ^{14}C decays by emitting β radiation.

2 A nucleotide consists of three basic parts:

i) a nitrogenous base – adenine, cytosine, guanine or thymine (DNA)/uracil (RNA)

ii) a pentose sugar – deoxyribose (DNA)/ribose (RNA)

iii) a phosphate group.

A DNA molecule comprises a double chain of repeating nucleotide subunits, joined together with hydrogen bonds.

3 Polypeptides and proteins consist of amino acid residues combined together by peptide linkages. Typically a polypeptide is around 20+ residues long, but above 50 residues in length the compound is always called a protein.

4 The form and position of DNA in bacteria is one very long, circular double strand of DNA in the cytoplasm, whereas in eukaryotes the DNA exists as very long double strands in individual chromosomes in a nucleus.

5 The universal genetic code implies that living things share a common origin, and that the hereditary material was present and functional at a very early stage in evolution.

5 Genetic engineering

1 The DNA of bacteria is a single, circular 'chromosome', with only one allele for each gene. This means that all genes are expressed (when activated), and not just the dominant alleles, as in eukaryotes. Also the DNA of bacteria does not require mRNA copies to be processed prior to translation (that is, the mRNA consists of exons only, see Figure 4.16, page 46).

2 A gene for resistance to an antibiotic may code for a protein that enzymically disables that antibiotic, on reaching the cell.

3 A gene that requires 'switching on' before being expressed may only function when, for example, its substrate is present. This means that the enzymatic proteins of the cell can all be actively engaged in currently required reactions.

4 The bulk of our foods and fibres come from cereals that may require fertilisers (particularly nitrogenous fertilisers) as they grow. Leguminous plants do not require these fertilisers, because of their nitrogen-fixing nodules. So, transferring these genes to cereals could reduce the need for fertilisers.

5 The DNA of identical twins is identical, whereas that of non-identical twins is not.

6 The 'genetic fingerprint' of child 2 shows that it is the offspring of the parents shown.

7 A person with a single allele for cystic fibrosis is a 'carrier', whereas someone with a single allele for Huntington's disease will become afflicted eventually.

6 Evolution

1 Sedimentary rocks are usually laid down under water, often under anaerobic conditions, from sediments washed in from the land. Objects that fall to the bottom (for example, dead organisms) are covered, compressed and eventually have their molecules reacted with or replaced by mineral ions.

2 The coast lines of Australia, southern Africa and South America can be fitted together, and the rock strata at these 'joins' are compatible.

3 a) An example of adaptive radiation found in insects is the way the mouthparts are adapted in different species for different diets;

b) in flowering plants, an example is the way flower parts are adapted for insect and wind pollination.

4 Gene mutations are abrupt changes in the chemistry of DNA, many of which can be repaired if the necessary enzymes are present.

5 If so much change can be induced in a few generations, then species must be able to evolve into other species by the gradual accumulation of minute changes, as environmental conditions alter.

6 The impact of a meteorite or asteroid from space or the violent eruption of a volcano are examples of events that might have caused violent and speedy habitat change over a substantial part of the surface of the Earth.

7

	Lamarck's theory of evolution	Darwin's theory of natural selection
1 Variation	arises by a natural tendency for progress	by chance
2 Rate of mortality among offspring	ignored	basis of natural selection
3 Inheritance of body features developed through excessive use	operates	impossible (in Neo-Darwinism)

8 See page 11.

9 Members of a local population are likely to have detectable resemblances because they are related by breeding.

10 The modal value = 7 lb, and the median of the birth weight data = 5.5 lb.

11 'Niche' means both the habitat an organism occupies and the mode of nutrition employed.

12 The teeth of an insectivorous tree-shrew would be fine and sharply pointed, whereas a vegetarian ape's teeth would have large crushing and grinding surfaces.

13 The head region must not overheat because its functions will be interrupted/impaired and the organism would become incapacitated, or might even die.

14 One of Darwin's finches of the Galapagos Islands (see page 62).

Glossary

Entries are *aides-mémoire*, rather than formal definitions.

adaptation The process by which an organism becomes fitted to its environment.
adaptive radiation Descent from a common ancestor, with divergence to occupy different niches.
altruism Behaviour by an organism beneficial to the genetic survival of another organism at the expense of itself.
amino acid Building block of proteins, of general formula $RCH(NH_2)COOH$.
amniocentesis Withdrawal of a small sample of amniotic fluid from around the fetus, 16–20 weeks into gestation, so that fetal cells can be examined cytologically.
analogous structure Similar in structure but of different evolutionary origin.
anticodon Three consecutive bases in tRNA, complementary to a codon on RNA.
autosome A chromosome (see *chromosome* below) that is not a sex chromosome.

bacteriophage A virus that parasitises bacteria.
bivalent (chromosomes) A pair of duplicated chromosomes, held together by chiasmata during meiosis.

catastrophism The theory that fossils are organisms of earlier creations which suffered mass extinction (and were replaced by freshly created organisms).
central dogma The idea that transfer of genetic information from DNA of the chromosome to RNA to protein (amino acid sequence) is irreversible.
centromere Constriction of the chromosome, the region that becomes attached to the spindle fibres in division.
centrosome Organelle situated near the nucleus in animal cells, involved in the formation of the spindle prior to nuclear division.
chiasma (plural chiasmata) Site of crossing over (exchange) of segments of DNA between homologous chromosomes.
chromatin A nuclear protein material in the nucleus of eukaryotic cells at interphase, which forms into chromosomes during mitosis and meiosis.
chromosome Visible in appropriately stained cells at nuclear division, each chromosome consists of a long thread of DNA packaged with protein. Chromosomes replicate prior to division, into chromatids. Contents of nucleus appear as granular chromatin between divisions.
chromatid One of two copies of a chromosome after it has replicated.
codon Three consecutive bases in DNA (or RNA) that specifies an amino acid.
convergent evolution Similarity between organs or organisms due to independent evolution along similar lines, rather than due to common ancestry.
crossing over Exchange of genetic material between homologous chromosomes during meiosis.

degenerate code The triplet code contains more 'words' (codons) than there are amino acids to be coded, so most amino acids are coded by more than one codon.
dihybrid cross One in which the inheritance of two pairs of contrasting characters (controlled by genes on separate chromosomes) is observed.
diploid condition Organisms whose cells have nuclei containing two sets of chromosomes.
DNA A form of nucleic acid found in the nucleus, consisting of two complementary chains of deoxyribonucleotide subunits, and containing the bases adenine, thymine, guanine and cytosine.

eukaryotic (cells) Cells with a 'good' nucleus, for example, animal, plant, fungi and protoctista cells.
euploidy A polyploid with a chromosome number an exact multiple of the haploid chromosome number.

F_1 generation First filial generation, that is, arises by crossing parents (P), and when selfed or crossed via sibling crosses, produces the F_2 generation.
founder effect Genetic differences that develop between the original breeding population and a small isolated interbreeding group of these organisms.

gene A basic unit of inheritance by which inherited characteristics are transferred from parents to offspring, consisting of a length of DNA on a chromosome.
gene pool All the genes (and their alleles) present in a breeding population.
gene probe An artificially prepared sequence of DNA made radioactive with ^{14}C coding for a particular amino acid residue sequence.

gene therapy Various mechanisms by which corrected copies of genes are introduced into a patient with a genetic disease.
genetic code The order of bases in DNA (of a chromosome) that determines the sequence of amino acids in a protein.
genetic counselling Genetic advance to potential parents on the risks of having children with an inherited disease.
genetic drift Random genetic changes in an isolated gene pool, not due to natural selection.
genetic engineering When genes from one organism are introduced into the genome of an unrelated organism.
genome The genetic complement (genes) of an organism or of an individual cell.
genotype The genetic constitution of an organism.

homologous structures Similarity due to common ancestry.
hybrid An individual produced from a cross between two genetically unlike parents.
hybrid vigour An individual that is heterozygous at many gene loci, and often more vigorous or healthy or more fertile as a result.
hydrogen bond A weak bond caused by electrostatic attraction between a positively charged part of one molecule and a negatively charged part of another.

inbreeding When gametes of closely related individuals fuse, leading to progeny that is homozygous for some or many alleles.
industrial melanism An increasing proportion of a darkened (melanistic) form of an organism, in place of light-coloured forms, associated with industrial pollution by soot.
interphase The period between nuclear divisions when the nucleus controls and directs the activity of the cell.
intron A non-coding nucleotide sequence of the DNA of chromosomes, present in eukaryotic chromosomes.

meiosis Nuclear division in which the daughter cells contain half the number of chromosomes of the parent cell.
mitosis Nuclear division in which the daughter nuclei have the same number of chromosomes as the parent cell.
mRNA Single-strand ribonucleic acid that is formed by the process of transcription of the genetic code in the nucleus, that then moves to ribosomes in the cytoplasm.
monohybrid cross A cross (breeding experiment) involving one pair of contrasting characters exhibited by homozygous parents.
mutagen An agent that causes mutation.
mutant An organism with altered genetic material (abruptly altered by a mutation).
mutation A change in the amount or the chemical structure (that is, the base sequence) of DNA of a chromosome.

nuclear pore Organised gap in the nuclear membrane, exit point for mRNA.
nucleic acid Polynucleotide chain of one of two types, deoxyribonucleic acid (DNA) or ribonucleic acid (RNA).
nucleus Largest organelle of eukaryotic cells, controls and directs the activity of the cell.
nucleolus Compact region of nucleus where RNA is synthesised.
nucleoside Organic base (adenine, guanine, cytosine, thymine) combined with a pentose sugar (ribose or deoxyribose).
nucleosome Repeating structural unit of chromatin, consisting of DNA wound around a protein core.
nucleotide Phosphate ester of a nucleotide, that is, an organic base combined with pentose sugar and phosphate.

outbreeding Crossing (breeding) of unrelated organisms, which increases heterozygosity.

phenotype The appearance (structural, biochemical, etc.) of an organism.
phylogeny The evolutionary history of a group of organisms.
plasma membrane The membrane (plasmalemma) of lipid and protein that forms the surface of cells (constructed as a 'fluid mosaic membrane').
plasmid A small circular length of DNA that is independent of the chromosome in bacteria, (R-plasmids contain genes for resistance to antibiotics).
polypeptide A chain of amino acid residues linked by peptide linkages.
polyploidy Having more than two sets of chromosomes per cell.
prokaryote Tiny unicellular organism without a true nucleus (it has a ring of RNA or DNA as a chromosome), for example, bacteria and cyanobacteria.
protein A long sequence of amino acid residues combined together (primary structure), which takes up a particular shape (secondary and tertiary structure).

reciprocal cross Cross between the same pair of genotypes in which the source of the gametes (male *vs* female) is reversed.
recombinant DNA DNA that has been artificially changed, involving joining together genes from different sources, typically from different species.
replication Duplication of DNA by making a copy of an existing molecule.
semi-conservative Each strand of an existing DNA double helix acts as the template for the synthesis of a new strand.
replicative division Mitosis.
ribonucleic acid (RNA) A form of nucleic acid containing the pentose sugar ribose, found in the nucleus and cytoplasm of eukaryotic cells (and commonly the only nucleic acid of prokaryotes), and containing the organic bases adenine, guanine, uracil and cytosine.

selection Differential survivability or reproductive potential of different organisms of a breeding population.
directional Selection favouring one extreme of the inherited variability of a population.
disruptive Selection favouring more than one phenotype within a population.
kin Selection operating on social insects such as ants and bees of genetically closely related members.
natural Selection by which evolutionary change comes about.
sexual Selection due to the struggle between individuals of one sex (usually males).
stabilising Selection favouring the existing mean of a population, leading to a reduction in variation.
self-pollination Transfer of pollen from the anther to the stigma of same plant (normally the same flower).
selfing Self-pollination or self-fertilisation.
sex chromosome A chromosome that determines sex rather than other body (soma) characteristics.
sibling Offspring of the same parent.
speciation The evolution of new species.
species A group of individuals of common ancestry that closely resemble each other and that are normally capable of interbreeding to produce fertile offspring.
spindle Structure formed from microtubules, guiding the movements of chromosomes in mitosis and meiosis.

template (DNA) The DNA of the chromosome, copied to make mRNA.
trait A tendency or characteristic.
transcription When the DNA sequence of bases is converted into mRNA.
transfer RNA (tRNA) Short lengths of specific RNA that combine with specific amino acids prior to protein synthesis.
translation The information of mRNA is decoded into protein (amino acid sequence).

Index